RECREATION AND FITNESS LEADERSHIP

SECOND EDITION

Patricia M. Leith

Debra L. Austin

Jillian Robertson

KINESIOLOGY
KBP BOOKS
PUBLISHER

Design by My1 Designs

Library and Archives Canada Cataloguing in Publication

Leith, Patricia M., 1947-
[World of recreation and fitness leadership]
    Recreation and fitness leadership / Patricia M. Leith, Debra L. Austin,
Jillian Robertson. -- Second edition.

Revision of: The world of recreation and fitness leadership / Patricia M.
    Leith, Debra L. Austin, Jillian Robertson.
Includes bibliographical references and index.
ISBN 978-0-920905-45-6 (bound)

    1. Recreation leadership--Textbooks. 2. Recreation--Management--Textbooks.
3. Physical education and training--Administration--Textbooks. 4. Physical fitness--
Textbooks. I. Austin, Debra, 1958-, author II. Robertson, Jill, 1964-, author
III. Title. IV. Title: World of recreation and fitness leadership

GV181.4.L43 2014   796.06'9   C2013-904543-0

Copyeditor: Patricia MacDonald
Proofreader: Patricia MacDonald

Distribution worldwide by
Kinesiology Books Publisher
212 Robert Street
Toronto ON M5S 2K7
Canada

www.kinesiology101.com
E-mail: kbp@kinesiology101.com
Fax: 416-966-9022

Dedications

My thanks to all those who have inspired and supported me – family, friends, colleagues, students, athletes, and especially my daughter, Stephanie.

"I am a part of all that I have met." – Tennyson, "Ulysses"

Patricia M. Leith

To my husband, Dave, for his ongoing support and his understanding. He never gets frustrated about all the time I spend away from home while working with students, coaching, or tripping.

I also want to acknowledge all the many students who have helped shape my life with their enthusiasm, their words of wisdom, or their appreciation. Thank you to you all. Being a writer on this book has been a fantastic experience. Many thanks to fellow authors Pat and Jill.

Debra Lea Austin

To my family…
Thank you for helping me realize my goals and for reminding me that no challenge is ever too big.

To those students who have passed through the doors . . .
Thank you for your honesty, enthusiasm, and energy!

Jillian Robertson

Author Team

Lead Authors

 Patricia M. Leith
*Lindsay CVI
(retired)*

 Debra Lea Austin
*Huntsville High
School (retired)*

 Jillian Robertson
*Georgian
College*

Contributing Authors

 E. J. Akesson
*Professor Emerita,
University of British
Columbia*

 A. Anderson
University of Toronto

 D. Brioux
University of Toronto

 J. Cressy
University of Toronto

 M.-J. De Souza
*Pennsylvania State
University*

 P. Klavora
*University of Toronto
(retired)*

 S. Lee
University of Toronto

 G. Leighton
*University of
Minnesota (retired)*

 L. M. Leith
*University of Toronto
(retired)*

 M. Locke
University of Toronto

 P. Maione
*Kinesiology Books
Publisher*

Reviewers

 K. Reid
*M. M. Robinson High
School*

 T. Lam
FITS Toronto

 P. Nalli
*St. Joseph
Secondary School*

 M. Wilkins
*Red Lake District
High School*

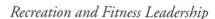

Prologue

> "We must be ready at any time to give up who we are for what we might become."
> *Anonymous*

Welcome to the world of recreation and fitness leadership. You have begun a journey that may have surprising outcomes. Our wish is that you will learn and grow through the knowledge presented in this text and the experiences the student workbook will lead you through.

Do you wonder if you have leadership ability? There is an old adage that "leaders are born, not made." Would you like the opportunity to prove this adage wrong? In Unit 1, you will read what researchers have discovered about leadership styles and characteristics over the last 60 years. A glimpse into the lives of outstanding Canadian leaders in sport, fitness, and recreation will build your appreciation of their contributions and give you examples to strive to emulate. You will learn and practice leadership skills that you can apply in all aspects of your life. You will also learn about the dynamics of group development and the factors that help groups become teams.

Have you ever wondered how the recreation programs and events in your community are planned and implemented? What about the organization involved in a major event such as the Olympics or even a provincial high school championship? Unit 2 will help you develop skills and knowledge that will allow you to plan, organize, and implement events for your classmates and school community to promote healthy, active living. You will discover the important role that recreation plays in our society and learn how to deal with barriers to participation.

Could you be an agent of "healthy change" in another person's life? By the end of Unit 3, you will have a good understanding of current knowledge in the areas of wellness, fitness, and nutrition. You will become familiar with a wide variety of lifestyle programs and learn how to measure a person's fitness level. You will learn about and practice mentoring so that you can help others improve their activity levels and eating habits. You will have a better appreciation of motivational techniques that can be used to encourage other individuals to participate in fitness and recreation activities.

Have you admired those who are able to handle the medical emergencies that are bound to occur when people are physically active? By the end of Unit 4, you will acquire the tools to foresee the risks that are inherent in all activities, learn how to manage these risks, and be able to prevent most accidents and injuries. You will be ready to plan and run safe fitness programs for individuals and groups. And when those inevitable accidents do occur, you will be familiar with the first aid techniques that enable you to deal with them.

Have you ever considered building a career around your love and appreciation of physical activity? Throughout the text you will find profiles of people who have pursued a wide variety of careers in sport, recreation, and fitness.

Enjoy this book, and happy learning.

P. M. L.
D. L. A.
J. R.

Contents

Leadership is action, not position!

Know the way, go the way, and show the way!

Keep fit, eat right, and have fun!

Better to be safe than sorry!

UNIT 1

LEADERSHIP

1 Theories of Leadership

2 Leadership Skills

3 Group Development

John Quincy Adams stated, "If your actions inspire others to dream more, learn more, do more and become more, you are a leader." Former Olympic rower Silken Laumann exemplifies this statement. Laumann suffered a gruesome leg injury just 10 weeks before the 1992 Summer Olympics in Barcelona. It took five operations and a gruelling rehabilitation schedule, but Silken competed and remarkably won the bronze medal. Her courageous comeback was admired worldwide. Today, Laumann is a noted inspirational speaker, the Kids Champion for the GoodLife Kids Foundation, and a member of the international board of directors for Right to Play, a program dedicated to reintroducing play into the lives of children in refugee camps. But Silken's true leadership has been in her own community. She had a vision, based on memories of her childhood, of youngsters playing in neighbourhood parks and open spaces. She knew that because of societal changes, this was not happening. So she made it happen. She went door to door in her community, talking to parents and sharing her vision. She urged them to bring their families to the local park one evening a week. And so it began. On Tuesday evenings families meet at the park and informal activities develop. The normally abandoned playground equipment bustles with activity. Children and adults join in pick-up soccer, Frisbee, and softball. Thus a community tradition was reborn. This is the essence of leadership. And anyone, including you, can do it.

In Unit 1, you will examine leadership styles and discover your natural tendencies. Then you will learn how to vary your approach depending on the nature of the group and the situation. You will develop your ability to facilitate group discussion, learn how to mediate differences of opinion, and learn to help groups reach decisions by achieving consensus. These skills will help you transform a group of individuals into a team focused on a common goal.

According to Vince Lombardi, "Leaders are not born, they're made. And they are made like anything else, through hard work. There is no genetic factor to leadership." This statement should reassure you that you have the potential to lead. What this course will provide is theoretical information and guided experiences. And as your knowledge grows, so will your self-efficacy and self-esteem.

In This Chapter:

CHAPTER 1
Theories of Leadership

In this chapter, you will learn about the following:

❶ The concept of leadership

❷ Canadian leaders in physical education and physical activity and their leadership qualities

❸ The development of leadership from a historical and societal perspective

❹ The effectiveness of various leadership styles in particular situations

3

> ## "The strength of the group is in the strength of the leader."
> ### Vince Lombardi

Good leadership is absolutely essential to any organization that shapes the way we live, work, or play. An organization without a leader is like a ship without a captain at the helm. Not everyone wants or has the ability to take hold of the ship's wheel, but those who do have certain characteristics in common: They are willing to shoulder responsibility, to take risks, and to dedicate themselves to the task at hand. Moreover, they tend to have a positive outlook and a clear idea of the goal to strive for.

What Is Leadership?

The leader is the vital link between the group and the goal. Several factors make up the qualities of **leadership**. Leaders help groups set goals; they help these groups envision the possibilities and make the commitment to pursue them. Leaders then employ a wide range of skills and strategies to facilitate the process of achieving those goals. Leadership can also be viewed as having a positive influence on the lives and behaviours of others. Both viewpoints suggest that a great leader is not someone who does great things but rather someone who inspires others to do great things. Our study of leadership will focus more on the first definition – the leadership of groups of people.

YMCA Definition of Leadership

We measure the effectiveness of a leader not in terms of the leadership he exercises, but in terms of the leadership he evokes; not in terms of power over others, but in terms of the power released in others; not in terms of the goals she sets up and the direction she gives, but in terms of goals and plans of action persons work out for themselves with her help; not in terms alone of products and projects complete, but in terms of growth of competence, sense of responsibility, and personal satisfaction among many participants.

Leadership versus Management

Leadership is the ability to influence others towards achieving set goals. It is often confused with management. Leading is more than managing or supervising. Leaders set the overall vision for the group and inspire the members to achieve results. Managers, on the other hand, direct or control operation or performance. They are concerned with logistics (e.g., all aspects of public relations, budgeting, planning, scheduling, acquisition, movement, maintenance and disposition of supplies, equipment, facilities, personnel, and the provision of services). A leader may show management ability or may delegate the organization of the minor details to someone else in the group. Leadership emphasizes interpersonal relationships and has a direct impact on motivation, whereas management does not.

Leadership versus Supervision

Leadership is also often confused with supervision. A supervisor oversees or inspects a group performing a task. Inherent in this definition is responsibility for the quality of the work done; thus supervisors have the role of passing judgment on the group members' performance. Although leaders may function as supervisors at times, they also encourage group members to set and achieve their own personal standards.

The Person at the Top

Can we assume that the person at the top of the hierarchy in an organization is a leader? Not necessarily. Sometimes leaders find themselves in their positions because of their assigned status, such as team captain, student council president, or community soccer coach. In these cases, the leadership label comes along with the position for which they have been appointed, elected, or hired or have volunteered to fill. If an individual acquires the title because of popularity rather than ability or because no one else would take on the role, sadly, leadership may be lacking. On the other hand, most people acquire or earn their status as leaders because of their actions or reputations. "Unofficial" leaders, ones who lack the requisite title, may be a source of either support or irritation to the official group leaders.

> *Leadership is the knack of getting somebody to do something you want done because he wants to do it.*
> Dwight D. Eisenhower

A leadership label is assigned automatically to the team captain.

> *Leadership is action, not position.*
> Donald H. McGannon

Two Contrasting Examples of Successful Leadership

It is much easier to provide examples of great leaders than it is to define leadership, especially when we apply the term across a variety of interpersonal settings. For example, in the world of sport and physical activity, it would be hard to find two better, yet contrasting, examples of successful sport leadership than Vince Lombardi and John Wooden.

Both coached teams to outstanding records, but their personal styles were at opposite ends of the spectrum. Legendary NFL coach Vince Lombardi was an extreme example of a task-oriented leader, whereas John Wooden (who coached the UCLA Bruins basketball team for 27 seasons) exemplified the people-oriented leader (see the box *Success Starts at the Top*), interested in the development of his players as individuals (see the section Behaviour Theory of Leadership, p. 13).

Success Starts at the Top

Vince Lombardi was a taskmaster who asked everything of his players and demanded total dedication to the goal of winning. He will always be remembered for his unprecedented success as coach of the Green Bay Packers professional football team from 1959 to 1967. Lombardi remains most remembered for his famous quote, "Winning isn't everything. It's the only thing." Not everyone *liked* working for Vince Lombardi, but almost every professional football player *wanted* to have him as a coach because he would bring out their best performances.

John Wooden coached 10 NCAA national basketball championship teams at UCLA, making him the most successful coach in U.S. college basketball history. Wooden is admired to a greater extent for his influence on the personal development of his players, which included building a foundation based on human values and personal characteristics embodied in what he called his "pyramid of success" (see the box *The Pyramid of Success*). Although his practices were very demanding, both physically and emotionally, there was always the sense of people having fun playing a simple game.

Canadian Leaders in Sport and Fitness

The Canadian physical activity and sport domain has been blessed with a large number of excellent leaders. These individuals have certain common characteristics, but they also have styles all their own.

Wayne Gretzky

Gretzky's NHL Career Highlights

► Thirteen consecutive 100-point seasons

► Four 200-point seasons

► Nine 50-goal seasons

► Eleven 100-assist seasons

► Sixty-one NHL records in all

Known as "the Great One," Wayne Gretzky became a household name in Canada and around the world. Widely considered the greatest hockey player of all time, he rewrote the NHL record books, winning four Stanley Cups, scoring 1,016 goals, assisting on 2,223 others, and amassing an amazing total of 3,239 points (including playoffs). He captained the Edmonton Oilers to notoriety, demonstrating consistent leadership on and off the ice. As executive director of the Canadian Olympic hockey team, Gretzky guided his country to a gold medal at Salt Lake City in 2002. In that same year, he established the Wayne Gretzky

Foundation, whose mission is to give underprivileged kids the opportunity to play the game, in part by donating equipment and ice time. The foundation has raised more than a million dollars for youth hockey. His charitable work doesn't stop there, however. Gretzky is an athlete ambassador and honorary member of the board of trustees of Right to Play, and he is the honorary chairman of Ronald McDonald House Charities of Canada.

THE PYRAMID OF SUCCESS

Competitive Greatness

Poise and Confidence

Condition, Skill, and Teamwork

Self-control, Alertness, Initiative, and Intentness

Industriousness, Friendship, Loyalty, Cooperation, and Enthusiasm

The Pyramid of Success: Reaching the Peak

John Wooden's philosophy of coaching and life is known as the Pyramid of Success. The pyramid consists of five layers of personal traits and attributes, each of which builds upon the layer(s) below it.

The base level consists of industriousness, friendship, loyalty, cooperation, and enthusiasm. These are the foundations of all that is to come. As a result of these traits, you can achieve your ambitions and become a truly sincere person.

The next level consists of self-control, alertness, initiative, and intentness. When committed to these, you will be adaptable to situations that you face, and honesty will become a part of your nature.

The third level encompasses condition, skill, and team spirit/teamwork. These traits bring about reliability and resourcefulness naturally.

Nearing the top, the fourth level includes poise and confidence. From this will come the strength to fight for what you believe in and the integrity to do the right things.

At the top is competitive greatness, which is what these building blocks lead to. But the culmination of competitive greatness is faith and patience, the highest virtues that can be reached.

Christine Sinclair

Christine Sinclair has taken women's soccer in Canada to a whole new level. Sinclair capped off a stellar collegiate career at the University of Portland in 2006 with a record-setting season and multiple awards, including her third West Coast Conference Player of the Year and the Honda-Broderick Cup as the college woman athlete of the year. She recently returned to the city to lead the Portland Thorns in the brand new National Women's Soccer League, wasting no time in being named the inaugural player of the month.

But Sinclair is best known in Canada for her international play. The two-time Olympian is captain of the Canadian national team and has participated in three FIFA Women's World Cup tournaments. After a controversial semi-final loss to the Americans at the 2012 Olympics, Christine led Canada to the bronze medal, finishing as the tournament's top scorer. She subsequently won the Lou Marsh Trophy as Canada's athlete of the year. Ten times Sinclair has been honoured as Canada's female soccer player of the year, and she's been nominated for World Player of the Year six times – and with good reason. She is the all-time leader in goals scored for the Canadian national team and sits third overall in international goals scored by a female player with 145.

David Patchell-Evans

"Patch" started off as a champion rower before a body-crushing motorcycle accident, coupled with debilitating arthritis, put him on the competitive sidelines. Enduring many painful hours in physiotherapy rehabilitation clinics taught David to appreciate what it takes to stay healthy. At that point in time, he devoted himself to helping other Canadians realize the importance of staying physically fit. In 1983 he bought his first fitness club. He now owns and operates more than 300 GoodLife Fitness Clubs across the country. Patchell-Evans was the key person in the establishment in 1993 of Canadian Fitness Professionals Inc. Can-Fit-Pro offers a variety of internationally recognized certification courses, publishes a bimonthly magazine, and presents conferences in several Canadian cities. With more than 400 activity and lecture sessions, the annual Toronto event is the largest fitness convention in the world, attracting around 7,000 fitness professionals each year. Patch is an inspiration for all those in the fitness field today.

Charmaine Crooks

Charmaine Crooks has an impressive association with the Olympic Games. The silver medallist has competed at five Olympics (the first female Canadian track athlete to do so). Elected to the International Olympic Committee (IOC) Athletes' Commission in 1996, the year before her retirement from competition, she has since served on the IOC Press Commission, the IOC Culture and Education Commission, the

IOC 2000 Reform Commission, and the World Anti-Doping Agency Foundation Board. Charmaine was a founding member of the IOC Ethics Commission, which developed the IOC Code of Ethics. As a member of the executive board of the Canadian Olympic Committee (COC), she played an integral role in bringing the 2010 Winter Olympics to Vancouver. She is the president of Olympians Canada and the chair of the COC Awards and Recognition Committee.

In 1994, Crooks founded NGU Consultants, a sports marketing, promotion, and production company. Believe it or not, she still has time to volunteer for Canadian and global charities focusing on youth, women, and sport. She is a founding international board member of Right to Play and a global athlete ambassador for Peace and Sport. Charmaine was inducted into the Athletics Canada Hall of Fame in 2012.

Steve Nash

Although he is small by NBA standards, point guard Steve Nash is big on talent. The two-time league MVP is known for his shooting, playmaking,

and ball-handling skills and is ranked as one of the top players in NBA history in several statistical categories. He is a three-time winner of the Lionel Conacher Award as Canada's male athlete of the year and was named an Officer of the Order of Canada in 2007.

Nash is well known for his charitable and humanitarian work. In 2001, he formed the Steve Nash Foundation, which assists children affected by poverty, illness, abuse, or neglect and creates opportunities for education, play, and personal development. He sponsors the Steve Nash Youth Basketball League in British Columbia and has supported GuluWalk, a Canadian charitable organization that raises awareness and funds for children in war-torn northern Uganda. In 2007, Nash received the J. Walter Kennedy Citizenship Award, given annually to an NBA player, coach, or trainer who shows "outstanding service and dedication to the community." A year earlier, *Time* magazine named him one of the 100 most influential people in the world.

Clara Hughes

A multitalented athlete, Clara Hughes is the only person to win multiple medals in both the Summer and Winter Olympics. After a stellar cycling career that included two Olympic bronze medals in 1996, Hughes returned to her first love – speedskating. In 2002 she gave us a glimpse of what was to come by capturing the bronze in the 5,000 metres. Four years later, Clara was on top of the podium. Her gold medal in the 5,000 and a silver in the team pursuit brought her Olympic medal count to five. Named Canadian flag-bearer for the Vancouver 2010 Olympics, Clara rounded out her medal collection with another bronze and then finished her Olympic career in 2012 by making a comeback in cycling. She is truly a competitor for all seasons.

But Hughes is more than just an elite athlete. She is also a public speaker, a television commentator, and a humanitarian. Clara sits on the international board of directors for Right to Play and is involved with a school program that introduces Canadian children to the benefits of sport and physical activity. She is the spokesperson for Bell Canada's Let's Talk campaign, part of the company's mental health initiative. In November 2010, Clara was inducted into Canada's Sports Hall of Fame.

Simon Whitfield

Simon Whitfield ran his first triathlon when he was 11 years old. He had found his calling, and Canada had found a true sports hero. At the 2000 Summer Olympics in Sydney, Australia, Simon overcame a multi-athlete bike crash and slowly worked his way to the front of the pack in the run, claiming the gold medal in an exhilarating finish. After an 11th-place result in 2004, Whitfield once again made an amazing come-

 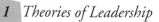

from-behind effort to capture a medal in 2008, this time a silver. In his final Olympic appearance at the London 2012 Games, he crashed early in the bike portion of the race. This time there would be no comeback, as he was forced to withdraw with a broken collarbone. Not long after the Olympics, Whitfield announced his intention to focus on long-distance racing, ending a triathlon career that also included a Commonwealth Games gold medal, 12 national championships, and 14 World Cup victories.

Whitfield has always represented his country proudly, and he was honoured to carry the Canadian flag into the Olympic Stadium in London. He is also honoured to be a role model for so many young Canadians, and he loves visiting schools to help children find and pursue their own dreams.

Hayley Wickenheiser

Arguably the greatest female hockey player in the world, Hayley Wickenheiser has three Olympic gold medals and multiple world championships to her credit. She joined the Canadian women's team in 1994 at the age of 15 and has been a mainstay on the national squad ever since. In 2003, Hayley made hockey history when she suited up with Finland's HC Salamat and became the first female player to notch a point in a men's professional game. Recent accolades include being named number 20 of the 25 Toughest Athletes in the World (*Sports Illustrated*) and among the top 10 Greatest Female Athletes in the History of Sports (QMI Agency).

Hockey is not Wickenheiser's only game. She also played softball for Canada at the 2000 Summer Olympics in Sydney, Australia, where she led the team in batting average. But hockey is where her heart lies, and Hayley's passion and dedication to her sport have helped raise the profile of women's hockey around the globe. Her support of organizations such as KidSport and Right to Play and her mentoring of young athletes through the Wickenheiser International Women's Hockey Festival ensure that the game of women's hockey will continue to grow.

Milos Raonic

There's a new kid on the block in professional tennis, and he's Canadian. Milos Raonic rocketed up the tennis rankings in 2011, rising from 156 to 31 and earning the ATP Newcomer of the Year award. He entered the top 20 in August of 2012 and has stayed there ever since. Now the highest-ranked male Canadian singles player in the open era, Raonic has won four career titles so far, with many more to come if he lives up to his expectations as the next great up-and-coming player on the ATP tour. With a seemingly endless supply of aces up his sleeve, Milos benefits

Recreation and Fitness Leadership

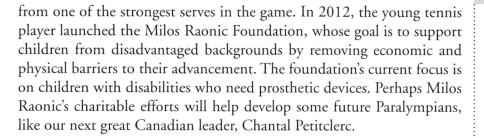

from one of the strongest serves in the game. In 2012, the young tennis player launched the Milos Raonic Foundation, whose goal is to support children from disadvantaged backgrounds by removing economic and physical barriers to their advancement. The foundation's current focus is on children with disabilities who need prosthetic devices. Perhaps Milos Raonic's charitable efforts will help develop some future Paralympians, like our next great Canadian leader, Chantal Petitclerc.

Chantal Petitclerc

When Chantal Petitclerc was 13 years old, she lost the use of her legs. At 18, she was introduced to wheelchair racing – and an amazing athlete was soon in the making. After winning two bronze medals in her first Paralympic Games in Barcelona (1992), she increased her medal count in Atlanta by winning two gold and three silver. At the 2000 Sydney Paralympics, Chantal added two more gold and two more bronze to her collection. Believe it or not, the best was yet to come. In Athens in 2004, she won five gold medals and repeated that feat four years later in Beijing. The most decorated amateur athlete in Canadian history, Petitclerc was named the 2008 recipient of the Lou Marsh Trophy as Canada's athlete of the year. She retired from competition as the most successful wheelchair racer in Paralympic history, with a total of 21 medals, including 14 gold.

A Companion of the Order of Canada and a member of the Athletics Canada Hall of Fame, Chantal is one of the most sought-after public speakers in the country. She is committed to promoting and developing sports for athletes with disabilities. She is a spokesperson for Défi Sportif and an ambassador for Right to Play. According to the Canadian Association for the Advancement of Women and Sport and Physical Activity, Petitclerc is one of the 20 most influential women in sport. It's not hard to see why.

Leaders or Celebrities?

Terry Fox

Although some of the individuals featured in this chapter are household names, many leaders are not. And many people who have achieved special recognition in sport – even "icon" status – have not necessarily displayed special leadership skills. For example, Terry Fox is recognized as an icon and a positive role model. Fox's right leg had to be amputated 15 centimetres above the knee because of cancer, but nevertheless, in 1980 he set out to run across Canada to raise money for the disease. He made it halfway across the country – a distance of 5,342 kilometres – when he had a relapse and was forced to abandon his quest. Fox died on June 28, 1981, one month before his 23rd birthday, but his legacy lives on. Every year the Terry Fox Run – the largest one-day fund-raiser for cancer research – is held in countries all over the world. In contrast, there have been many outstanding athletes, such as Terrell Owens and Barry Bonds, who never endeared themselves to their teammates or served as positive role models for young people.

Studying Leadership

Leadership is a fascinating topic to study. The question of how to get people to cooperate for the purpose of achieving shared goals has been approached from many perspectives for study and understanding. Five different, though not entirely incompatible, approaches have emerged and will be discussed in this section.

Trait Theory of Leadership

The **trait theory** had its origin in the **great man theory** of leadership. This viewpoint maintained that great leaders have personality traits that make them perfect candidates for the leadership role. In other words, great leaders are born, not made.

If you were to describe a leader based on the general comments presented in today's media, you would likely list qualities such as intelligence, decisiveness, charisma, enthusiasm, bravery, strength, self-confidence, and integrity. These are characteristics we can associate with some of the great leaders of our time. Over the years, researchers have tried to determine whether effective leaders do indeed have certain personality traits that set them apart from their peers. A summary of the personality traits in which leaders differ from nonleaders includes the following:

- Drive and ambition
- The desire to lead and influence others
- Honesty and integrity
- Self-confidence
- Intelligence
- In-depth technical knowledge related to their area of expertise

Generally speaking, however, a summary of these studies indicates inconsistent conclusions and a number of dead ends. For this reason, trait theories have been largely dismissed as predictors of good leaders. It appears that possessing certain personality traits only makes it *more likely* that an individual can become an effective leader. The potential leader must still behave in an appropriate fashion, and that approach can vary markedly from one situation to another. This observation led to the next stage in leadership research.

Personality Theory of Leadership

Although it is impossible to consistently predict leadership ability based on personality traits, **personality theory** suggests that becoming more aware of your own strengths and preferred behaviours in group situations

Mark Messier is an example of an individual who possesses certain personality traits that make him an effective leader. The Mark Messier Leadership Award is presented each year to the NHL player who best exemplifies great leadership qualities both on and off the ice.

" We can often do more for others by correcting our own faults than by trying to correct theirs.
Anonymous

Recreation and Fitness Leadership

will help you understand when and how you will step up to the front and lead. Completing a personality investigation process, such as Myers-Briggs, True Colors, or Personality Dimensions, will give you insight into your own behaviour in a group and the behaviour of others.

For centuries, researchers have tried to categorize people into groups. Remember references to the four humours in Shakespeare? Hippocrates, an ancient Greek physician, devised this interpretation of a person's personality and health based on the quantity of blood, black bile, yellow bile, and phlegm in his or her body. Modern researchers examining human behaviour find that they can accurately categorize people into four or five types.

Personality Dimensions workshop leaders take participants through a paper and pen process to identify how much of each of four main personality types they possess. Participants discover their main and secondary "colours."

"Golds" are organized, like structure and rules, and are very dependable. "Greens" are curious, innovative problem solvers. "Oranges" are active, fun loving, and adventuresome. "Blues" are warm, empathetic individuals who use their strong communication skills to strive for harmony in a group.

We usually have a preferred way of functioning. It's natural, comfortable, and effortless. But because we are all a blend of the four types, we can function from other perspectives when circumstances demand it. It simply requires more effort.

No one type is better or worse than another. Each has its strengths and its weaknesses. That's why it's important to understand all the types so you can capitalize on your strengths and build on your weak areas.

GOLDS
Organized
Dependable
Prefer structure

GREENS
Curious
Innovative
Problem solvers

ORANGES
Active
Fun loving
Adventuresome

BLUES
Warm
Empathetic
Seek harmony

You can see that these different personalities may behave differently when placed in a leadership situation. Groups will function more successfully when a blend of colours is present. For example, a group of four that has a member with each colour as his predominant type is a well-rounded group. Relationships are promoted, and the task will be accomplished within the set timelines in a blended group such as this.

Trying to write your name with your nonwriting hand is similar to functioning in one of your nonpreferred colours – possible but difficult and uncomfortable.

Behaviour Theory of Leadership

Personality theory bridges the gap from trait theory to **behaviour theory**. After all, what is the difference between calling a person "well organized" (personal characteristic) and describing the habits (behaviours) that lead to that description?

Two researchers at Ohio State University questioned whether there is something unique about the way effective leaders behave. Using a statistical technique known as factor analysis, they narrowed a list of more than a thousand leader behaviours down to two distinct **leadership dimensions**:

task and relationship. These terms have been in use now for more than 60 years. Note that the term *people* is often used interchangeably with *relationship*.

Leadership based on **task orientation** is characterized by an emphasis on achieving performance tasks or goals. Behaviours typical of this leadership style include the following:

▶ Achieving goals and overcoming barriers that prevent success

▶ Concentrating on defining and achieving performance goals

▶ Assigning responsibilities for individual performance

▶ Establishing a well-defined authority hierarchy

▶ Viewing group members predominantly in terms of what they can do to accomplish the goals

▶ Providing explicit instructions

▶ Using both rewards and punishments to control behaviour

Leadership based on **relationship orientation** is characterized by an emphasis on interpersonal relationships, with less attention devoted to achieving performance outcomes. Also called supportive leadership, it includes the following key attributes:

▶ A genuine personal interest in the individual team members' feelings

▶ The tendency to be friendly and approachable

▶ Respect for team members' opinions

▶ Encouragement of group members to express their feelings and concerns in a nonthreatening environment

▶ A striving for harmony within the organization

▶ The provision of security

▶ An emphasis on positive rewards rather than punishment or reprisals

Further research refined the two behavioural categories of leadership by showing how leaders exhibit varying degrees of each dimension, as shown in Figure 1.1.

Comprehensive Theory of Leadership

The recognition that few leaders consistently use only one dimension and, in fact, can and do modify their approach led to the next stage of thought about leadership. It became increasingly clear to those studying leadership that predicting leadership success was far more complex than isolating a few traits or preferable behaviours. The missing ingredient was a consideration of the context in which leadership occurs. Separate studies looked at (1) the personalities, characteristics, dispositions, and behaviours

Leadership based on task orientation incorporates various forms of punishment – such as running stairs or laps in the gym – to control behaviour.

Recreation and Fitness Leadership

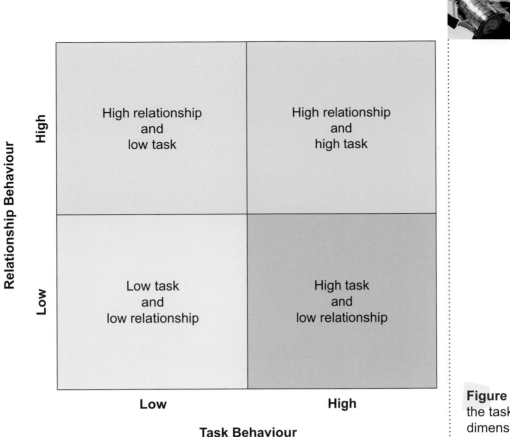

Figure 1.1 The interaction between the task and the relationship dimensions of leadership.

of the group members and (2) situational factors such as environment, barriers, and time constraints. Eventually all the observations and conclusions of many studies were merged to form a **comprehensive theory** of leadership. This approach states that leadership success is a function of the leader's behaviour, the group members' characteristics (see Figure 1.2), and situational factors. If any one of these elements changes, it affects the outcome or effectiveness of leadership.

Individuals who have	Individuals who have
• low affiliation needs, • high achievement needs, • high acceptance of authority, • low need for independence, • low tolerance for ambiguity, and • a preference for material rewards	• high affiliation needs, • low achievement needs, • low acceptance of authority, • high need for independence, • high tolerance for ambiguity, and • a preference for intrinsic rewards
tend to thrive under a ***task-oriented*** leader.	work more effectively for a ***relationship-oriented*** leader.

Figure 1.2 Individual group member characteristics that can affect leader effectiveness.

The group leader needs to be sensitive to the characteristics of each group member. Typically there will be differences between the members. In some cases these differences are overlooked, and all members of the group are treated the same (e.g., army boot camp). But in most cases, a leader will need to select appropriate ways to work with each member on a personal basis.

So how does this awareness of group members relate to the dimensions of leadership? See Figure 1.3 to find out.

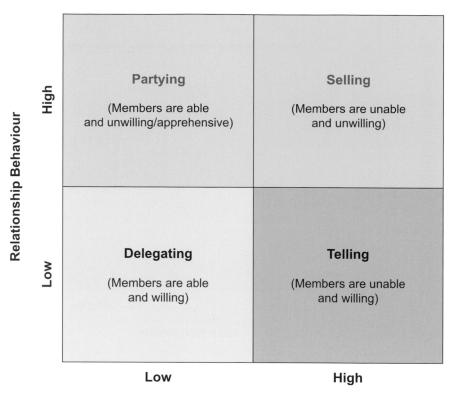

	Low	**High**
High (Relationship Behaviour)	**Partying** (Members are able and unwilling/apprehensive)	**Selling** (Members are unable and unwilling)
Low	**Delegating** (Members are able and willing)	**Telling** (Members are unable and willing)

Task Behaviour

Figure 1.3 Leadership dimensions plus group member characteristics.

Like a babysitter, the "telling" leader must act more like a teacher and supervise closely.

To summarize, when the leader recognizes that there are group members who lack the necessary skills to complete the project and also appear to be disinterested in being part of the group, the leader needs to be persuasive (**selling** – members are unable and unwilling). Think of a car salesman trying to build trust while simplifying the purchase process.

To interact most effectively with group members who are committed to the group but lack the background knowledge and experience, the leader must give directions, supervise closely, and be more of a teacher (**telling** – members are unable and willing). Think of a babysitter.

For group members who have the ability but are not working together, the leader needs to be more like a cheerleader. Enthusiasm is catching, and the leader must do the "throwing." Sometimes this may involve providing the kinds of rewards that the group likes or cajoling the group members into complying (**partying** – members are able and unwilling/apprehensive). Motivation is the key.

Finally, if the group members are working cohesively and are capable, the leader need only assign the tasks necessary for the completion of the project (**delegating** – members are able and willing). The group assumes the responsibility for decisions and implementation.

The circumstances surrounding a leader–follower relationship may also have a profound impact on leader effectiveness. Sport provides convincing evidence that the characteristics of the situation in which a leader finds herself are closely linked to the success that leader will enjoy. Magazines and newspapers are filled with stories of individuals who have been successful in leadership roles in one environment, only to relocate and be considered failures in another. Figure 1.4 outlines the factors that can influence leader effectiveness.

A ***task-oriented*** leader will excel when	A ***relationship-oriented*** leader will excel when
• the task is structured, • the degree of stress is high, • roles are clearly defined, • the group is large, and • deadlines must be met.	• the task is unstructured, • the degree of stress is low, • roles are unclear or flexible, • the group is small, and • time constraints are loose.

Figure 1.4 Factors in a situation that can influence leader effectiveness.

Situational Theory of Leadership

One particular theory of leadership has gained strong support among management development specialists. This model, called the situational theory of leadership, has been included in leadership training programs at more than 400 of the Fortune 500 companies, and over one million managers a year are being taught its basic premises. Situational theory maintains that just as a parent needs to give up control as a child matures and becomes more responsible, leaders must also learn to relinquish some of their normal control. Implicit in this theory is the notion that leadership styles range from highly autocratic (directive) through democratic (participative) to highly laissez-faire (see Figure 1.5). This suggests that the most effective leadership behaviour depends on the followers' ability and motivation.

Autocratic (Directive) Leadership Style

Many characteristics of autocratic leaders are the same as those of task-oriented leaders, but the key that distinguishes this style from others is that the autocratic leader makes all decisions and may feel no need to justify them to the group. The autocratic leader is very much "in charge." He directs the group by command or by polite request that has the same effect. A leader should use this style when the group needs complete direction, perhaps when group members are novices and respect the leader's superiority. Groups that cannot work through a group decision process, due to unfamiliarity with the process or too many strong differences of opinion, need an autocratic leader. This style is very effective in times of crisis when decisions must be made

When the police must respond to a crisis situation and decisions must be made quickly, a directive leadership style has its advantages.

and carried out quickly, so it is well suited to organizations that have a clear line of command, such as the military or police. "The buck stops here" is certainly true of the autocratic leader's ultimate responsibility for every decision and action of the group.

Democratic (Participative) Leadership Style

The **democratic** form of leadership is often referred to as **team management** because the leader empowers the group members to contribute to the overall organizational objectives. This leader shares information and power in the decision-making process. Key attributes of this style of leadership include the following:

- The utilization of group goal setting

- Open negotiation of problems or differences of opinion with team members

- The delegation of control over their own performance progress and outcomes

- A genuine sharing of the team's successes and failures

When the leader demonstrates a democratic form of leadership, all group members are empowered to contribute to the overall objectives of the group.

A very important feature of this leadership style is the value placed on achieving group consensus (i.e., every group member is convinced to agree with the group's decision). Although it can be time consuming to reach consensus, it is worthwhile because it ensures that all group members buy into and fully support the decision. When disagreement still exists, the democratic leader retains the right to make final decisions.

To clarify, the term *democratic* in this instance does not refer to taking a vote. Voting is not the best way to make decisions: Those who voted against the plan may assist only half-heartedly, may act self-righteously

Recreation and Fitness Leadership

if something goes wrong ("I told you so!"), or may even go so far as sabotaging the plan.

Laissez-Faire Leadership Style

A laissez-faire leader likes to be kept informed but steps back from decision making, preferring to act as a resource, providing support or direction when appropriate or when asked. This style of leadership is very effective when the group has become competent and is functioning well. It is the style that tends to foster leadership development in the group members. A laissez-faire leader is not threatened by emerging leadership. She must not make the mistake of abandoning the group but instead must retain responsibility for seeing that it continues to function and to react to changing situations. This approach is the exact opposite of the autocratic style of leadership discussed previously.

> " Even if you are on the right track, you'll get run over if you just sit there. "
> *Will Rogers*

Leader-Centred						Follower-Centred
AUTOCRATIC			DEMOCRATIC			LAISSEZ-FAIRE
Leader makes decision and announces it.	Leader makes decision and "sells" it.	Leader presents decision and invites feedback.	Leader makes tentative decision subject to change.	Leader presents problem, welcomes suggestions, makes decision.	Leader defines limits and asks group to make decision.	Leader permits group to function independently within set limits.

Figure 1.5 Continuum of leadership behaviour.

Benevolent Dictator

A nonrecommended leadership style is the benevolent dictator. This leader goes out of his way to ask group members for advice, puts on a show of considering their feelings and opinions, but then makes administrative decisions without taking the solicited advice into consideration in the decision-making process. Initially, this person is viewed quite favourably by the members, since they believe their feelings and opinions count. But over a short period of time, they quickly learn what is really happening in the organization. This in turn leads to strong feelings of resentment because team members feel they have been treated with complete disrespect. Leaders with this style do not normally last long.

Can Leadership Be Learned?

It is generally agreed that leadership can be learned through experience, but to what extent can it be learned (and fostered) when taught formally? Many institutions depend on the assumption that leadership can be learned in this way. Many of you may have already experienced leadership training within recreation or religious organizations to which you have belonged. CIT (counsellor in training) programs are a staple of summer camps. Local military cadet programs offer excellent leadership training opportunities. The Ontario Educational Leadership Centre offers courses for students involved in student government and intramural activity councils, among others. And certainly, this is the assumption under which we, the authors of the text and your teachers, are operating.

However, developing as a leader is a lifelong day-by-day learning process that is built on continued self-examination, introspection, and self-searching honesty. As a person pursues the goal of becoming a leader, she learns from failures, acknowledges wrong turns, and makes amends when necessary. It is a learning process that begins and ends with oneself. In the process of developing leadership skills, people need to work with what they have, learning to refine their strengths and working to improve their weaknesses. Although many leadership skills can be learned in the classroom, practical experience followed by personal and group reflection offer a better and more lasting avenue for learning. It is the intent of this text to provide you with the theoretical knowledge that will underpin the structured learning experiences provided by the student workbook.

Leadership training within recreation settings, such as summer camps, assumes that leadership can be learned through practical experience.

Putting It All Together

Early studies of leadership focused on personality characteristics. More recently, personality inventories have proved useful in understanding individual patterns of leadership. Two broad dimensions of leader behaviour have been proposed. The concepts of "task" and "relationship" orientation permeate most of the theories of leadership. The task dimension has been referred to as directive and production-oriented. The relationship dimension has been termed supportive and people-oriented.

The early trait and behaviour theories do not provide reliable yardsticks for leadership behaviour. The ability of either theory to predict leadership success is just not that strong. A significant breakthrough occurred when comprehensive theories of leadership were developed. With this approach, situational factors and group member characteristics are included in predicting leader effectiveness.

The value of flexibility, as in shifting from autocratic to democratic to laissez-faire styles as a group changes over time, is now recognized. Developing as a leader is a lifelong process – good leaders continue to learn and grow in their leadership roles.

Key Terms

autocratic leadership style
behaviour theory of leadership
benevolent dictator
comprehensive theory of
  leadership
delegating
democratic leadership style
great man theory
laissez-faire leadership style
leadership

leadership dimensions
partying
personality theory of leadership
relationship orientation
selling
situational theory of leadership
task orientation
team management
telling
trait theory of leadership

Review Questions

1. What are the differences between leadership, management, and supervision?

2. Research a sports hero and assess his or her leadership traits. Determine if this person is a celebrity, a role model, a team leader, a visionary, and so on. How wide is this person's influence (e.g., team, general public, institution)?

3. Briefly describe the five theories of leadership.

4. List three personality traits that leaders are likely to possess. Which do you think is most important?

5. What are the four personality dimension colours? Describe the characteristics of each personality type.

6. Do you think it is better to be a task-oriented leader or a relationship-oriented leader? Name two advantages of each style. Can you think of any disadvantages?

7. Describe the three leadership styles of situational theory.

8. To what extent do you think leadership can be learned?

9. Recall people who have led groups that you belonged to. Select one who was a great leader in your opinion. List this person's qualities and actions that earned your respect.

10. Recall a leader you have had who was not successful. Try to account for this, considering personal characteristics, the group, and the situation.

In This Chapter:

CHAPTER 2
Leadership Skills

In this chapter, you will learn about the following:

❶ The communication process and the barriers to effective communication

❷ Communication skills and strategies that help develop positive relationships (e.g., the ability to express ideas and to listen and respond to others)

❸ The types of conflict and its common causes

❹ Strategies to minimize and resolve conflict

❺ Factors affecting the decision-making process

❻ Techniques to bring about organizational change, such as time management skills

23

> "A good leader takes a little more than his share of blame; a little less than his share of credit."
>
> Arnold H. Glasgow

In Chapter 1, we examined the various theories of leadership, their conflicting results, and several different leadership styles. By now, you should be aware that leadership does not come with an easy set of instructions on how to go about your day-to-day tasks. But research does indicate that certain leadership tasks can be learned and developed. In other words, to be an effective leader, there are certain areas where you will need to display competence.

Any effective leader displays competence and skill in four important areas: communication, conflict management, decision making, and time management. This chapter reviews some of the accepted guidelines so you will be able to develop your skills in each of these four crucial areas. These techniques will greatly enhance your ability to be an effective leader that people will want to work with.

The Communication Process

Because we spend almost 70 percent of our waking hours communicating – speaking, listening, reading, and writing (or typing) – it seems obvious that one of the most serious flaws of a potential leader would be a lack of effective communication. The term **communication** basically means sending a message to a receiver. This message can be sent in many forms, yet how do you know if the message was received or understood? Ideas can be shared only if the message reaches the receiver; however, the message must be completely understood in order to be effective. The leader who fails to recognize these concepts is certain to have limited effectiveness in his organization or group.

Although perfect communication is an ideal that can never be achieved, a thorough understanding of the communication process, knowledge of the effectiveness of different types of communication, the development of good listening skills, and the use of paraphrasing and feedback are essential for improving overall communication effectiveness.

A communicated message is effective only if it is received and understood, which requires good listening skills and feedback.

The Communication Model

Before any type of communication can take place, a **message** with a purpose must be formulated. This message is then passed between the **sender** and the **receiver** as shown in Figure 2.1. The message is converted or encoded to a **symbolic form** (e.g., oral speech, written words) and then passed via a particular medium or **message channel** (pen and paper, e-mail, radio, phone, direct contact or conversation, notes, dance, music, body language, video) to the receiver. The receiver then retranslates or decodes the message from the sender. The final result is transference of meaning from one individual to another. If the communication is "**one-way**," then the sender can only assume the message was received and understood. If the communication is "**two-way**," then the receiver can ask questions if necessary, and the sender can offer **feedback** to clarify.

A message can be passed via numerous message channels, including direct conversation, phone, radio, music, or e-mail.

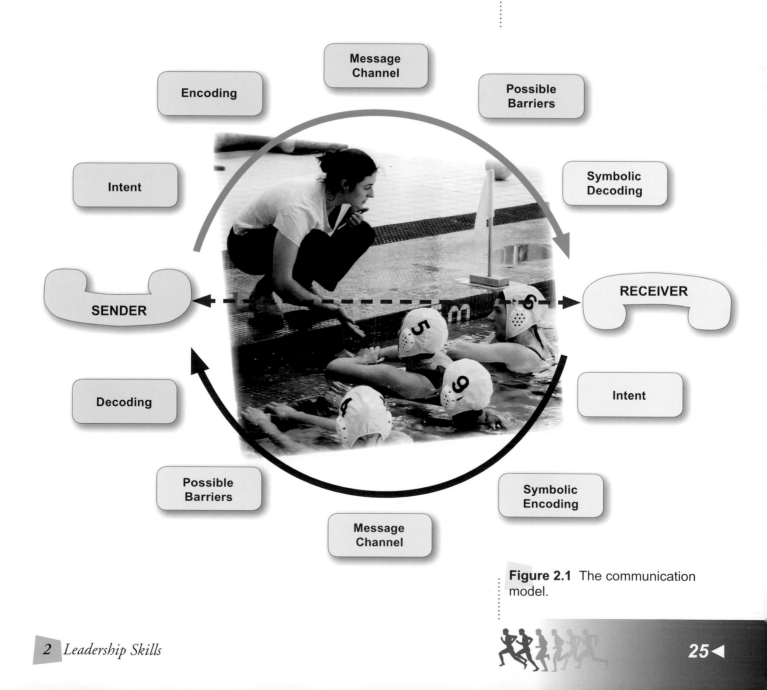

Message Channel

Encoding

Possible Barriers

Intent

Symbolic Decoding

SENDER

RECEIVER

Decoding

Intent

Possible Barriers

Symbolic Encoding

Message Channel

Figure 2.1 The communication model.

Not all communications contain all the components in the communication model, but communication is usually best when it does. For example, one-way communication does not have any feedback, and this can lead to misinterpretations of intent and breakdowns in communication.

Let's take a brief look at the different components of the communication model.

Sender The sender formulates a message by encoding, or putting a particular thought into words (or music, body language, gestures, stance, expressions, pictures, video, and so on).

Message The final product of the encoding is the message. There are many different methods or mediums in which a message can be sent, including words (oral or written), music, and nonverbal or body language. For example, when we speak, speech is the message; when we write, the written words constitute the message; and when we use body language, our gestures, our body position, and our facial expressions all convey a message.

Nonverbal cues such as body language, gestures, and facial expressions convey a lot of information in the messages we send.

Message channel The medium through which the message is sent is considered the message channel. Examples include television, e-mail, MSN, phone, radio, bulletin boards, announcements, and flyers.

Receiver The person or population group to whom the message is directed by the sender is referred to as the receiver.

Decoding The message must be understood or interpreted by the receiver. This process is called decoding. If the receiver has any preconceptions about a particular topic, this may change how he perceives a message. Have you ever played the game Broken Telephone? As you may know, Broken Telephone involves a number of people passing verbal information from one to another. Each person gets one opportunity to pass the message to the next in line. There are no opportunities for feedback, and because you have to whisper, a natural barrier to communication is present. Invariably, the message gets distorted.

Example

Primary message:
The primary message could be that "Johnny got an A on the test and he sat beside Jane, who is the smartest person in the class."

Resulting message:
By the time the message gets to the last person, it might sound as if "Johnny got an A on the test only because he cheated off Jane, who is the smartest person in the class."

Many factors are at work, but people often fill in missing information based on their own personal experiences or beliefs. This is not unlike what happens when office gossip spirals out of control as it is passed on from one person to another. In the end, the truth gets twisted.

Feedback The last step in the communication process is feedback. This stage illustrates to the sender whether or not the intended message was received successfully and decoded correctly. A very popular technique to verify understanding is called **paraphrasing**. The sender asks the receiver to summarize in his own words what he just heard. The sender then determines the accuracy of the response and gives further clarification if necessary. Some communication in the leadership setting does not initially lend itself to feedback, but this step is always important, whenever possible, to ensure full understanding.

Barriers to Effective Communication

When considering the communication process, it is important to realize that there are many potential barriers. A good leader must be able to anticipate these barriers and use strategies to eliminate or minimize their effect on the communication process. In general, the common reason why most groups encounter problems is a breakdown in the communication process within the group. Often, the communication breakdowns are due to communication barriers. Examples of communication barriers include filtering, selective attention, defensiveness, information overload, differing gender styles, poor listening skills, physical or environmental barriers, and body language.

Filtering

When the sender of a message purposely communicates information that she thinks will be viewed favourably by the receiver, it is referred to as **filtering**. The key ingredient in filtering is telling someone what you think he wants to hear. For example, telling your teacher that the class was really interesting and informative, even if you don't really believe that, in the hope that the teacher will raise your mark is an example of filtering. Another example of filtering is when an injured athlete minimizes the seriousness of an injury because she wants her coach to perceive her as being "tough" and committed to team goals.

Selective Attention

Individuals receiving messages invariably see and hear things based on their own needs, experiences, and motivations. This **selective attention** means that we tend to hear and see selectively to reinforce our personal

> **Comparing One-way and Two-way Communication**
>
> **One-way Communication**
> - Message is sent to a receiver
> - Message moves in only one direction in the communication model
> - No opportunity for feedback or clarification
> - Original message may or may not be accurately received or understood
> - Examples include posters, e-mail, school announcements, radio and TV ads
>
> **Two-way Communication**
> - Message is sent to a receiver and feedback is returned to the sender
> - Message moves in both directions in the communication model
> - Opportunity for feedback and clarification
> - Original message is more likely to be received and understood
> - Examples include phone conversations, MSN, chat lines, group discussions

Sometimes athletes try to minimize the seriousness of an injury to maintain their reputation of toughness and commitment to the team.

perspectives, and we base our interpretations on our personal value systems. For example, a man who believes that women are poor drivers will look for situations to support his viewpoint rather than assess all situations equally. Similarly, if you don't particularly like someone, a message from that person will be perceived more negatively than if it had come from another individual. This highlights the old adage that no one truly sees reality – we interpret what we see and call it reality.

Defensiveness

When individuals are feeling threatened, they tend to react in a manner that hinders their ability to understand any form of communication. Rather than listening (or reading) and really trying to comprehend the message, these people often respond aggressively, perhaps by making sarcastic comments, refusing to answer a question by saying "no comment" or changing the subject altogether, verbally attacking others, or questioning the sender's message and motivations. For example, if your coach tells you that you are not putting out enough effort, you may find it tempting to respond that "the drill was stupid in the first place." This **defensiveness** seriously hinders effective communication and does not solve the problem.

Information Overload

Human beings can process only a limited amount of information. With the increased information processing necessitated by today's ever-increasing number of phone calls, text messages, e-mails, TV programs, and so on, we are faced with **information overload**. An overwhelming array of data is available today. As a result, people invariably resort to weeding out, ignoring, tuning out, forgetting, or passing over information that they normally would have read or thoughtfully considered. Either way, the result is lost information and less effective communication.

Since we are capable of processing a limited amount of information, receiving phone calls, text messages, and e-mails can create an information overload, which can lead to lost information and ineffective communication.

Gender Styles

Current research indicates that men and women use oral communication for very different reasons. This means that gender has the potential to become a serious barrier to effective communication between the sexes. Research suggests that men talk to emphasize status, whereas women talk in an attempt to make a connection. For example, if a man tells you what type of car he drives or what sport he plays, he may hope you are impressed by his choices, but a woman may just be looking for common ground to start up a conversation.

Poor Listening Skills

Many individuals are poor listeners. This is likely because active listening is hard work – it is much more tiring than talking. It is interesting to note

that the average person speaks at the rate of approximately 150 words per minute, but we have the capacity to listen at the rate of more than 1,000 words per minute. It is also generally more satisfying for most people to talk than to listen. So when someone talks, we hear. But how often do we fully listen? Listening involves an active search for meaning, whereas hearing is passive. See the box *Active Listening Skills* later in this chapter on page 37 to learn how to improve your listening skills.

Trying to get the attention of an entire group of students can be difficult if some of them exhibit poor listening skills.

Physical Barriers

There are many examples of physical barriers that prevent, distract, or inhibit effective transfer or interpretation of a message, resulting in a breakdown in communication. For example, the receiver may have a hearing impairment (or the sender a speech impediment), the sun might be in the receiver's eyes (preventing him from seeing the sender clearly), or there might be background noise.

Another common example of a physical distraction is having equipment (such as a ball) readily available to the receiver. This may distract her from listening to the sender's message. For example, if a teen has a basketball in his hand, what is he likely to do with it? Usually, he would want to dribble or shoot the ball. If you are giving instructions in a leadership situation and half the class are dribbling their basketballs, there is a sound barrier and their attention is not focused on you. If the students are all running around the gym, they are even less likely to hear you.

To minimize the barriers to communication in a noisy gym environment, it is a good idea to gather the group in a corner to help keep your voice contained when giving instructions.

Physical Communication Barriers and Possible Solutions

- **Receiver has a hearing impairment** – Use sign language, pictures, or other forms of visual communication.

- **Outside in the bright sunlight** – Position the group you are communicating with so they have the sun to their backs to ensure they can see you and will be more likely to listen. You will need to face the sun, but it is less likely that the group will be distracted.

- **Windy or noisy situations** – Make sure your group is close to you for instructions, or try to move away from the wind or noise temporarily to give instructions. You may need to ask that your group meet in a corner of a noisy gym to help keep your voice contained. Outside on a field or in an outdoor education situation such as a lake, you may need to use hand signals or whistles if necessary.

- **Equipment** – It is usually best for the receivers not to have any sports equipment available (e.g., basketballs) if you want to ensure they are not distracted.

- **Attention span of listeners** – Minimize complex instructions. Keep your instructions simple and brief in order to keep the group's attention.

Body Language

A verbal message that is contradictory to your body language may also distract or confuse communication. For example, if you tell someone, "I am happy to see you," but your arms are crossed and there's an angry expression on your face, your message is going to create confusion. Your body language is saying, "I'm mad at you," even if your words are saying, "I'm happy to see you." In these situations, the leader who is sending a message must attempt to minimize this barrier to communication by manipulating the situation.

Direction of Communication

In a team or working group, communication can flow vertically or laterally. The vertical dimension is composed of two separate categories: upward and downward. We will now briefly examine each of these directions.

Upward

Upward communication helps the leader stay informed about his team members' goals, performance efforts, feelings, morale, and organizational

Recreation and Fitness Leadership

Summary of Barriers to Communication

- **Filtering** – The sender of a message purposely communicates information that he thinks will be viewed favourably by the receiver of the message.

- **Selective attention** – Individuals invariably see and hear things based on their own needs, experiences, and motivations when they receive a message from a sender.

- **Defensiveness** – When feeling threatened, we tend to react in a manner that hinders our ability to understand, and rather than listening (or reading) and really trying to understand a message, we may respond aggressively.

- **Information overload** – We can process only so much data or information, and presenting too much data will invariably cause your audience to "tune you out." The result might be weeding out, ignoring, forgetting, or passing over information that normally would be read or heard thoughtfully.

- **Gender styles** – Research suggests that men talk to emphasize status, whereas women talk in an attempt to make a connection.

- **Poor listening skills** – Many individuals are poor listeners, perhaps because active listening is such hard work, much more tiring than talking.

- **Physical barriers** – Barriers (such as background noise) prevent, distract, or inhibit effective transfer or interpretation of a message, which causes a breakdown in communication.

- **Body language** – If your body language contradicts your verbal message, confusion is bound to arise.

concerns in general. As indicated by the term, this type of communication flows from a lower to a higher level in the organization. Upward communication is very important – it provides the leader with suggestions that have the potential to improve the group's overall effectiveness. This type of communication can be oral, written, or nonverbal.

Downward

When we think of leaders communicating to their followers, or coaches instructing their athletes, we are referring to downward communication. It is usually used to assign goals, provide job or skill instruction, provide performance feedback, and point out problems that are in need of attention. Downward communication is often oral or nonverbal, but it can also be provided in written form by means of e-mail or formal letters, such as a letter from the school principal to a student who is having conduct issues.

Lateral

When communication occurs among members at the same organizational level, such as students in a particular class, fellow teachers, or athletes

Lateral communication among teammates, both on and off the court, can improve team cohesiveness and foster a stronger sense of team solidarity.

on a team, this is termed **lateral communication**. The main value of lateral communication is to save time and facilitate coordination. In other words, if the group decides in advance about a chosen approach to a problem, this can then be communicated to the leader with a feeling and showing of solidarity. Lateral communication can also serve a role in team member bonding. As with the other levels, lateral communication can be oral, written, or nonverbal.

Types of Conflict

> "Most people evaluate events in their lives according to how they will be personally affected. Leaders think within a broader context.
> *John C. Maxwell*

Generally, conflict arises when there is a disagreement about how to best solve a particular problem. Conflict may be about something that is really personal and important to you, or it can result from a disagreement between two or more people or even a number of different groups of people. In any of these situations, finding the best solution to a problem or conflict involves rationally considering the various possibilities as well as showing empathy for the points of view of the other parties involved. Before we learn how to solve conflict, let's review the different types of conflict.

Personalized versus Depersonalized Conflict

Conflict can be categorized as either personalized or depersonalized, as seen in the continuum depicted in Figure 2.2. When people are in opposition to one another, a **personalized conflict** exists. Emotional reactions and feelings often arise, and having to work with this person may be annoying, confrontational, or offensive to the people involved. Most important, it may cause an unproductive work environment. When a conflict stems from a difficult situation or problem, the conflict can be considered **depersonalized**, and a rational resolution process without emotion is possible. For example, if your group is asked to choose the colour of the gymnasium in your school, then you may be making a depersonalized decision based on your school colours. But if you and your parents are making colour choices for your own room at home and your favourite colours are not included, then any conflict over paint colour may become personalized.

Figure 2.2 The depersonalized–personalized conflict continuum.

Recreation and Fitness Leadership

Often, however, a conflict that starts as depersonalized becomes personalized as individuals become invested in a particular point of view. For example, a community group might be raising funds to build a playground for the local children and must decide the best location. Ideally, this depersonalized issue could be resolved rationally by evaluating pros and cons of the available sites. However, individuals may choose to defend a certain location for any number of reasons (it may be closer to where they live, they may not like the people who are supporting the other locations, and so on), and the conflict turns into a "personal crusade" (i.e., a personalized conflict). The group members might have very strong feelings about the issue and communicate them verbally or nonverbally to others, and the others might resent the fact that the decision is being affected by biased opinions.

Intrapersonal versus Interpersonal Conflict

Internal conflict, or having to make a tough decision all on your own, can be called intrapersonal conflict. A person who has developed a clear set of personal values and a strategy for making decisions faces less stress than these dilemmas often present for others less prepared. People are happiest when their actions match their personal values and most distressed when they feel forced to behave in ways that conflict with their values. In the previous situation (choosing a site for the local playground), each individual needs to decide between voting for the option that makes the most logical sense for the community (the most pros and the least cons) and the option that is most advantageous for his or her family.

Conversely, conflict between two or more individuals, where each holds an opposing view, is considered interpersonal conflict. If a community member gets into an argument with his neighbour over the location of the park, the conflict is interpersonal.

*While **intrapersonal** conflicts refer to internal conflicts between personal actions and values, **interpersonal** conflicts occur between two or more individuals with opposing views.*

Intragroup versus Intergroup Conflict

When a group is split on an issue, an intragroup conflict occurs. The committee that is responsible for making the decision about the playground is likely to initially experience intragroup conflict. The best decisions, the ones that are most strongly supported afterwards, are those where the group reaches a consensus. In other words, by the time the vote is taken, the decision is unanimous. Everyone must agree it is the best course of action. If there are still members who disagree, they may fail to volunteer their support and may even attempt to sabotage the future of the project.

An intergroup conflict exists when entire groups are in conflict with each other. Still using the playground example, if the town splits into "People for the North End Park" and "Support the South End Park" groups, complete with yard signs, flyers, and campaigns, then you will have an intergroup conflict.

Common Causes of Conflict

Besides reviewing the different types of conflict, it is also important to understand the factors that can cause conflict. If you are aware of these factors, you will understand conflict better and therefore be able to resolve it easier.

Differing Goals, Needs, or Values

Playing on the same team with individuals who do not share the same ethics and values can create conflict among individual team members.

If your goals differ from those of the people you are interacting with, you may place different value on various outcomes. For example, if you value group harmony, and you are working in a group with someone who is more concerned about getting a task completed than about keeping group members happy, your group may experience conflict. Also, if you personally place high value on sportsmanship and sport ethics, you may find it extremely difficult to work with teams that have players who cheat or don't follow rules.

Rivalries and Personal Ambitions

If you are at a tryout for a basketball team and don't pass the ball to an open competing player, then try for an improbable layup to outshine others, you might be putting personal ambition ahead of the needs of the team. Also, sport rivalries get heated at times, and fair play is not always adhered to. If your school has a long-running rivalry with another school, this may lead you to experience conflict if you are unexpectedly asked to play with these rival players in the High School All-Star Classic.

Avoidance of Responsibility

You might feel conflict if group members do not complete their responsibilities. For example, if your group assigned a task to someone and she didn't meet her timeline, you might blame her for the poor mark you got on the project. Working with people who do not complete the work they are assigned can cause confusion, and it ultimately leads to frustration and low group morale.

Carelessness in Job Performance

If someone on your team does not play with the intensity you expect or put forth day in and day out, or if someone in your group hands in an incomplete draft of your event plan, this might cause conflict. If your personal work expectations are not matched by the others in the group, then you may have trouble trusting the quality of the work submitted by the other group members. You may be tempted to do all the work yourself, or you might be really demanding on the other members to ensure their work is up to your standards. In either case, conflict is very likely to occur.

Overlap in Job Responsibilities

If more than one person or group is assigned to the same task when planning an event, conflict and disorder may arise if they do not work on the task in a coordinated manner. The different individuals or groups involved may think they are "wasting their efforts" because of the duplication or may feel they are not trusted to fulfill their responsibilities. In either of these situations, the individuals or groups might not give a 100 percent effort, assuming that others will work even harder to complete the assigned task. If both groups assume the other is doing the work and don't communicate, the task may not get done at all and the timelines may not be met. As well, the message that each of these groups sends out to the target group may differ, causing confusion as well as conflict.

Personal and Group Stress

Stress often brings out the worst in people. When we are under elevated amounts of stress, we often experience problems with both our intrapersonal and interpersonal communication skills. It is our listening skills that suffer first. We may not listen to what others are saying because we are upset, and we often have trouble empathizing with their situation. Often, our body language does not match what we are saying, and we may be more verbally aggressive or self-serving than normal. Stress is a very common factor in group conflict. Whenever you or your group is under stress, such as difficulty meeting deadlines or disagreement about an event, conflict often results. Stress can change how you look at situations, and you need to be careful to be assertive and not aggressive or passive.

Prejudice

Prejudice can have a negative impact on any group. Whenever someone judges another person based on race, religion, colour, gender, or sexual orientation, conflict is almost inevitable. When Jackie Robinson broke the "colour barrier" in 1947, the conflict within the sport of baseball, and even with his own teammates on the Brooklyn Dodgers, was well documented.

Misunderstandings

Misunderstandings often result from poor communication in a group. If a group doesn't use clear messages and there is a misunderstanding,

Jackie Robinson

Prejudging another person or persons based on race, religion, colour, or sexual orientation can cause conflict and turmoil within a group. Sometimes it takes the courage of one individual to break the cycle of prejudice.

clarifying the situation will be difficult. For example, if one group member makes a major change in the event plan without consulting others in the group, then the other members might question the motivation behind the change and feel slighted unless it is reviewed and discussed. Also, gossip is a dangerous method of communication, and the message invariably gets changed extensively before it ever completes the full circle. Feelings are often hurt as a result of the misunderstandings that arise from gossip, and it should be avoided. For example, if Luke spreads rumours about Maya—his biggest competition in the race for class president—he is engaging in a form of gossip.

Techniques to Improve Your Conflict Management Skills

> "You will go through tough times again in your life. Always, always remember these three words: Responsibility. Determination. Courage. And don't ever give up on you."
> *Danièle Sauvageau*

In any group or team, conflicts are an inevitable part of life. The ability to properly handle these conflict situations is an important skill for any recreational leader's portfolio. There are a number of widely used approaches to conflict resolution, and good leaders will use more than one depending on the situation. Several approaches to **conflict management** are presented in this section.

Active Listening

Active listening involves asking the right questions to better understand how someone else is feeling and why. You need to do more than just listen or hear the person's words. It requires you to try to understand her needs. Asking open questions allows the other person to tell you more. Questions such as "How would you like things to be?" allow for more information to be shared than asking, "Would you like things to be different?" Open questions encourage exploration of the issue and show you are interested in the other person's ideas.

Win–Win

In a **compromise** situation, one party will give up some of what he really wants and take less to allow the other party to get some of what she wants. Thus, neither party gets all of what he or she is really looking for. In a **win–win** situation, you must "think outside the box" and explore how to meet the needs of both parties at the same time.

> **Example 1**
> Both Tim and Sally need the last lemon in the fridge. After further discussion, it turns out that Tim wants to make a cake using the lemon rind, and Sally wants the pulp of the lemon to make lemonade.

Active Listening Skills

Improve your listening skills by practicing active listening:

- Remember to make eye contact.

- Show you are interested in what the other person is saying.

- Avoid distracting actions or gestures, such as looking at your watch.

- Ask questions for clarification and to ensure understanding of the message.

- Use nonverbal cues, such as head nods or hand gestures, to convey interest.

- Use paraphrasing if necessary to ensure understanding.

- Avoid interrupting the sender; let her complete her thoughts.

- Don't "over-talk" – remember that knowledge is composed of two parts: having a lot to say and knowing when not to say it!

Active listening involves more than just hearing someone else's words. Try to show interest in what the other person is saying by making eye contact and avoiding distracting actions. The man in this picture is not practicing active listening skills.

Example 2

Two groups want to use the same gym at the same time. But after clarification and discussion, it turns out that one group of six students wants to play three-on-three basketball and needs only one basket, and the other group needs only half the gym to do a Pilates workout and can close the gym's dividing door.

As a group leader, you may be called on to help group members explore the win–win situation. If the parties involved simply compromise, then each party must give up something of value, which is a passive response. With compromise, there is no clear loser, but there is no clear winner either. If someone has to compromise to help meet your needs, it may not necessarily solve the problem – and in some cases neither party is happy. In other words, if a compromised solution is reached to help both parties live with their differences, those differences still exist. Sometimes compromise is the best solution because each party intends to give up something. The challenge is to do everything possible to make your solution win–win.

Using "I" Messages and Being Assertive

Assertive people have developed a wide range of respectful strategies for resolving conflict. They use a problem-solving approach that strives for the win–win resolution. They are attentive, active listeners who accept the other person's views as valid, and they are able to communicate their own feelings, needs, and wishes directly, honestly, and openly using "I" messages. People who are assertive behave in ways that meet their own needs, but not at the expense of compromising anyone else's needs. A person effectively uses an "I" message when he communicates his emotions, identifies the situation that is causing these feelings, and proposes a solution without blaming anyone directly.

Example

"Dad, when I am studying in my room and you yell at me from the kitchen to 'empty the trash right now,' I feel annoyed because I think studying is important. It makes me feel that you think I can't manage my time or my chores, but I think I am quite capable of it. In the future, I would appreciate it if you came to my room and asked me to do the chore, and I will do it when I take my next break from studying."

Mediation

A process in which a neutral third party (a mediator) helps the participants resolve their differences or conflict without aggression or coercion is called mediation. Mediation means negotiating disputes so that the people involved have their needs met and are willing to attempt to resolve their differences.

The mediation process has several steps:

❶ *Establish a respectful environment.* Make rules clear (e.g., physical violence, name calling, threats, and personal insults will not be tolerated), and allow each person a chance to speak uninterrupted.

❷ *Identify the problem.* Ask each person in turn to describe the problem, then attempt to restate and summarize what you heard; make sure each person agrees with your summary of her statements.

Recreation and Fitness Leadership

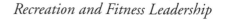

❸ *List the alternatives.* Brainstorm a list of realistic solutions from both sides.

❹ *Select the best alternative.* Narrow down choices and look for a win–win solution if possible. If not, can everyone at least "live with it"? Be realistic, respectful, and reasonable.

❺ *Write out a plan.* Record details and give everyone a copy. Decide on a date to meet to re-evaluate the current plan.

❻ *Evaluate at a later date.* Make necessary adjustments that everyone agrees with.

A neutral third party, or mediator, can help defuse a conflict between individuals by negotiating a peaceful resolution.

> **Example**
> Jenny heard a rumour about herself and thinks her former best friend Elise started it. Jenny is really angry and asks her friend Chandra to be there when she talks to Elise. Chandra is a friend of both girls and agrees to mediate. She encourages Jenny and Elise, who are willing to try to resolve their dispute, to tell each side of the issue and listen to each other. They discuss alternatives together and find a win–win solution. The girls write down the plan and agree to meet in a week to re-evaluate.

Adjudication

A process in which a neutral third party listens to all sides of a dispute and then makes a judgment based on the available information is known as **adjudication**. This takes responsibility for resolving the conflict from the disputants and hands it over to the adjudicator (usually an authority figure such as a parent, teacher, older sibling, or group leader). The adjudicator, sought out by one or more of the individuals involved in the conflict, must have her authority accepted by all parties or else her decision will be ignored.

> **Example**
> Every time Janice and her friends walk down a certain hall in the school, a group whistles and makes comments. The group thinks it is a joke, but the girls are intimidated and annoyed. They have asked the offending students to stop, but the problem persists. The girls ask their health teacher to solve their problem. The teacher has authority to reprimand the group and can execute further consequences if the misbehaviour continues.

A very common example of adjudication occurs when a professional athlete feels he should be paid the same as other players in the league who are at the same talent level, and the team management believes the athlete is not worth the money he is asking for. So the player and the team agree to go to arbitration to solve the problem. The arbitrator's decision is final.

Avoidance

Another method of dealing with conflict is to avoid it. However, this does not offer a permanent way of resolving the conflict, but it is an extremely popular short-term solution. The main positive value of **avoidance** is that it gives conflicting parties a chance to cool down. A person who avoids dealing with conflict is usually taking a passive stance. If this person puts others' needs before his own, takes the blame for others, attempts to apologize when it is not necessary, fails to make eye contact, allows himself to be intimidated, or shows other evidence of poor self-esteem, he may be reacting passively to the conflict. It is often the easiest method, but the problem with avoidance is that it is a passive technique that may not solve the problem but could intensify it and often delays its resolution.

> **Examples**
> Staying home from school to avoid doing a presentation in your science class and walking out of a group meeting because you don't agree with the event your student council is planning for the senior prom are examples of avoidance.

Accommodation

The technique known as **accommodation** occurs when one of the conflicting parties makes a conscious decision to place another person's viewpoint or needs before or above her own. This approach may be viewed by some as passive because it sometimes involves making personal sacrifices, often at the expense of your own needs. A sporting example occurs when a hockey player has a chance to score an open-net goal but instead passes the puck so that his teammate can score his third goal and record a hat trick.

Accommodation may also involve an element of empathy towards an opponent, such as discontinuing a full-court press in basketball to keep the score from getting too high. If a person perceives that she has an advantage over an opponent because of superior skill or experience, she may choose not to exert this to her advantage. Coaches may play their inferior (bench) players more and "sit" their superior players to give an unskilled opposing team the chance for a closer score. The outcome may be the same, but the opponent is not embarrassed and respect is often earned.

Rather than running up the score on an opponent when the game is in hand, coaches will often make a conscious decision to sit their superior players in favour of the bench players to keep the score respectable.

When an individual acknowledges a personal mistake, or accepts another person's point of view because this second viewpoint is backed by others, this is also a form of accommodation. However, if we always accept everyone else's viewpoints just to avoid conflict, then we are acting passively, and this method may encourage the conflicting party to expect similar compliance in different situations in the future.

Sporting Example

An inspirational story of accommodation occurred in a high school football game in the United States. The coach of a state championship team received a phone call from the coach of an inferior team, asking if one of his players (who had a mental disability) would be allowed to run one play at the end of their upcoming game. Little did the coach of the inferior team know, the opposing coach not only agreed but also told his team to allow the disabled player to run with the ball and score a touchdown, which was an unprecedented display of class. This was unheard of, and it did not bode well with some of the players, with some of the parents, and with the school administration because a shutout in that final regular-season game—which was almost certain against this inferior team—would give the team a state record for fewest points allowed in a season. The coach did not care about the record and insisted that his players allow this person to score a touchdown.

When the mentally challenged player entered the game for the last play and the ball was snapped to him, all the players on the opposing team stopped and watched him run slowly towards the end zone with the ball. The coach of the disabled player looked on in utter surprise and disbelief that his player was being allowed to run to the end zone. When he scored after being told several times which way to run, the disabled player did not even know how to celebrate. All he knew was that he had done something good, and he cheered as his teammates piled on top of him.

The final whistle blew and the game was over. The players on the winning team gave the disabled player a standing ovation, the fans were going absolutely nuts, and the coach of the disabled player was in tears as he walked across the field to embrace the other coach. The shocked coach could not believe that his opponent had allowed the player to score a touchdown, ruining a chance at a long-standing state record. It was one of the greatest displays of respect and accommodation in high school sports history.

> "Show class, have pride, and display character. If you do, winning takes care of itself.
> *Paul Bryant*

In summary, there are many strategies to reduce conflict. It is best not to rely on any one strategy. The effective leader will learn to recognize that every situation is unique and choose the best style of conflict management to fit the given situation. The student workbook contains exercises to help you examine your predominant style of conflict management and explore other possible solutions.

The Decision-Making Process

Decision making is a process that occurs as a reaction to a problem or an available opportunity. A problem usually involves a discrepancy between the status quo and some other preferred state of affairs, and it requires a consideration of alternative courses of action. Opportunities, on the other hand, occur when something unplanned happens, giving rise to ideas about new ways of proceeding to take advantage of that opportunity. An example of a problem is when an organization or sports team member experiences poor morale and dissatisfaction. An example of an opportunity is when the president of the athletic association steps down, and the group must secure a new student leader for the athletic program.

The Decision-Making Model

When presented with a decision to make, a leader should follow the IDEAL model of decision making presented in Figure 2.3. The model entails five steps arranged in a specific order. First, a problem must be identified before it can be solved. Alternative courses of action must be examined, and new ideas about ways to proceed must be carefully evaluated. At this point, the best course of action needs to be determined and the pros and cons of each action examined. Then it is important to act and later learn from the results of your actions.

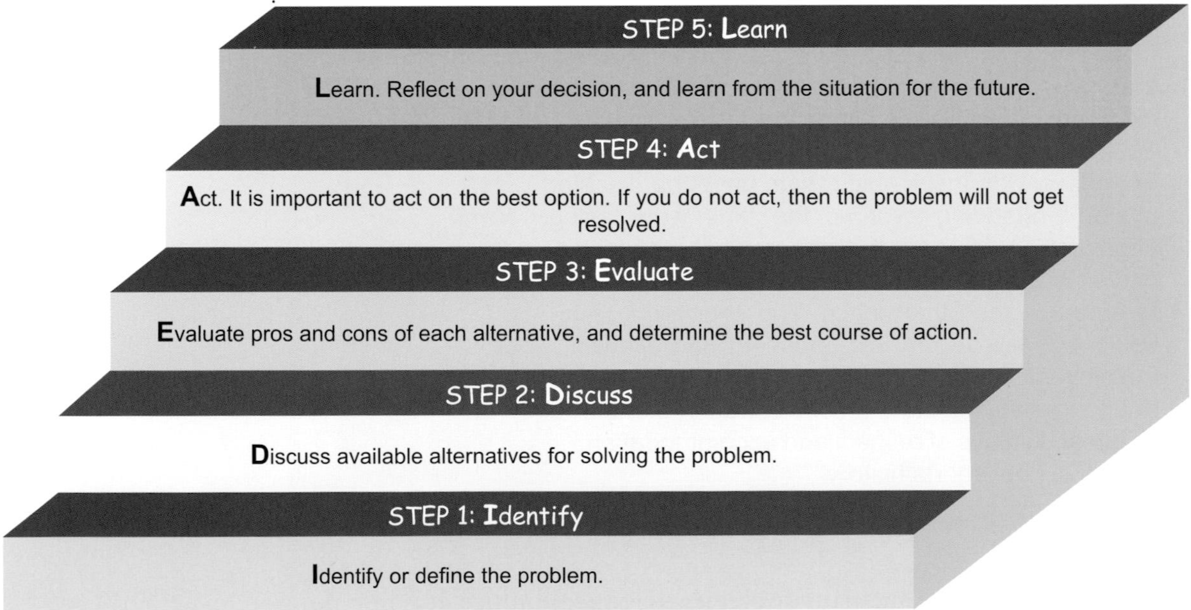

STEP 5: **L**earn

Learn. Reflect on your decision, and learn from the situation for the future.

STEP 4: **A**ct

Act. It is important to act on the best option. If you do not act, then the problem will not get resolved.

STEP 3: **E**valuate

Evaluate pros and cons of each alternative, and determine the best course of action.

STEP 2: **D**iscuss

Discuss available alternatives for solving the problem.

STEP 1: **I**dentify

Identify or define the problem.

Figure 2.3 The IDEAL model of decision making. Each step needs to be followed in order.

Following the IDEAL model gives a leader an objective way to make decisions. Rather than relying on subjective feelings or the overall attractiveness of an option, you are using rational criteria and considering all factors, weightings, and alternatives. This method can be used when making almost every type of decision.

Unfortunately, decision makers in many sports organizations are not always rational. In many instances, they do not carefully assess problems, identify relevant criteria, develop alternatives, and painstakingly evaluate every alternative to calculate the best solution. In fact, most decisions in the real world don't follow the IDEAL model. People are usually content to find an acceptable or reasonable solution to a problem rather than the optimal one.

Factors Affecting Decision Making

When a person arrives at the point of making a decision, several internal and external factors may affect how the final decision is actually made. Some of the common factors that influence decision making include judgmental shortcuts and individual decision-making styles. Judgmental shortcuts could lead you to make decisions based on previous outcomes or experiences that are similar but not necessarily the same as the current situation. If you take a shortcut without taking a thorough look at all the unique factors involved in a new situation, the decision could be wrong. Your decision-making style can also influence the effectiveness of your decision. If your style of decision making involves discussion with the parties involved, then you are less likely to overlook key factors in that decision. If you generally make decisions without involving others or without proper consideration of all factors, then the decision may be flawed.

*Although **the IDEAL model** provides leaders with an objective and rational way to make decisions, many factors come into play that may affect the final decision.*

Internal versus External Judgments

If you continue to play a sport that you no longer enjoy just because you recently purchased new equipment or paid for a membership, you are being influenced by a previous decision. This is considered an **external judgment** or influence. If you participate in a sport or activity just because your parents encourage you to, then you are again being influenced externally.

If you play this same sport because you "think it is cool" – even though you don't really enjoy the activity – then this may be an **internal judgment** or influence. Internal judgments are based on the values you place on outcomes and activities. If you place value on personal health, then you will be more likely to eat well, get plenty of sleep, and get regular physical activity. Internal judgments can also be negative; for example, if you care too much about what people think of you, then your decisions are more likely to be governed by peer pressure and not based on right and wrong.

Parental encouragement often influences the activities we choose to participate in, especially when we are young and impressionable.

SPIETH

Time Management

> "One of the best ways to save time is to think and plan ahead; five minutes of thinking can often save an hour of work.
> *John C. Maxwell*

A person's ability to effectively allocate his time and resources in order to achieve personal objectives is known as **time management**. This is an important skill for a leader to have. The better we are at managing our time, the more we can prioritize and accomplish, ultimately resulting in a greater sense of overall well-being. A very important spinoff of this skill is that it reduces stress and results in a more positive work–life balance. This provides us with the opportunity to be happier and more productive at work, rest, and play. An old saying summarizes this philosophy well, suggesting that we should "work smarter, not harder."

The person who continually feels she has no time to think or breathe can expect to experience burnout or stress-related illnesses at one point or another. Instead of allowing this to happen, it is important to acknowledge that now may be the time to cut back. Focus on doing fewer things more effectively rather than many things quite poorly. Time management does not mean filling every hour of every day. In reality, it means allowing some downtime in the day for unexpected circumstances that will invariably arise and allocating time for recreation and leisure activities.

You can't actually "manage" time, since there are only so many hours in every day and the clock keeps ticking no matter what. However, you can manage yourself in order to be more efficient with your time. You can focus on getting your "best work" done – on time – by using all your available resources. The following time management strategies will help you manage your time in a way that will result in your best work as well as give you a healthy balance in your life.

In order to achieve a positive work–life balance, it is important to allocate time for recreation and leisure activities.

Plan and prioritize   There is an old adage that states, "Failing to plan is planning to fail." Proper planning is absolutely essential for effective time management. The 5 or 10 minutes you spend organizing your schedule can result in a net savings of many hours during your total workweek or the length of an individual project.

Prepare "to-do" lists   Following from the preceding point, it is a good idea to make a list of everything you wish to accomplish each day. Prioritize the list according to the importance of completing each task. Include items that absolutely must be done; items that should be done, time permitting; and tasks that can wait until tomorrow. Break especially complex tasks into manageable steps, and specify a time frame for completing each step.

Draw up a schedule Schedule your daily activities according to the priorities you have set. Attack those projects that are absolutely critical first, then distribute your time over the other items on your list in order of priority and flexibility. For example, doing your homework before calling your friend about an outing tomorrow is prioritizing your activities.

Follow the "80/20" rule It has been speculated that 80 percent of our results are achieved from 20 percent of focused time. This suggests that we should devote more time to doing useful activities, tracking whatever it is that makes that 20 percent so productive, and then make the transition to allocating more time to productive work.

Plan some "downtime" Don't forget to incorporate downtime in your daily schedule. We all need a break every now and then to rest up and recharge our internal batteries. Ironically, research in the area of organizational behaviour has repeatedly shown that you can actually get more work done if you take several short breaks than if you choose to work straight through the day.

Identify your optimal working time This concept has also been referred to as your biological "prime time." Each one of us has a time of the day when we are most effective in our work efforts. It is therefore a good idea to schedule the most urgent and critical tasks during this optimal time, then plan the less demanding and less important tasks for other periods of your day.

Minimize distractions Organize your work environment in a manner that will increase your chances of completing the planned task. Sometimes it is necessary to go to your room instead of sitting on the couch in front of the TV. Make sure you have a comfortable work area or desk. Turn off your phone, your iPod, and your computer, or at least avoid responding to MSN messages or checking your Facebook account when you need to be focused on a task. If these steps fail, then it would be wise to simply go somewhere you can complete your project without distractions, such as the library.

Delegate responsibility to others A balanced division of labour within a group is absolutely crucial for any leader's ultimate success. When delegating tasks to others, ask yourself these three questions: (1) Is this something only I can do? (2) If not, to whom can the task be appropriately assigned? (3) Is this person adequately prepared to complete the task successfully? Then distribute the work according to your answers. Remember, if you try to do everything yourself, you could easily become overwhelmed.

Going to the library can increase the chances of completing an assigned task by minimizing common distractions encountered at home or at work.

Don't procrastinate Procrastination is one of the biggest time wasters in any organization. If a task absolutely must be performed, then there is no time like the present to complete it. After all, your responsibility will not simply go away by putting the task off until tomorrow. Another problem with procrastination is that it leaves you with little or no time to review your work, incorporate feedback, and ensure that the final product is accurate and of sufficient quality to reflect well on your efforts.

Putting It All Together

Becoming an effective leader involves four distinct areas of competence. Regardless of the situation, leaders are invariably responsible for promoting effective communication, managing conflict, making effective decisions, and managing their time wisely.

Communicating effectively requires a thorough knowledge of the communication process, and leaders must know how to overcome the many potential barriers to effective communication. When people work in a group setting, conflict often arises. Good leaders know which conflict management approach to use in a given situation and can execute these strategies well.

By utilizing the IDEAL model of decision making and being aware of individual differences in decision-making styles, leaders can make more effective decisions. Finally, there is only so much time in a day, and leaders must practice meticulous time management. Each of the four skills just outlined can be learned and developed by following the guidelines offered in this chapter.

Key Terms

accommodation	IDEAL model of decision making
active listening	information overload
adjudication	intergroup conflict
assertive	internal judgment
avoidance	interpersonal conflict
communication	intragroup conflict
compromise	intrapersonal conflict
conflict management	lateral communication
defensiveness	mediation
depersonalized conflict	message
downward communication	message channel
external judgment	one-way communication
feedback	paraphrasing
filtering	personalized conflict
"I" messages	receiver

selective attention
sender
symbolic form
time management

two-way communication
upward communication
win–win

Review Questions

1. Describe the communication process, and identify the key components.

2. In your own words, explain the differences between one-way communication and two-way communication. List two examples of each type of communication, and describe two problems that can arise while using one-way communication.

3. List four common barriers that you might experience when communicating in a leadership setting. Discuss strategies for overcoming barriers to communication.

4. Describe the three directions of communication, giving an example of each.

5. Explain the differences between intrapersonal, interpersonal, intragroup, and intergroup conflict. Describe two causes of group conflict, and discuss strategies to correct or avoid these within a group.

6. How does stress increase the chance of group conflict?

7. List several observable and measurable ways you can improve your active listening skills, and think of two personal examples.

8. How does active listening improve communication and help resolve conflict?

9. Identify a problem or decision that you need to address in the near future, and outline exactly how you would use the IDEAL model to arrive at an objective solution to this problem or decision.

10. Outline in detail how you can incorporate three of the time management strategies in your daily life.

In This Chapter:

CHAPTER 3
Group Development

In this chapter, you will learn about the following:

❶ The classification of groups and why people join them

❷ The five stages of group development

❸ Factors that impact effective group development

❹ The importance of developing trust within a group or organization

❺ Group decision making and its by-products

> *"Coming together is a beginning;*
> *Keeping together is progress;*
> *Working together is success."*
> Henry Ford

Have you noticed that when individuals interact in groups, they act differently from when they are alone? This occurs not just in a social context but also when people come together in groups to undertake projects. Working cohesively, in concert, often produces superior results over individual efforts. In this chapter, we examine the basic concepts regarding groups and demonstrate how an understanding of groups can help leaders function more effectively.

Defining and Classifying Groups

Groups and teams are not the same thing. Groups can range from several strangers standing together at a bus stop, to an elementary grade 5 class, to colleagues working on a project. Teams, on the other hand, can include a sports team, a hospital emergency room team, or a group that has worked together and evolved into a team unit.

Work Groups

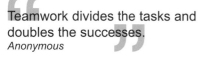
Teamwork divides the tasks and doubles the successes.
Anonymous

A work group interacts in order to share information, eventually making decisions that will help each group member perform within the areas of his own responsibilities. Work groups do not engage in collective work that requires everyone's participation. This means that the performance of the group is only the sum total of each individual group member's contribution. For example, teachers at a high school will meet to discuss topics about the upcoming school year, changes to the building, and staff changes, and each department will update the others on new initiatives taken on by their departments. The teachers leave the meeting with information and ideas that they can implement within their own classes.

Work Teams

A work team, on the other hand, represents a small number of individuals with complementary skills who are working towards a common result, a

Recreation and Fitness Leadership

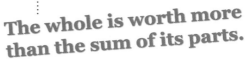

performance goal, and personal accountability. A work team exemplifies **positive synergy**, where the result of the group's performance is greater than the sum of individual member inputs. Simply put, the group is successful because all group members work together towards a common group goal.

> ## When a Group Becomes a Team
>
> Work groups evolve into work teams when the following conditions are met:
>
> - The members of the team share in the overall leadership – each may assume the leadership role at different times.
>
> - Accountability is shared by the team as a whole, and responsibility is shared equally among team members.
>
> - The mission of the organization or group is developed by the team itself, not an outside source; the goals of the group are also created by the group itself.
>
> - The team works continually, not just at regularly scheduled times.
>
> - The overall effectiveness of the team is measured in terms of team outcomes and goals rather than individual outcomes and goals.

The whole is worth more than the sum of its parts.

Two heads are better than one.

SYNERGISM: the action of separate substances that in combination produce an effect greater than that of any component taken alone.

You can probably think of many personal experiences involving students, administrative councils, athletic councils, church youth groups, or summer camps that relied on work teams to accomplish the objectives of the group. However, simply creating a team does not automatically improve organizational success. The leader, also known as the team leader or **project manager**, must identify and take full advantage of each group member's strengths. For example, the teachers within the physical education department meet to create an extracurricular events calendar for the year. After the work team brainstorms to come up with possible activities and events, the individual teachers volunteer to organize specific activities based on their personal interests and expertise. The project manager/team leader helps the work team choose activity leaders within the group, but each group member also has the opportunity to assume a leadership role. Each

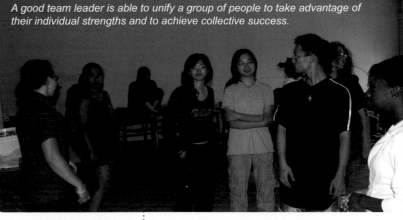

A good team leader is able to unify a group of people to take advantage of their individual strengths and to achieve collective success.

work team member assists with the other activities involving planning and supervision. The work team pulls together to achieve collective success.

In the following sections of this chapter, you will learn that successful work teams have certain characteristics that make them effective and efficient units. Therefore, the leaders of any organization need to recognize these characteristics and ensure that they are present in the team members. We start by analyzing the underlying stages of group development to see how groups actually evolve.

The Five-Stage Model of Group Development

Figure 3.1 The five stages of group development.

It is generally accepted that groups and teams pass through five specific developmental stages: forming, storming, norming, performing, and adjourning. This sequence is depicted in Figure 3.1.

Although team development does not always follow this step-by-step sequence, a general process exists whereby a group of individuals come together, engage in actions and reactions, and finally emerge as a cohesive work team. Sometimes groups will become stuck in a stage for a period of time or may revert back to a previous stage until all members are ready to move forward. This can and will occur occasionally, and the team leader must allocate time for the group to deal with the issues and then move forward. A leader's understanding of group formation will help her use strategies that promote overall team harmony. For this reason, we now turn our attention to the five stages of team development.

Forming

The process of group members familiarizing themselves with one another is called **forming**. The group members have just been introduced to each other. The forming process begins with a good deal of uncertainty about the group's purpose, structure, and overall leadership. For example, think of times when you have worked with youth groups, such as coaching athletes or volunteering your services at a summer camp. At this point, you will remember how team members assess one another's strengths and weaknesses, engage in social comparisons, and determine the probability of work team success. They also engage in "testing the waters" to determine which behaviours are seen as acceptable and which are not. Testing the waters may involve pushing a personal point of view to see how the group will react. Will they accept your point of view or will they offer resistance?

Every group goes through a period of forming, during which members become acquainted and assess one another's strengths and weaknesses.

Storming

The second stage of group or team formation can be quite volatile, hence the term **storming**. This stage of development, also termed *infighting*, is characterized by conflict and open rebellion – not exactly the recipe for team cohesion. These power struggles are typical of the storming stage, which is almost always characterized by intragroup conflict. The members seem to accept the existence of the group but continue to resist the constraints that the group imposes on individuality. Another confounding factor is that there is also conflict over who will ultimately control the group. When this stage of group development is complete, a relatively clear hierarchy of team leadership will have emerged (Figure 3.2).

It is important to note that some groups never completely emerge from the storming stage. A group such as this will always be less able to complete task goals because of all the interpersonal problems and conflict. Storming is both necessary and beneficial for the group since each person needs to understand the other group members and the strengths, weaknesses, characteristics, and skills that they bring to the group.

This sets the stage for the norming process.

Norming

When groups are able to resolve the interpersonal conflict inherent in the storming phase, they reach the next phase of development, **norming**, where close relationships develop and the group starts to exhibit cohesiveness. Team members increasingly become organized, and individual cooperation evolves. All of a sudden, a sense of group identity and camaraderie is apparent. At this point, the group develops norms, which are acceptable standards of behaviour, group goals, or values that are shared by all group members. Once agreed on, norms act to influence the behaviour of the group members. The norming phase can be considered complete when group structure becomes solid and the group recognizes a common set of expectations regarding correct group behaviour.

Performing

In this phase, when significant task progress is being accomplished, the group has reached the **performing** stage of development. This becomes noticeable when a group just seems to come together well to perform individual functions for the benefit of the team. The team structure is completely functional and acceptable to individual members at this point. The total energy of the group has moved from getting to know one another to performing the specified task at hand in an appropriate fashion. When work teams are formed, performing is the team leader's ultimate goal.

Adjourning

For permanent work teams, task performance is the final stage in overall group development. But there are also times when a temporary committee, team, or task force is put in place. This occurs most often when a group within an organization has been assigned a limited task to perform, within a particular time frame. Once that task has been completed, an **adjourning** stage takes place. At this point, the group prepares to disband, replacing the overall team goal of task performance with simply wrapping up activities. When this happens, some members are happy the job has been completed, while others experience a sense of loss of the team camaraderie that has evolved over the group/team formation process. This stage has also been

Group Development – Forming to Adjourning

Stage 1: Forming

You are a member of a group that has been asked to create and implement a volleyball tournament. You are meeting the other group members for the first time. The team leader has provided information and direction.

Stage 2: Storming

Your group meets to determine the course of action for the volleyball tournament. Areas of responsibility for each group member need to be distributed, and a chairperson must be appointed. Officiating, scheduling, registration, refreshments, advertising, promotions, and set-up and take-down of equipment are some of the areas of responsibility that require leadership. The group must decide who is best suited for each area based on each person's interests and expertise. Not everyone will be happy with the area assigned to her. This could involve storming until the roles are assigned and the group is ready to move on to the organization of the tournament.

Stage 3: Norming

Your group now begins to organize the volleyball tournament. Meeting once a week, each member updates the group on the progress within his area of responsibility. The group offers support and advice on challenges that arise, and individuals volunteer to assist if necessary.

Stage 4: Performing

The volleyball tournament is under way, and the group is working well together. The group members meet early in the morning to set up for the day and go over last-minute items. During the day the group members work together, helping each other and the participants in the tournament.

Stage 5: Adjourning

The volleyball tournament was a success, and the group meets to evaluate the event and wrap up any loose ends. The group enjoyed organizing and implementing the event and looks forward to volunteering for another tournament during the year.

Recreation and Fitness Leadership

called *re-forming*. If the experience was positive, members may decide to work together on a different project because they want to continue to develop the relationship or they enjoy interacting with each other.

Factors Affecting Group Development

Just as groups can be seen to consistently pass through a sequential series of stages in becoming a team, several important factors play a large part in this overall developmental process. In this section, we highlight the observation that groups have a common set of principles that shape the behaviour of all participating members.

Group Norms

If you have ever played golf, you know that golfers do not speak while their opponent or partner is putting on the green. Similarly, it is customary for spectators at a tennis match to remain quiet while the ball is in play. The reason for this is that certain **norms** operate in any given group. In other words, the members of that group share acceptable standards of behaviour that are considered to be appropriate.

Of special importance to the project manager or team leader is that groups exert considerable pressure on members to comply with previously established standards. When individuals violate group norms, other members often move to punish or correct the deviant behaviour. An exemplary leader will therefore strive to understand the norms operating in any group or work team so that he can better interpret individual and group behaviours and make the necessary recommendations for positive change.

Acceptable standards of behaviour vary from one group to another. For example, golfers do not speak when a playing partner or opponent is putting on the green (above), and students normally raise their hands when they have something to contribute to the group (below).

Group Size

The size of a group definitely affects overall team behaviour. However, the effect of size varies positively or negatively depending on the purpose and goals of the group. For example, smaller groups are generally faster than larger groups at completing assigned tasks. Smaller groups with three to seven members can often make decisions quickly with less discussion and interruption. Group consensus is much easier. Larger groups can bring forth more opinions; thus it can take longer to hear all ideas and arrive at a group decision. A volleyball tournament group consisting of six members – each member assigned a specific area of responsibility – performs well because the group is an optimal size with separate tasks delegated to each member. If a group is assigned one or more problem-solving tasks, then larger groups will generally outperform their smaller counterparts. This occurs because large groups (12 or more members) are good at achieving diverse input from team members and excel at fact-finding ventures. See an example in the box *Size Matters*.

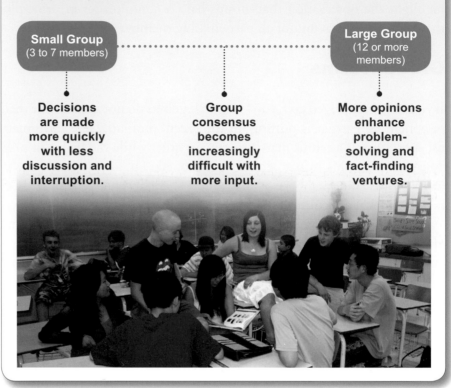

Size Matters

Deciding between a larger or smaller group to form a work team often depends on the ultimate goal for that collection of individuals. A large group of 15 students meet to brainstorm possible solutions to vandalism at their school. This group has been asked to provide possible solutions to the problem. Since there are no real tasks involved and the group will meet only once and then disperse, a larger group format is deemed to be more effective. Many ideas are brought forward by individuals in the group, and the principal will take these ideas and determine which one(s) to implement.

Small Group
(3 to 7 members)

Large Group
(12 or more members)

Decisions are made more quickly with less discussion and interruption.

Group consensus becomes increasingly difficult with more input.

More opinions enhance problem-solving and fact-finding ventures.

Leadership Dimensions

Another factor affecting group development is the **leadership dimension** expressed by the team leader. Good leaders are insightful and versatile. They can assess a group's stage of development and choose the dimension that will bring the group forward in its progress. The four dimensions are based on the variables of relationship and task.

High Relationship/Low Task

This dimension works best when the group is still in the forming stage of development but is faced with a task that has a strict deadline. Although the group is just coming together, the leader must ensure that the group is working on the task and is moving quickly through the forming, storming, and norming stages. Relationships among members within the group and with the leader are very important at this stage to ensure that the group forms cohesively and moves towards completing the task on time.

For example, a group meets to plan a corporate picnic. The group members spend some time at their first meeting getting to know each other by introducing themselves and discussing why they volunteered to sit on the picnic committee. Therefore, at this point the relationship of the group is more important than the task at hand, hence high relationship/low task.

High Relationship/High Task

This dimension is appropriate when the team leader is working with the group on the task as well as building relationships within the group. The group has now formed and is progressing on time with the task. The group itself has moved through the forming stage and is almost through the storming stage of group development.

The leader or chairperson of the corporate picnic committee works on building group relationships but at the same time sets timelines for tasks to be completed for the picnic. To be ready for the event day, the group members must get to work, but they also must get along and work cooperatively to get these jobs done on time.

Low Relationship/High Task

This dimension becomes critical when the group is moving out of the storming stage. The leader works diligently on the task while the group works through the norming stage of development. The task has a timeline that must be met, and the relationship of the group has moved to a point where members have established their responsibilities and **roles** (i.e., the expected behaviour patterns that accompany their positions) and can focus on the tasks. The picnic committee now knows each other's strengths and weaknesses and chooses tasks to match individual strengths. The group members work within their assigned roles.

Low Relationship/Low Task

This is the appropriate leadership dimension when the group is in the performing stage. The leader now offers advice when needed, but the group essentially functions on its own. The group members work well together and understand the implications of the task deadline. Although the group requires little leadership, the leader may need to step in temporarily to assume one of the other situational leadership dimensions and bring the group back on track. Challenges and setbacks requiring situational leadership intervention often occur in group settings, so leaders must be prepared to adapt, adjust, and mediate conflict.

Leader's Behaviours

Leaders can demonstrate task or relationship behaviours (see Chapter 1). Task behaviours are often seen when working on jobs with set deadlines.

> You may be on top of the heap, but remember, you are still part of it.
> *Anonymous*

A good leader is versatile, which means the leadership dimension expressed by the team leader should change – depending on the group's stage of development.

Relationship behaviours, on the other hand, are actions that help the group work together cohesively. However, the leader is not the only one who exhibits these behaviours. A wise team leader, especially one who is moving from total control of the group to relinquishing control, recognizes that group members often take on these leadership behaviours as well.

Task behaviours that help keep the group on track and moving towards completing the task at hand include the following roles:

Initiator – generates new ideas and suggests solutions to existing problems.

Elaborator/Clarifier – expands on existing ideas and may restate ideas.

Summarizer – pulls ideas together and ensures consensus.

Recorder – records details for current and future progress.

Time keeper – makes sure the group observes time limits and deadlines.

Relationship behaviours, on the other hand, keep individuals within the group feeling wanted and valuable. They include the following roles:

Encourager – responsive to individuals on a personal level and makes everyone feel important.

Gate keeper/Involver – ensures everyone has the opportunity to contribute ideas.

Mediator – helps keep harmony in the group by suggesting compromises.

Custodian – keeps checking to ensure that the group doesn't violate basic values.

Just as task and relationship behaviours or roles can have positive influences on a group, **negative behaviours** will often surface as well. It is important to be aware of these influences and nip them in the bud. Negative behaviours include the following roles:

Blocker – opposes others' ideas and continues to get off topic and not listen.

Joker – tries to be the centre of attention and may make fun of others' ideas.

Dominator – tries to impose his own ideas at the expense of others.

Hidden agenda – uses the team to fulfill her own personal gains.

Dependent – has no ideas of his own and depends on others for ideas and opinions.

Group leaders need to be aware of these negative roles and work with individuals displaying these behaviours to turn the negative into positive.

Group Cohesiveness

Groups almost always differ in their cohesiveness, or the degree to which individual members are attracted to a group – and each other – as well as the motivation to remain in that group. Cohesiveness is an important concept because it has been linked to the group's overall productivity. In terms of developing group cohesiveness, and hence productivity, a team leader is advised to consider implementing the following recommendations:

► Reduce the size of your group.

► Try to increase the time team members spend together.

► Invite and encourage team members to "buy into" the group's goals.

► Physically isolate the group as much as possible.

► Impress upon the team members the valued status of the group and the difficulty of gaining membership in that group.

► Try to reward the group members equally rather than individually.

► Encourage competition with other work groups or work teams.

Since cohesiveness can increase a group's overall productivity, team leaders should encourage group members to spend more time together, even outside of the usual group setting.

To promote group cohesiveness, your group should contain a blend of the four personality dimension colours (see Chapter 1). This ensures not only that the group moves ahead with the task at hand but also that the relationship of the group is promoted. Blues and Golds can be extremely helpful in promoting both the task and the relationship dimensions.

Group Composition

Most group or team activities require a variety of background knowledge and skills. Heterogeneous groups, or groups composed of dissimilar individuals, are more likely to have diverse information and abilities. When a work group or work team is diverse in terms of gender, age, personalities, educational background, task specialization, and experience, there is an increased likelihood that the group will possess the needed skills to successfully complete its tasks. The bottom line is that diversity promotes group conflict, which stimulates creative alternatives, which in turn lead to improved decision making.

Heterogeneous groups that are composed of diverse individuals bring a wider range of personalities, backgrounds, skills, and experience to the table than a group made up of similar individuals.

For the purpose of team building, a team leader could ensure that each colour – blue, gold, orange, and green – is represented within the group, and depending on the reason for the group's existence, members of a particular colour can be added or omitted. For instance, if the group has been created to complete a predetermined task with a tight deadline, then one orange, one blue, and one green individual should be included along with several gold members. If, however, the group has been created to brainstorm possible advertising methods for an upcoming event, then each colour should again be represented but with an emphasis on orange and blue members.

Group Selection in a Gym Class

Leaders often have the task of dividing a large group into smaller ones to form teams for games, tournaments, or relays. Avoid setting up a negative, self-esteem-draining scenario in which you select the captains and they take turns choosing their team members. No one wants to be the last one picked!
  Here are some options:

▶ **When it is important that the teams be balanced in skill:**

(a) Set the teams up ahead of time based on your observations of members' skills, strength, size, or speed.
(b) Select team captains and have them distribute the group members between them privately. No doubt they will try to create balanced teams!

▶ **When size or skill matters:**

(a) Line participants up by height and number off (e.g., every second person: 1, 2, 1, 2, 1, 2, and so on).
(b) Ask participants to pair up with someone who is the same size and strength, or who runs about the same speed, and split the pairs up to form two teams.

▶ **When the groups may be heterogenous:**

(a) Divide on the basis of favourite food, sock or shoe colour, birthdates, brand of toothpaste, and so on.
(b) Line up randomly and number off.

No one wants to be picked last, but there are many creative ways to select groups that will preserve students' self-esteem.

  Recreation and Fitness Leadership

Preselected Groups

Sometimes a leader is put in charge of a preselected group. The group may have been together for some time or chosen prior to the appointment of a leader. The leader is now faced with the challenge of making this group work. It is important to determine which group members possess which strengths and then promote these within the group. The Personality Dimensions workshop mentioned in Chapter 1 can assist the leader with this discovery. Knowing personality dimension colours within the group, the leader can assign tasks to suit each person. For example, within the corporate picnic committee, the Blues organize the decorations and entertainment, the Greens schedule the events and prepare the menu, the Golds take meeting minutes and organize the registration, and the Oranges prepare the games and contests. As a group, the members will discover their own strengths and how they can positively contribute to achieve the group goals and the task at hand.

> "I start with the premise that the function of leadership is to produce more leaders, not followers."
> *Ralph Nader*

Developing Organizational Trust

High-performance teams are characterized by high mutual trust among members. The individuals believe in each other's integrity, character, and ability. But trust is fragile – it takes a long time to develop, it can be easily destroyed, and it is hard to regain once it has been lost. Five key dimensions underlie the concept of trust.

Integrity

Integrity refers to honesty and truthfulness. This characteristic appears to be the most important when someone assesses another's trustworthiness. Your integrity is crucial to your ongoing relationships with classmates, team members, and peers in any administrative task you take on, such as student council representative or summer day camp counsellor.

Honesty and integrity are crucial characteristics that all summer day camp counsellors must possess to maintain the necessary level of trust among all participants and team members.

Competence

Competence refers to a person's technical and human relations skills. The bottom line is that employees or classmates will not listen if they believe the team leader does not know what she is talking about. You have probably already noticed this same tendency in the different work groups you have been a member of, such as church groups or athletic councils. It is critical that followers respect the leader and trust that person's ability to carry out his responsibilities.

Consistency

Consistency reflects an individual's predictability, reliability, and good judgment in handling various situations. People quickly notice if a leader does not practice what she preaches. It is therefore important to attempt to act consistently across the numerous situations that will arise in your organization. A major problem occurs when you treat people differently because of your personal feelings for those individuals.

Loyalty

Loyalty reflects the willingness to protect and save face for another person in your organization. The whole idea of trust is that you can depend on someone to not act in his own best interest behind your back. You will likely have no problem remembering a time when you stood up for a friend or classmate because you felt that was the right thing to do. This example is exactly what loyalty is all about!

Openness

Openness refers to the overall willingness of a leader to share ideas, information, and feelings freely. People often wonder, "Can I rely on this person to give me the full truth, regardless of the situation?" Openness is also very important in your interpersonal relationships. Your friends, classmates, and team members need to perceive that you are open to their suggestions and in tune with their feelings.

Following are some valuable suggestions for building trust with a group's members:

A good team leader will share ideas, information, and feelings freely, but he will also make each group member feel comfortable doing the same by demonstrating honesty, dependability, and openness.

▶ *Always, always tell the absolute truth.* Never lie or withhold important information from anyone. Since integrity is critical for the development of trust, a leader must be seen as a person who tells the truth, no matter what the consequences.

▶ *Always be fair with team members.* Before making decisions or taking action, remember to consider how others will see these actions in terms of objectivity and fairness.

▶ *Always keep your promises.* Trust develops only when people believe they can rely on a leader to remain dependable. This means you must always keep your word.

▶ *Demonstrate confidence in your role as leader.* Admiration and respect from followers is a by-product of demonstrating professional and technical abilities. Pay particular attention to demonstrating communication, interpersonal, and job-related expertise.

▶ *Demonstrate consistency in your actions.* People really need consistency from a leader. So remember to take the time to completely understand your beliefs and values, and then follow these principles to guide your decisions.

▶ *Do everything possible to maintain confidence.* People tend to trust those individuals who are discreet and reliable. When a follower tells a leader something in confidence, that person needs to know it will not be discussed with others in the organization.

▶ *Practice openness with your classmates, employees, or followers.* It is also important to be candid about problems and fully disclose all relevant information.

▶ *Don't be afraid to speak your true feelings.* If a leader can become comfortable with sharing personal feelings, the followers will gain a better understanding of that person, and they will respect the leader more for this.

The Group Decision-Making Process

Today, a large majority of decisions within organizations are actually made by groups, teams, committees, or task forces. In this section, we briefly examine the group decision-making process. We begin by analyzing the effectiveness of individual versus group decisions.

Individual Decision Making

The major advantage of individual decision making is *speed*. Individuals do not need to hold meetings, listen to everyone's concerns, and discuss alternatives. So, if a decision needs to be made quickly, it is best made by an individual. In addition, individual decisions have a clearer accountability, since everyone knows who made the decision and who is responsible for the outcome. Finally, individuals make more consistent decisions than their group counterparts. This is likely due to the fact that individuals approach different problems with the same set of personal values, while a group can fluctuate from decision to decision.

Group Decision Making

Group decision making, on the other hand, has its own distinct advantages. First of all, groups are able to generate more complete information and knowledge than are individuals. By pooling the resources and experiences of several people, groups can bring more input into the decision-making process. Groups also offer increased diversity of viewpoints, so more approaches and alternatives are presented. In addition, group decisions lead to a higher acceptance of the solution, since several people offered input in the process and often see their suggestions in the final product.

Individual decision making can be more advantageous when decisions must be made quickly, but groups are able to generate more ideas and information by pooling the resources and experiences of many people.

The bottom line is that groups make higher-quality decisions than do individuals because the expertise and experience of several people have been incorporated into the final decision.

This leads to the obvious question, "Who makes better decisions – individuals or groups?" In reality, it depends. At certain times, decisions are handled best by individuals. Individual decision making is preferred when the decision is relatively unimportant and doesn't require employee input for success. It is also appropriate for individuals to make a decision when they have all the information required to do so. When the corporate picnic committee meets, the leader or chairperson books the room and orders refreshments. The group does not need to be involved in these decisions.

Overall, in terms of quality decision making, groups are almost always superior – they generate more alternatives, are more accurate and more creative, and produce higher-quality decisions than do individuals. But groups are less efficient in their decision making – they use up more time and resources to come to an ultimate decision. Group consensus is the optimum in group decision making. Consensus occurs when the entire group agree on the decision made. All members support this decision and agree to abide by it.

Groupthink

Be aware of groupthink, which can affect decision making in a negative way. Groupthink is best understood by asking yourself if you have ever felt like speaking up in a group setting but decided against it for one reason or another. One possible explanation could be shyness in terms of sharing feelings or ideas in a group. More likely, it is very possible that you have been the victim of **groupthink**, where individual group members are so concerned about reaching agreement with other members that the desire for consensus overrides the best possible viewpoint for solving the problem. Common symptoms of groupthink include the following:

► Individual members of the group tend to rationalize any resistance to their original assumptions.

► Group members pressure hesitant individuals to support the majority viewpoint.

► To appear in consensus with others, those who question the group opinion remain silent about their original misgivings on the issue.

► The group interprets member silence as a distinct "yes" vote for the majority opinion.

Any one of these symptoms leads to poor decision making, including incomplete analysis of the issue, lack of a proper information search, interpretation of information from one side only, and failure to reconsider earlier rejected alternatives.

Groups generally make higher-quality decisions than individuals because more people have had input into the final decision. Can you think of scenarios when this is not the case? When do individuals have an advantage over groups?

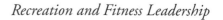

Recreation and Fitness Leadership

Brainstorming

A technique known as brainstorming has been used as one acceptable method of overcoming pressures to conform within an interacting group. **Brainstorming** employs an idea-generation process that specifically encourages the group members to offer any and all alternatives without fear of criticism from the team leader or other participants.

In a typical brainstorming session, 6 to 12 individuals sit around a table. The team leader then states the problem in a clear and simple manner. At this point, the members "freewheel" as many suggestions and alternatives as possible within a specified length of time. Absolutely no criticism is allowed, and every alternative is recorded for future discussion and analysis. For example, you may use this strategy to determine ways in which your school council or sports team can take their performance to the next level. Opinions generated in this type of discussion can often lead to creative ways of improving team effectiveness.

The main value of brainstorming is simply generating new ideas or alternatives. Then, each individual in the group silently and independently ranks the different ideas presented. The final group decision is made objectively by selecting the solution with the highest aggregate rating from the team members. The major advantage of this technique is that it can be conducted in a formal meeting, yet it permits the independent thinking that is usually restricted by groupthink in the traditional interacting group.

Brainstorming can be used as an effective technique to generate ideas and alternatives to many problems. This reduces the pressures to conform within a group and encourages creative solutions.

Putting It All Together

Group decision making has its advantages and disadvantages. Although groups usually arrive at better decisions, they are not without their own set of problems. Conflict is a normal occurrence in team development and as such should not be discouraged. Groups pass through specific stages in their development sequence, and a wise leader will anticipate and understand each of these phases.

The behaviour of individuals in groups is always more than the sum total of individual input. When people interact with others, they respond quite differently from when they are alone. Groups can be seen to have a common set of principles that guide the behaviour of all participating members. The most noteworthy of these include roles, norms, group size, cohesiveness, and composition.

Group effectiveness and success are determined by how well the group members set goals and objectives, utilize the resources available to them, trust each other, and minimize and deal with conflict as it arises. The leader must be observant and willing to facilitate the group through all the stages of group development. It is challenging to be an effective group member, but the rewards are often well worth the effort.

Key Terms

adjourning	norms
brainstorming	openness
cohesiveness	performing
competence	positive synergy
consistency	project manager
forming	relationship behaviours
groupthink	role
integrity	storming
leadership dimension	task behaviours
loyalty	work group
negative behaviours	work team
norming	

Review Questions

1. What is the major difference between a work group and a work team? Provide a notable example of each.

2. Describe the five-stage group development model.

3. Briefly outline the various factors that affect group development, providing examples from your personal past experiences.

4. List and briefly explain the four leadership dimensions when it comes to groups.

5. Identify when task behaviours and relationship behaviours are most appropriate, and give some examples of each.

6. List seven factors a leader should consider when promoting group cohesiveness.

7. How can diversity improve decision making?

8. Briefly describe the five dimensions underlying the concept of trust?

9. Who makes better decisions – individuals or groups? Explain your answer, and suggest when each would be most appropriate to make decisions.

10. Outline the advantages of utilizing the brainstorming decision-making strategy. Can you think of any disadvantages?

 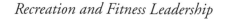

Recreation and Fitness Leadership

> **NAME:** Kevin French
> **OCCUPATION:** Program Director, King Day Camp and Outdoor Centre
> **EDUCATION:** Outdoor Recreation Technician, Seneca College, King Campus

▶ *What do you do?*

As the program director for King Day Camp and Outdoor Centre, I am responsible for designing and implementing all of the outdoor experiential activities we offer throughout the year. In addition, I am responsible for creating the risk management practices that govern how those programs run. I also hire, train, and evaluate the program staff who work for the camp and outdoor centre. The position is a year-round job with a tremendous amount of variety and interaction with a wide range of people.

▶ *What is unique about your job?*

The outdoor component of my job is what makes it so unique in the recreation field. Each season of the year sees us working with a different sector of

the public (summer – children age 4 to 16; spring – school-age children; fall – school-age children and college students; and we work with corporate groups throughout the year). To be able to use the outdoor experience as a tool for developing people is a wonderful opportunity for all who work in this sector of recreation.

▶ *What was your motivation for pursuing this field?*

I have had some tremendous outdoor experiences in my life that have helped develop me as a person. My goal is to provide the same experiences for people whom I interact with through my career.

▶ *How competitive is the field?*

With the seasonal nature of the outdoor field, there are very few full-time jobs. Individuals who make the choice to work in this sector will usually work seasonal contracts, which can become tiring and make it difficult to establish roots in one place. The competition for full-time jobs therefore is very real.

▶ *What career advice would you give to students interested in this area?*

Become a generalist in many different aspects of the outdoor experience in the beginning, and as you experience different work opportunities in the outdoor field, look to specialize in one or two areas. It's very easy to get wrapped up in the "cool" factor of the hard skills (mountain biking, skiing, climbing, and paddling are examples) associated with outdoor jobs. Be sure to take the time to develop your "soft" skills (group development, communication skills, and conflict resolution, to name a few). You should also obtain a minimum of a standard first aid certificate (wilderness first aid is a good idea if you plan on working in wilderness-based areas) and also a swim certification through the Lifesaving Society (in 2007 the minimum most employers will require is a Bronze Medallion; however, look for that to change in the coming years).

UNIT 2

FACILITATION OF RECREATION AND LEISURE

4  Leisure, Recreation, and Wellness

5  Needs Assessment

6  Event Coordination

7  Promoting Participation

"Play has been man's most useful preoccupation." This quote by Frank Caplan, a pioneer in the development of children's educational toys, shows the value of including recreation in our lives. Thankfully, our modern society is becoming more and more aware of the importance of balancing work and play. What we do in and with our leisure time potentially makes us more fulfilled as human beings as well as more productive in the workforce. What's more, there is ample evidence that our level of physical activity in our free time plays a major role in our health.

In Unit 2, you will discover the importance of recreation in our society as well as explore some of the factors that prevent participation. Since recreation and leisure provide the framework for active living, how effectively we overcome these barriers will play a large part in the long-term health of our population. With this in mind, you will develop the skills to plan, organize, promote, and implement events that encourage healthy, active living. Further, you will be able to draw upon this knowledge throughout your life, as a volunteer in your community or as a recreation professional. There is high demand for enthusiastic, committed individuals to manage recreation programs and facilities, both in the nonprofit and commercial sectors.

You will also learn how to choose the programs and activities that best suit the needs and abilities of the participants. Creating and providing events and activities that meet an individual's or group's needs for amusement and exercise can provide you with a feeling of great accomplishment. Just think about it: How many people will be taking their first steps towards health and wellness in a program that you designed?

In This Chapter:

CHAPTER 4
Leisure, Recreation, and Wellness

In this chapter, you will learn about the following:

❶ The definition of leisure, recreation, and wellness

❷ The evolution of recreation in society

❸ The benefits of and potential barriers to recreation opportunities

❹ How to become physically active

> "Don't drop out, drop in.
> Don't cop out, compete.
> Don't exit, excel."
> Pierre Elliott Trudeau

Health is an important resource for living, but it is very specific to people's lives. Consider the ways recreation, leisure, and wellness are expressed in your own life and the ways you set out to contribute to your health through being physically active, spending time with friends and family, enjoying time to contemplate the world around you, and challenging yourself to reach new heights. To achieve good health, it is important to personalize the information presented and to reflect on the various dimensions of health from your own perspective to make them relevant to your daily life.

What Is Leisure?

Leisure is free time that can be spent as you see fit. Think about how you spend your time each day. When you eliminate the necessary tasks that you must complete each day, such as work, school, sleep, meals, chores, and grooming, what is left? Your mental list now includes all the activities and pastimes that make up your leisure time.

We schedule our leisure time each day so that we can participate in the activities that we enjoy. This time can be spent with family, with friends, in solitude at home, or out in the community. The possibilities are endless!

Unstructured free time can be used to daydream, read a book, listen to music, nap – anything you want to do; it's not necessarily planned use of time, but it's not necessarily wasted time, either. It is your body's chance to rejuvenate itself.

What does leisure mean to you?

Leisure Defined

- Leisure is "time when one is free to relax and do as one wishes."

- Leisure is "freedom from time-consuming duties, responsibilities, or activities."

- Leisure is "the time when you are not working or doing other duties."

- Leisure is "time spent in or free for relaxation or enjoyment."

Recreation and Fitness Leadership

What Is Recreation?

Recreation is participation in an activity that you enjoy. The various definitions (see the box *Recreation Defined*) imply that the activity will improve us or restore us in some way.

Recreation Defined

- Recreation is "the refreshment of one's mind or body after work through activity that amuses or stimulates."

- Recreation is "refreshment of the strength and spirits after toil; amusement; diversion; sport; pastime."

- Recreation is "an activity that diverts or amuses or stimulates."

Recreation is very personal. Some students enjoy playing sports, whereas others enjoy watching TV, downloading music, or playing video games. What one individual views as work, another may view as the perfect recreational activity. Many people consider cooking and baking an enjoyable and relaxing hobby; others find peace in their gardens, pulling weeds and planning where each plant would look best. However, there are also people who view these activities as dreaded chores. These people might prefer to spend time reading books by their favourite authors. They may even join a book club (i.e., a group) in order to compare their evaluations of a book with other book lovers. Other people do not enjoy reading and read only when necessary. Recreation, therefore, is an individual preference, and it can be performed alone or as part of a group.

Recreation is very personal. What may be relaxing and enjoyable to one person may be considered a chore to another.

Work or Play?

Personal perceptions of activities can dictate whether a specific activity is regarded as recreation or work. For example, Gerry does not own a car and there is no public transportation from his house to his work. He must ride his bike to work each day, rain or shine. He is thinking of finding a part-time job in order to save money to purchase his own car. In contrast, Sam loves to ride his bike and is planning to join a cycling club in his community. Gerry clearly views his bike riding as work and nothing more, while Sam enjoys riding purely for the pleasure of it.

So where did the concept of recreation come from? Recreation has historically been dependent on social class. The working class (feudal system) had little leisure time, although annual celebratory events were held, with festivals, dancing, contests, and so on. The ruling class had far greater amounts of leisure time, during which they participated in formal balls and sporting matches, such as polo and fox hunts, as well as garden parties and teas.

Renaissance Period (1350–1600)

During the Renaissance period, upper-class citizens involved themselves in activities such as painting, music, literature, science, and education. A well-educated man could ride, fence, dance, and paint, among other things. This era involved a great cultural movement in the arts and education, and people became more civilized in their pursuits.

Reformation Period (1500s–1600s)

In the 1500s and 1600s, in what was known as the Reformation period, the Protestant work ethic was introduced to colonial America. At first, hard work, or toil, was necessary to ensure survival, but over time, hard work came to be valued as the road to economic success, social acceptance, and religious superiority. Recreation and leisure were earned through daily hard work. Perhaps this is where the motto "work before play" originated. If you had ample time for recreation and leisure, you were considered lazy and a loafer.

Industrial Revolution (1700–1900)

During the Industrial Revolution of the 1700s, working-class people did not have the time or energy for recreation. Twelve-hour work days were common, and labourers worked six days a week. Leisure opportunities were few and far between for these blue-collar workers. Three social classes emerged, from the poorer blue-collar worker to the middle class and finally the wealthy upper class. New wealth from industrialization created the new middle class, and a new group of upper class became competition for the already established elite.

There was no mingling of the classes during this era. For the poorer working class, recreation included visiting the taverns or pubs and attending fairs and exhibitions. The middle class attempted to model themselves after the upper class by pursuing more sophisticated recreation activities such as playing the piano, singing, and drama. Of course, during this time, the upper classes enjoyed many forms of recreation such as bird watching, fishing, cricket, polo, and fox hunts.

Roaring 20s

The Roaring 20s bring to mind pictures of carefree young people touring in the newly invented automobile or dancing the Charleston in speakeasies – illegal after-hours clubs. During this time, recreation and leisure became more popular, and people began to recognize the need to enjoy leisure time once and a while. They worked hard so that later they had the time to enjoy a little recreation and leisure. Although work was still regarded as important and recognition was given to those who embraced the strong work ethic, people began to socialize more, organizing dances, outings, and family functions. Dancing was extremely popular, and public dance halls, tea rooms, Broadway musicals, and movie theatres opened. Jazz made its debut, and professional sports such as tennis, golf, and football emerged from the amateur circuit. Gambling also became a popular form of recreation.

Depression Years (1929–1945)

During the Depression years, recreation became less formal. People came together and played their musical instruments or had picnics at the local beaches and went swimming. Square dances and get-togethers to make ice cream were the norm. Big bands and swing music were popular, and many nights were spent around the radio, listening to this music or broadcasted sermons and soap operas. Movies now had sound, and many people escaped the stresses of everyday life by attending the movie theatres on a regular basis.

Modern Era (1950–Present)

Fundamental changes to recreation and leisure occurred in the 1950s. Average middle-class citizens began to have discretionary income (i.e., extra money that could be earmarked for fun and leisure). They wanted to finish work each evening to enjoy a night out, read, or watch television. With transportation faster and much more convenient, people could begin to travel for enjoyment instead of just for work, and with an increase in yearly incomes, people could retire earlier and enjoy themselves.

Municipal multipurpose recreation facilities that include

Do we live to work or do we work to live?

a swimming pool, gymnasium, fitness centre, ice rink, and possibly a library are present in many cities. This provides one-stop shopping for an entire family's recreation interests. But at the other end of the spectrum, technological advancements have taken over for physical activity. One example is that you no longer need to get off the couch to change the channel on the TV. Entertainment is provided by way of televisions, video game consoles, computers, and mp3 players. Technological entertainment can now travel in cars, on planes, or to remote locations (e.g., Game Boys and portable TV/DVD units). Gone are the days of roughing it! We are in constant communication with each other, on a much larger scale than in the past. Unfortunately, these technological advancements have caused us to be more physically inactive than any generation before us. Although technology can provide many hours of recreation, we need to recognize that it does not necessarily promote a healthy and active lifestyle.

Recent Developments

Recreation has become increasingly important in our society. Families look forward to evenings and weekends when time can be spent together doing the things they enjoy as a group. This can include camping, weekends at the cottage, ski days, hiking, movie nights, and attending community events. Our society has recognized this shift in family priorities from working long hours and weekends and has adapted programs and facilities within our communities to reflect this trend. Trail systems, skateboard parks, waterfront boardwalks, parklands with benches, playground equipment, shaded areas, sport pads, and walking paths are becoming mainstream because they offer something for the whole family to enjoy.

Recognizing the importance of recreation and sports as part of a healthy and active lifestyle, parents spend time driving their children to sports activities, watching their games, and volunteering. It has become a form of social entertainment for parents. Although family recreational activities are on the rise, separate activities for adults remain strong, such as adult sports leagues, golf, skiing, and fitness memberships.

If you were to ask those within the workforce today if they enjoy their careers, many would say that they enjoy what they do, but they make sure they have time to enjoy their recreation pursuits as well. In fact, recent studies suggest that people are willing to sacrifice larger salaries for more time off.

Recreation and Fitness Leadership

Benefits of Recreation

Aside from the obvious physical advantages of active participation in recreational activities, recreation also provides various other personal, social, economic, and environmental benefits. Brief descriptions of these benefits are provided in this section.

Beyond the Physical

Participation in recreational pursuits not only affords positive physical health benefits but also provides opportunities for children to develop self-esteem, self-confidence, perseverance, humility, dedication, and respect for others; to explore their skill potential; to learn friendship, teamwork, and communication skills; and to share good times with others. Physical activity and recreation are embedded in a more holistic perspective on health. In other words, health is the capacity of an individual to interact with his or her environment and to work towards fulfilling his or her potential.

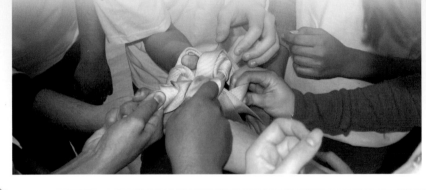

Participation in recreational pursuits provides opportunities to learn about friendship, respect, communication, and teamwork.

Personal Benefits

Participation in recreation can energize you and improve your self-esteem and physical appearance.

▶ Promotes physical fitness and active living

▶ Develops fine and gross motor skills through physical activity

▶ Improves self-confidence

▶ Gives a more positive outlook on life

▶ Decreases stress

▶ Creates a more positive self-image

▶ Provides the opportunity to learn new skills

▶ Improves problem solving, tolerance of others, and leadership

"We do not stop playing because we grow old; we grow old because we stop playing."
George Bernard Shaw

- ► Promotes spiritual growth

- ► Gives you the opportunity to take calculated risks and set reasonable and attainable short-term and long-term goals

> **Example**
> Noreen is a dog lover! Apart from the companionship and amusement she gets from her dog Precious, she gets exercise walking with her pet twice a day, rain or shine. Every two weeks, Noreen spends an evening helping her local kennel club with its seniors project. She takes Precious to nursing homes in her area. This work gives Noreen the satisfaction of feeling she is contributing to her community.

Social Benefits

Recreation gives you the chance to meet others and to socialize with your friends. You can try new things and challenge yourself while enjoying the company of others.

- ► Provides opportunities to develop friendships

- ► Improves social skills and reduces feelings of alienation and antisocial behaviours

- ► Introduces new learning environments – auditory, practical, and visual learning opportunities

- ► Promotes sharing, nurturing, and understanding of others

- ► Builds strong family ties that lay the foundation for community pride and satisfaction

- ► Promotes ethnic and cultural harmony and integration of all populations

- ► Improves conflict resolution and group development

> **Example**
> The Cooper family wants to spend more time together. They decide to set aside Sunday afternoons for family time. Sometimes they go out together to take a walk, to go shopping, or to visit a museum, or they stay home and play board games.

Economic Benefits

People who participate in active recreation are generally healthy and in good physical condition. This decreases the likelihood of absences from

Recreation and Fitness Leadership

work and reduces the financial demand on our medical system. Recreation activities can bring money to your community through attendance and sponsorship.

► Lowers medical costs because people are healthier

► Lowers job absenteeism because a healthy, active workforce is a productive workforce

► Increases job stability and productivity

► Creates jobs and spurs economic growth

► Builds a sense of community and presents community fund-raising opportunities

► Decreases crime and vandalism

► Inputs large sums of money into the local economy (e.g., from special events)

► Boosts tourism by offering programs and facilities that bring money into the community

Example
Jack is extremely passionate about rock climbing. As a teenager he was introduced to the sport during a PE class field trip to an indoor climbing gym. Now he plans several challenging climbs each season. In the winter he maintains his fitness and practices his techniques indoors. He earns some extra money teaching beginners; this income offsets the costs of purchasing the necessary climbing equipment.

Environmental Benefits

Although some recreational activities can be somewhat destructive to the environment, many can actually be quite helpful.

► Protects and preserves environmentally sensitive areas

► Results in cleaner, well-maintained facilities

► Preserves cultural and historical sites

► Increases public awareness and participation in environmental issues

► Improves community image

Factors Affecting Our Recreational Interests and Pursuits

Not everyone has a clear sense of what it means to be healthy and how to achieve wellness through recreation. This confusion is partly influenced by our early educational experiences, our families, our peers, the culture in which we live, and the media. A closer look at the influence these factors have on how we choose to spend our recreation and leisure time will help us understand more about the lifestyle choices we make.

Early Educational Experiences

We are introduced to recreation early in our lives. Junior and senior kindergarten are filled with recreation opportunities such as sand play, water play, arts and crafts, music, drama, and gym. In the classroom, children can revisit the activity centres they enjoy the most. From these early experiences that expose us to a wide variety of activities, we learn that we can make choices when it comes to our participation. We can continue to select the activities we enjoy at school, but we can also register for programs that offer these activities within our communities.

While participating in recreation, we develop and refine our social, emotional, physical, physiological, psychological, and cognitive skills. We learn to cooperate with others, remain physically active, establish friendships, build self-confidence, and continue our healthy, active lifestyles.

Example
Sadie has learned to share, wait her turn, and listen to others and their ideas in her preschool playgroup. This recreational experience provides motor skill and social skill development in a playful, fun, and active environment.

Family Influences

Our parents teach us a great deal about wellness and the importance of quality recreation and leisure time. Traditional family attitudes and actions send strong messages about health, well-being, and a general sense of life satisfaction. Parents that value physical activity, for example, introduce their children to sports, games, and recreational pursuits at an early age. Most young people today get their start in dance, gymnastics, hockey, tennis, volleyball, skiing, and swimming because of their parents' interests, attitudes, and enthusiasm for these same activities.

Adults encourage us as children to play with toys, join sports teams or clubs, and take lessons for activities in which we have expressed an interest. From these early introductions, we are able to modify our activities as we grow older to those that we enjoy and feel most comfortable with.

We can choose from recreational or competitive activities or even "introduction to" programs. Participation in such "how to" programs gives us the opportunity to try something new. If we enjoy the activity or quickly pick up the skills, we can move on to a more challenging level. The skills we develop from recreational activities can encourage us to continue with the activity and possibly move from a recreational level to a more competitive level.

Traditional family attitudes and values about physical activity and recreation are passed on to children at an early age.

Social (Peer) Influences

As we continue to grow as individuals, our recreational interests and pursuits become increasingly influenced by our friends and a growing social network. Therefore, it is important to choose our friends wisely.

Many people decide to become active participants in sport and recreational pursuits because of the social benefits incurred in meeting new people and in spending time with old friends. In fact, social interaction is one of the most compelling reasons for committing to an active lifestyle. It is therefore important that we establish and maintain these social networks and foster related healthy activities within these communities. Participation in physical activity, recreation, and leisure pursuits can be a common experience shared among all people.

Cultural Influences

Views about recreation and leisure have evolved over time and are understood differently across cultures. We do not live in a vacuum. Whether people have access to affordable and safe opportunities to be active may be a key determinant of how we choose to pursue leisure. How easy is it to fit activity into a crowded schedule? How expensive is it to join a fitness facility

Our friends can have a huge impact on the recreational pursuits we choose to follow.

or club? Do students have opportunities to enrol in health and physical education programs, or are they forced to enrol in compulsory courses that are needed for postsecondary education or the workplace?

Different cultures can encourage or forbid certain forms of recreation. For instance, some cultures and religions forbid dancing, while others embrace it as a form of creative expression. North America is a much more sedentary culture, and with the excuse of busy schedules we drive everywhere we go. Many other countries frown upon the use of motor vehicles except when necessary, and people walk whenever they can. Children often participate in the sports that their families can afford. Skiing and golf are perceived as expensive activities, while soccer and basketball are affordable options because minimal equipment is required.

Our choices regarding recreation and leisure are affected by cultural influences, including access to public parks, designated bike paths, and other facilities.

Media and Other Influences

The media has "hyped," commercialized, and distorted interpretations of what it means to be healthy and what can be expected from participating in sport and other recreational activities.

One of the greatest distortions that has emerged as a result of the commercialization of sport and physical activity is body image. Stereotypical versions of the ideal body shape and size have resulted in drug abuse, eating disorders, and a host of other mental and physical problems. Advertisers like to emphasize the shortcuts to success or, at least, the "look" of success.

The pursuit of health and wellness through recreation is more about finding out who you are – as you journey towards personal improvement and aspire to achieve your individual potential – than it is about being the toughest, beating the competition, or trying to achieve some unrealistic ideal.

Some advertisers and certain forms of media are slowly realizing that it is okay to be a recreational player rather than a competitive player. Many commercials now depict families and people of all ages engaging in recreational activities.

Barriers to Recreation and Leisure Pursuits

If recreation provides so many positive outcomes, what holds us back? There are several significant barriers that prevent us from participating regularly in recreational activities.

Recreation and Fitness Leadership

Economic Factors

An important barrier is related to economic factors. For example, large families with lower household incomes may not be able to enjoy certain recreation programs because of high program registration fees, equipment costs, and possibly transportation issues if the location of the recreational activity is not near their home.

However, recreation doesn't need to be expensive. In fact, many activities are free. Go for a walk along the beach or around the block in your community. Visit your local park or public gardens. Go skating or swimming outdoors or at a local community centre. Check out the public hiking trails. Play tennis or basketball at the community courts. Challenge your friends to a game of tag or hide and go seek. The opportunities for inexpensive recreation and leisure are limited only by your imagination.

Some recreation programs and activities – such as golf – can be quite expensive, which creates a barrier to participation for individuals with lower household incomes.

Perceived Lack of Necessary Physical and Social Skills

People often feel they lack the proper skills to effectively participate in an activity. This perception along with a poor self-image holds people back from the satisfying experience that recreation can give. They believe that if they can't do something well, then they shouldn't do it at all – but this is not true. Just because you have never tried an activity before or you don't think you are a "natural" at a particular activity doesn't mean you can't do it. "Try, try again" should be your motto, because in recreation no one fails. Besides, it's fun to try new things!

Time Constraints

Although most parents are committed to giving their children the opportunity to experience the joy of participation, time can become a real issue for families with working parents. The scheduling of activities is often not convenient or may conflict with work schedules and the need to get home, prepare dinner, and then head off to the recreation activity. Sometimes the constant rushing can make the recreation opportunity seem too much like work and not enough like fun.

When fearful that we lack the proper skills to effectively participate in an activity, we often make up excuses. A popular excuse is that the activity will take too long to learn and commit to on a regular basis. However, you can always make time for things that are important. Once you have found something that you enjoy, make sure you set aside time for that activity on a daily or weekly basis.

Work and Family Commitments

"I can't exercise because I have to work" and "I need to be home with my family" are common excuses, but the reality is that it is possible to accommodate both job and family while recreating, too! Can you squeeze in an activity during your lunch hour? Does your place of employment have a workout room on the premises? Can your family participate in your favourite activity, too? Would they enjoy it as much as you do?

As mentioned earlier, an active workforce is a productive workforce. With this in mind, many businesses are promoting physical activity by renovating or designing new workplaces that include on-site fitness centres for their employees. And family activities such as bike riding, bowling, or playing Frisbee make it possible to combine leisure with family time. No more excuses!

Other Constraints

The list of possible constraints is a long one, but there are solutions for every problem.

Lack of motivation, poor self-image If you think you can't do something, then most often you won't try it. For many, a poor self-image can lead to a lack of motivation to participate in activities as well as decrease the urge to try something new. But everyone is good at something – the key is finding an activity in which each person can excel.

Although some individuals might look at age and gender as barriers to participation, our society now offers a myriad of programs for all ages and genders.

Lack of structures or facilities Your community may not have an indoor running track or a fitness centre with treadmills, but you may have beautiful trails and hills to run. Recreation allows for adjustments and modifications to programs for maximum participation and program options.

Age and gender Our society now offers a variety of programs for all ages and genders. These programs also incorporate the various skill levels (introduction, beginner, intermediate, and advanced/competitive).

Lack of participants Sometimes programs are cancelled because of a lack of registrants. Can the program be modified to allow for smaller groups or changed to a drop-in format? With minimal commitment, perhaps more people will participate.

Recreation and Fitness Leadership

Lack of available resources Resources can include facilities, staff, equipment, supplies, and money. Is there a program running that offers some of your preferred program characteristics? Do you have a second choice? Is there another location that may offer what you are looking for?

Physical or mental challenges Recreation programs and activities are easily modified to accommodate everyone. Take wheelchair basketball, for example. Anyone can play!

User fees for program or facility admittance User fees are standard for most facilities and programs. There are organizations and funds available to subsidize those who could benefit from programs but who are financially unable to afford the registration or user fee.

Time when the programs occur Although many recreation facilities offer several dates and times for programs, sometimes none will accommodate your schedule. You can check other facilities in your area for similar programs or ask for a more convenient time and day for the next program offering.

Equipment and supplies not provided by the program Sometimes program registration fees also attach an equipment or supply list and costs. Look at the list. Can you borrow some of these items? Can you purchase used items rather than new?

Quality of facility maintenance Sometimes participants judge a facility by its appearance. Is it in good condition? Is it clean? Is it spacious or crowded all the time? Does it have the amenities you are looking for? Check around until you find a facility you are comfortable with.

Overcrowded facilities Overcrowded facilities not only are dangerous but also can turn people away. If you enter a building with large crowds, you may feel intimidated by the numbers or believe there is no room for you. Ask the staff if there are times when the facility is usually less busy, and try to avoid peak hours.

Location of facilities and programs Are the facilities and programs within a reasonable distance for you? Can you walk, drive, or take public transportation to the facility or program? Can you sign up with a friend and take turns driving?

Most recreation programs and activities can be modified easily to accommodate individuals of all abilities.

Health and Wellness

Various definitions of health and wellness have been introduced into North American culture in recent years. What do these terms mean to you? What steps have you taken to achieve a more balanced life?

Aterm that we are hearing much more frequently these days in discussions of recreation and leisure is *wellness*. This term has been introduced into North American culture by practitioners of alternative or nontraditional health therapies, often rooted in Eastern medicine. So what is wellness?

Definitions and Dimensions

Health can be defined as "the capacity to lead a satisfying life, fulfill ambitions, and accommodate to change." This modern definition recognizes that health is a dynamic, ever-changing process of trying to achieve one's individual potential.

Wellness, on the other hand, can be defined more broadly as the combination of health and happiness (see the box *Wellness Defined* for more definitions of wellness). It is the concept of achieving balance in one's mental, physical, emotional, social, environmental, and spiritual life (see the box *Dimensions of Wellness*).

Wellness Defined

"Wellness is an active process of becoming aware of and making choices toward a more successful existence."

"Wellness is the personal experience of physical and mental health – measurement is self-reported health status."

"Wellness is the concept of practicing all the things that keep one well. It involves maintaining good nutrition, exercise, stress-control, and good personal and familial social relationships."

"Wellness is a dynamic state of health in which an individual progresses towards a higher level of functioning, achieving an optimum balance between internal and external environments."

Health and wellness encompass a lifestyle that includes the joys of physical activity as an integral part of daily living. Although we ultimately make the decisions about our own health and how we choose to live our lives, these choices are not made in isolation from the environments in which we live.

Wellness is reflected in the way a person chooses to live his life and is therefore dependent on the individual's capacity to effectively interact with his environment and to build and maintain physical, mental, social, and spiritual well-being throughout his lifespan. Wellness involves having a deep understanding of what it means to care for oneself in relation to others and the environment. In short, wellness is making informed choices and taking responsibility for the way we live our lives.

Wellness is all-encompassing, and each dimension should be fulfilled in some way to ensure personal balance (Figure 4.1). For instance, Georgia enjoys going to the gym three times a week with her friends to unwind and relieve the stress of the day. Georgia's participation in this activity combines the social, emotional, and physical dimensions of wellness. Olivia enjoys walking each evening to reflect on the day's events and loosen up her muscles. While taking in the fresh air, she likes to stargaze and identify certain constellations as she comes to appreciate the vastness and order of the universe. This simple activity combines the emotional, environmental, physical, and spiritual dimensions of wellness.

Physical

Social

Environmental

Career

Spiritual

Intellectual

Emotional

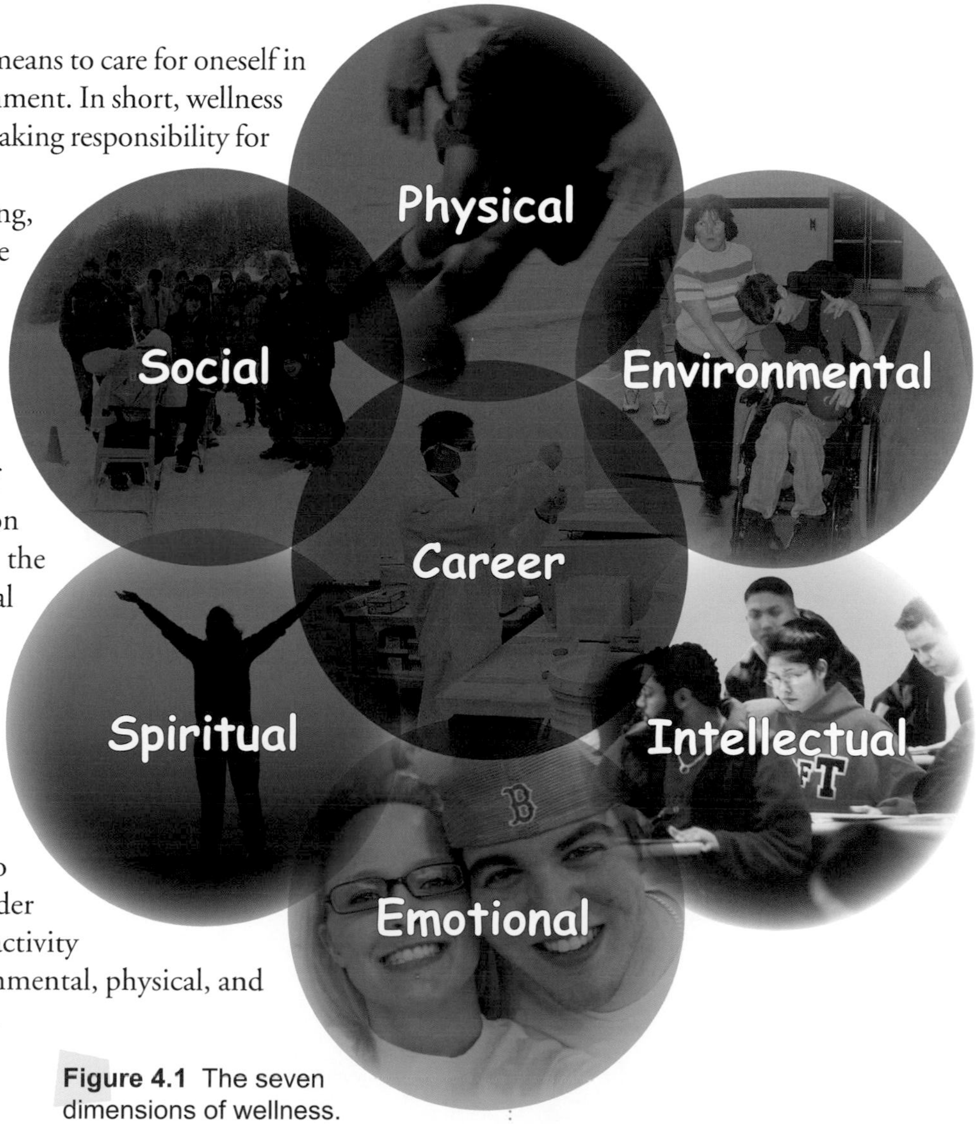

Figure 4.1 The seven dimensions of wellness.

Get Moving for Better Health

Regular exercise and a proper diet are crucial for overcoming the threat of obesity in Canada. Approximately 63 percent of Canadians do not participate in sufficient physical activity to achieve good health. This means that only 37 percent are physically active! Inactive individuals leave themselves at risk for future health problems, including the following:

- Obesity
- High blood pressure
- Diabetes
- Depression

- Heart disease
- High cholesterol
- Stroke
- Premature death

Did you know that you should participate in at least 30 minutes of moderate-intensity physical activity every day? You should try to mix cardio, endurance, flexibility, and strength exercises. Activities can be done 10 minutes at a time and should become part of your daily routine. Some simple ways to fit more activity into your day include taking the stairs instead of an elevator or escalator, getting off the bus a few blocks before your destination, and walking to a friend's house instead of driving.

The threat of obesity in Canada is growing, as is the list of health problems associated with our increasingly sedentary population.

Putting It All Together

Becoming more active can be as simple as taking the stairs instead of an escalator, walking or cycling instead of driving, or getting off the bus a few stops before your destination.

Recreation and leisure provide the framework for healthy, active living. Being active strengthens your body, relieves stress, provides you with an opportunity to make friends, and allows for skill development. Participation can be rewarding and fun, too! As we grow older, our recreational interests change and can be influenced by family, friends, geography, time, resources, and other factors.

Wellness is about achieving a balance of the mental, physical, social, emotional, and spiritual elements of your life. Pursuing recreational and leisure activities plays a major role in achieving this important balance. Society recognizes the importance of recreation, leisure, and wellness in our everyday lives, and our governments now realize that a healthy population is a less expensive population. ParticipACTION, Body Break, and participation challenges are promotional strategies to deliver the message that recreation and leisure are essential services available to everyone.

How Can I Become More Active?

Canadians value physical activity and recreation as an important part of their lives. There are many ways to become more active:

- Take calculated risks and set reasonable goals for yourself – little ones that are easily achievable at first.

- Find a friend to participate with you.

- Start out doing just a little each day – 10 minutes at a time.

- Build on your successes.

Healthy, active living is your responsibility. You can choose those activities and programs that you enjoy while keeping your personal wellness in mind. Remember, wellness is dependent on your capacity to interact effectively with your environment and to build and maintain physical, mental, social, and spiritual well-being.

Key Terms

barrier

health

leisure

lifestyle

recreation

toil

wellness

work

Review Questions

1. In your own words, define and differentiate between the terms *leisure* and *recreation*.

2. Explain recreation during the Industrial Revolution.

3. Explain recreation during the modern era.

4. List three personal, social, economic, and environmental benefits of recreation.

5. What factors affect our recreational pursuits?

6. What are the barriers to recreation?

7. Pick three barriers to recreation and explain how they can be overcome.

8. What is wellness?

9. What are the dimensions of wellness?

10. How can you become more active in recreation?

In This Chapter:

CHAPTER 5
Needs Assessment

In this chapter, you will learn about the following:

❶ The importance of doing a needs assessment before organizing a health, physical education, or recreation event

❷ Applying appropriate research skills when conducting a survey to identify the needs of a target group

❸ Synthesizing information from a survey and incorporating conclusions into preparations for an event

❹ Community partnerships available to support the findings and participate in the plan

> "Acting without thinking is like shooting without aiming."
> B. C. Forbes

We are always in a hurry, rushing from here to there, and we do not always pay complete attention to details or why we are doing what we are doing. Sometimes we create solutions for problems or needs that we think we have, but if we take our time and identify what is important to us and to potential participants, we often see that what we believe is important isn't always as significant for others as we may think. Needs assessments provide concrete results that identify true factual needs.

What Is a Needs Assessment?

To determine the recreation activities that your targeted participants prefer, you must conduct a needs assessment. A needs assessment is a tool that reveals the opinions and wishes of potential participants through the analysis of personal feedback. Conducting a needs assessment involves gathering personal information and gaining knowledge about a specific group in a certain subject.

Needs assessments help you identify and assess the needs of the population you are examining. Through needs assessments you become aware of the population's feelings, beliefs, and attitudes as well as identify the issues that are important to them. You can also determine what has been done in the past and whether or not these approaches were successful.

Needs Assessment Tools

Several different types of needs assessment tools are available, including surveys and questionnaires, telephone interviews, focus groups, statistics, community interest checklists, public meetings, and your own professional expertise and knowledge about the subject area and the **target group**. You can use one or several of these methods to gather your information.

Remember that gathering information may require you to use several needs assessment options because not everyone will be able to respond to all assessment tools. You must be aware of the abilities and restrictions of your respondents. Those who cannot read, for example, may require a focus group or verbal interview. Respondents with special needs or who do not speak English as their first language may require various forms of assistance or alternative needs assessment methods.

Surveys and Questionnaires

Surveys assess the needs of the community or evaluate program quality or customer satisfaction with recreation facilities, programs, or services offered. In most instances, surveys use a questionnaire as the data-gathering technique.

A **questionnaire** is a series of questions or statements on paper. Questionnaires are simple but effective methods of gathering information from your potential participants. The questions asked should be short and to the point, in simple English, and easy to understand and respond to. In addition, an easy scoring system or rating scale should be in place. To keep the questionnaire short, decide which questions are necessary to give you the information you need and which questions would be useful to know now and possibly in the future.

The questions need to be placed in a sensible sequence that is logical to the respondent. The order should proceed from general to specific. This allows the respondent to feel comfortable when beginning the survey or questionnaire. Each question should consist of one topic only. Those completing the questionnaire could become confused if you require them to respond to more than one area of information at a time.

When using questionnaires, you can expect about a 10 percent return rate from the number distributed. If you mail surveys to your target group, include a self-addressed stamped envelope to encourage respondents to mail back their information.

When mailing surveys to your target group, it is a good idea to include a self-addressed stamped envelope to encourage respondents to mail back their information.

Cover Letter

You must attach a cover or introductory letter to your questionnaire. This short letter should outline the purpose of your survey/questionnaire, tell respondents why their input is important and what will happen once the results have been tabulated, identify a contact person for more information, and give the due date for completed surveys/questionnaires.

Key Points

Surveys and questionnaires should have a cover letter and should be

- short,
- straightforward,
- easy to understand, and
- presented in a logical sequence.

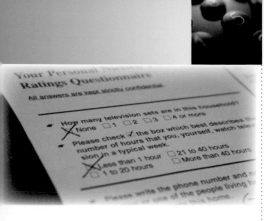

Constructing the Questionnaire

A well-designed questionnaire does not impose on the patience of the respondent. It should be possible to move through the questionnaire rapidly, without becoming bored and without having to reread questions because of ambiguity. An easy-to-complete questionnaire is more likely to be properly filled out.

Questionnaires are used for a variety of different reasons, and very often the purpose dictates the type of questions asked. So, question type is one decision to be made during questionnaire development. In this section we present various types of questions that could be used when developing questionnaires.

Multiple Choice Questions The format of **multiple choice** should be used whenever possible. These types of questions are the easiest to answer and are also less time consuming for the respondent.

> **Example**
> Which municipal community centre do you use the most?
>
> (A) Centreville
> (B) Churchview
> (C) Parklane

Rating Scales Questions For questions that require **rating**, the scale should range from 1 to 5 or from 1 to 7, but no larger (see Example 1). Normally, a 5 or 7 rates as the most positive response, and 1 is the most negative. Using an odd-numbered rating scale gives the respondent a middle number to select if he feels indifferent to the question or if he doesn't know the answer.

Allowing the option of "I don't know" can be useful if those completing the survey/questionnaire have little or no knowledge of the subject. You must be careful when using this option, however, since it can reduce the ability to effectively analyze your responses later on.

A five-point rating scale may also use negative, positive, and zero signs. For example, – – and – represent negative responses, + and + + represent positive responses, and 0 stands for a neutral response (see Example 2).

To avoid confusion, the rating scale that is chosen should be used consistently throughout the survey.

> **Example 1**
> Please rate your satisfaction with the recreation activities provided by your local municipal recreation department.
>
> | 1 | 2 | 3 | 4 | 5 |
> |---|---|---|---|---|
> | Not satisfied | | Somewhat satisfied | | Very satisfied |

Example 2

Select the response that best reflects your feelings about the dance class you are presently taking.

– –	–	0	+	+ +
Not satisfied		Somewhat satisfied		Very satisfied

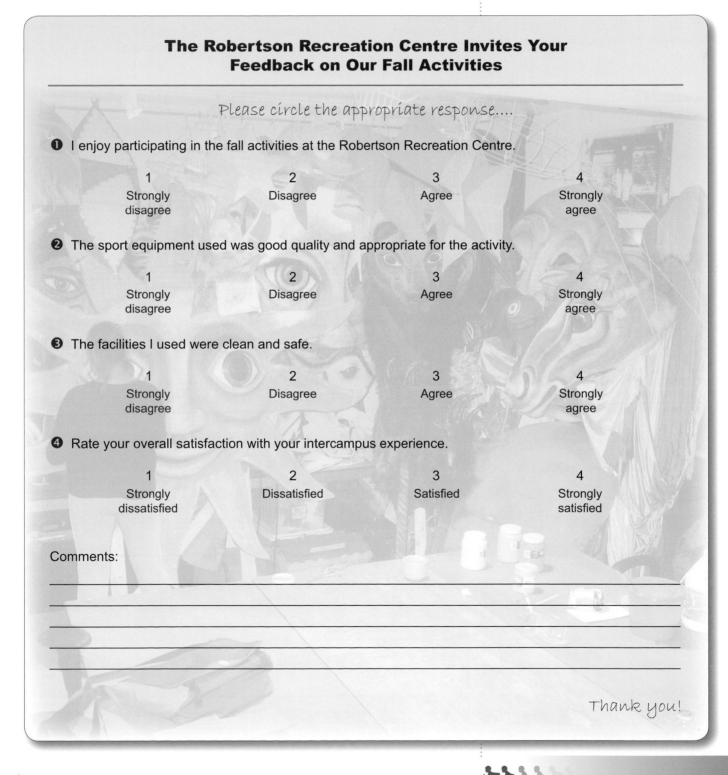

The Robertson Recreation Centre Invites Your Feedback on Our Fall Activities

Please circle the appropriate response....

❶ I enjoy participating in the fall activities at the Robertson Recreation Centre.

1	2	3	4
Strongly disagree	Disagree	Agree	Strongly agree

❷ The sport equipment used was good quality and appropriate for the activity.

1	2	3	4
Strongly disagree	Disagree	Agree	Strongly agree

❸ The facilities I used were clean and safe.

1	2	3	4
Strongly disagree	Disagree	Agree	Strongly agree

❹ Rate your overall satisfaction with your intercampus experience.

1	2	3	4
Strongly dissatisfied	Dissatisfied	Satisfied	Strongly satisfied

Comments:

_____

_____

_____

_____

_____

Thank you!

Listed Options Questions If you ask a question that lists options or preferences, you should always include "Other" as a potential choice in the event that the respondent does not use or has no knowledge of the choices provided.

> **Example**
> Which of the following recreation activities do you currently participate in?
>
> | | | |
> |---|---|---|
> | Basketball | Volleyball | Ball hockey |
> | Ice hockey | Baseball | Lacrosse |
> | Badminton | Skateboarding | Cycling |
> | Gymnastics | Weight training | Other |

Closed-Ended Questions Multiple choice, rating scales, and options lists are all **closed-ended questions**. They direct the respondent to answer using the possibilities provided. These formats make the purpose of the questionnaire evident, and at least one of the potential answers will be right for each respondent. Collating the data from these questions is a simple task.

Open-Ended Questions Another common format uses **open-ended questions**, which simply pose a question and then provide space on the page for the respondent's answer. Open-ended questions could be included in a questionnaire for several reasons: (1) There are too many possible responses to include (e.g., year of birth); (2) you do not want to impose response categories on the respondent; and (3) you may want to give the impression that the respondent is being asked to offer an opinion.

Open-ended questions must be used sparingly. If you ask too many open-ended questions, those completing the survey may feel that the questions are taking too long and will limit their writing where possible.

Open-ended questions can be useful in certain cases, but these types of questions should be used sparingly. They are difficult to quantify, which makes collating the final data more difficult.

> **Example**
> Please explain why you are interested in participating in the annual ball hockey tournament.
> _____
> _____
> _____
>
> What is the one thing you would like to see changed at your school?
> _____
> _____
> _____
>
> In your opinion, what is the single best thing about your school's intramural program?
> _____
> _____
> _____

Recreation and Fitness Leadership

Should this occur, you will not receive all the necessary information. However, when used appropriately, these types of questions provide an excellent change of pace for the respondent.

Note that data obtained from open-ended questions are difficult to quantify in a final report, but they do provide a rich source of quotations.

Leading Questions Avoid using **leading questions** that could result in skewed responses. Leading questions can often force the respondent to answer in a manner that goes against how she really feels about the topic. Questions should be specific, but allow for a positive or negative opinion. A leading question (e.g., How wonderful was the Christmas parade this year?) should be stated more objectively (How satisfied were you with the Christmas parade this year?).

Telephone Interviews

Telephone interviews are similar to surveys but add a more personal touch. A telephone interviewer asks the questions to the respondent and documents his answers. Questions asked through telephone interviews should be direct and relevant to the topic area. Usually the participants for this type of needs assessment are selected by random sampling. A random sample can be taken by balloting (i.e., drawing names) or by choosing every 10th number (or any number) in the telephone directory or on the census list that you have received from the municipal office. You count down to the 10th name and underline it – this is the person you will try to contact. If you cannot reach the 10th person, then you will attempt to contact the 9th person. Furthermore, you must determine which of the household occupants will provide you with the most accurate information and ask for that person.

When the goal is to survey a random group of participants, telephone interviews can add more of a personal touch.

Sampling the Population

Populations can be large, and it is often impractical and financially unfeasible to measure all variables for each member. Sampling is thus essential. Data collected on a sample can then be generalized to estimate or predict the needs of the populations.

The larger the sample, the more accurately it will represent the population and the smaller the error in prediction. Therefore, it is important to maximize the sample size, sometimes while working within tight financial and time constraints.

In random sampling, each member of a larger population has an equal opportunity of being selected into a sample. This method is unbiased and more likely to represent the population needs under consideration. A biased sample contains some type of systematic error and is not as good a representation of the population needs.

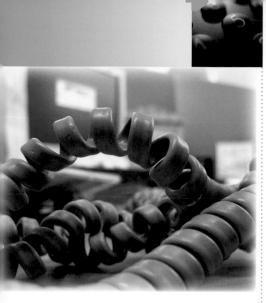

Here are five steps to follow when conducting a telephone interview:

❶ Call each selected respondent.

❷ Explain the purpose of the telephone interview, and state how long it will take to answer the questions. Ensure the respondent that you are not selling anything.

❸ Read each question clearly, and document each response.

❹ Repeat the question if necessary, but do not offer any personal opinions.

❺ Stay focused until you complete the interview.

Remember that not everyone is receptive to telephone interviews. It may be a busy time in the person's household, and she may decline participation. Politely thank her for her time and move to the next phone number. Don't call back unless you are invited to do so by the respondent.

Focus Groups

Focus groups provide feedback and varied opinions that are not restricted by closed-ended questions, rating scales, or multiple choice selections. Groups meet and discuss their thoughts and views on topics using open-ended questions. These discussions often lead to new and innovative ideas that can improve products and services.

Focus groups will do the following:

▶ Test your own assumptions about what you think people want or need

▶ Provide opinions and attitudes about your needs assessment topics

▶ Create enthusiasm about the topic

Focus groups are often organized to generate innovative ideas on a specific topic using open-ended questions, which hopefully leads to improved products and services.

Planning a Focus Group

Preplanning is critical in order to present yourself and your topic in a professional manner. Here are five steps for planning a focus group:

❶ What do you want the focus group to accomplish? What is the purpose of the focus group session?

❷ Who will your participants be? Will they represent a broad population base? A good focus group generally has 6 to 12 participants. Issue invitations, then follow up with confirmations of attendance.

❸ What questions will you ask? Are these questions easily understood, clear, and simply stated? A focus group session of one to two hours should have between four and seven questions. The session should begin with one or two introductory questions and move to general and then more specific questions.

❹ Which location will suit your needs for the focus group session? Find the right facility and room for the group and book it.

❺ What materials, equipment, and supplies (e.g., refreshments, flip-chart paper, pad and pens, name tags) will you need for the session?

Successful focus groups have strong facilitators who lead the group through the process and ensure that the questions are answered in detail. A good facilitator keeps the group on track, deals with outspoken participants, and encourages quieter members to voice their opinions. The facilitator must be familiar with the needs assessment and the information to be gathered. He should have a complete script, with the welcome and introduction, the purpose of the focus group, session questions, and closing remarks written out prior to the session.

Organizing a successful focus group session depends on preplanning – finding and booking the right location and being equipped with all the necessary materials and supplies.

Focus Group Format and Sample Questions

1. Welcome and introduction

2. Purpose of the focus group

3. Ground rules for discussion

4. Sample questions

   (a) What recreation programs at Robertson Recreation Centre are important to you?

   (b) What difficulties or challenges do you face in programs you have registered for at Robertson Recreation Centre?

   (c) How can we deal with these challenges?

Interest Checklists

Interest checklists allow respondents to check off the activities they have participated in recently or those they would like to have offered in their community. It is important to carefully select which activities to include on the form; list only those that you have seriously considered offering. Because it is impossible to list all possibilities, you can add an "Other" checkbox with a blank to allow respondents to add activities they are interested in but that are not listed.

Public Meetings

Public meetings create a great atmosphere for debate about community issues, providing community information and gathering ideas for future possibilities. Although this method of information gathering and dispersion can be very time consuming to organize, it is usually a one-time event.

To hold a public meeting, you must do the following:

▶ Determine the date, time, and location of the meeting

▶ Book a location

▶ Prepare your presentation

▶ Create and deliver public service announcements to the public

▶ Organize the speakers for the presentation

▶ Select a meeting chairperson/facilitator who is knowledgeable and able to effectively guide the group through presentations and question-and-answer periods

▶ Arrange refreshments

▶ Book, set up, and take down necessary audio and video equipment

▶ Collate the information gathered and prepare a public document with the findings and discussion results

Public meetings offer a good opportunity to debate community issues and to generate ideas for future planning.

A Summary of Needs Assessment Tools

Surveys and Questionnaires

Pros
Anonymous
Distributed to a large group
Not overly time consuming
Small staff required
Easy to administer

Cons
Low return rate – about 10 percent
Lengthy process
Is the addressee the actual respondent?
No clarification if respondent has questions
Mailing lists – are they current?

Telephone Interviews

Pros
Not expensive
Easy to organize and implement
Can cover a wide geographical area
Can keep calling back until you speak with someone

Cons
Interviewer may have biased tendencies
Must train the interviewers
Can you get a good representation from all areas?
Hang-ups and uncooperative respondents

Focus Groups

Pros
Inexpensive
Convenient and not overly time consuming
Provide a creative atmosphere for idea sharing

Cons
Controlled by the facilitator
Skill level of the facilitator must be very high
Qualitative data only
Limited in the number of people that can participate

Interest Checklists

Pros
Easy and quick to complete
Easy to tally
Minimal staff required
Inexpensive
Can cover a large geographical area

Cons
People may think it is time consuming because of the columns
Can be time consuming to tabulate
Return rate is lower

Public Meetings

Pros
Large numbers
Low cost
Low time commitment
Everyone can be heard
Those who have an interest will attend

Cons
Recording all comments is difficult
Sometimes crowd can be one-sided
Crowd may have a leader that does all the talking
Leader in the audience can sway others

Organizing and Displaying Data

Before conclusions can be drawn from collected information, the data must be collated and organized systematically.

When surveys are conducted and data are collected, a lot of information with potential value is gathered. However, before any real conclusions can be drawn from collected information, the raw data must be organized systematically. The information from your target group must be collated, organized, and presented properly to gain a clear picture of the group's perceived needs and wants. If you used surveys/questionnaires or telephone interviews, the collation simply requires adding the numbers of yes or no responses or adding the scale number responses. If you used public meetings or focus groups, simply group the similar comments to determine how many people felt a certain way. You can create columns with positive and negative headings and list the comments according to their nature.

The following are areas you should summarize:

► Number of surveys/questionnaires distributed or number of people contacted by phone

► Number of responses

► Number of participants in public meetings or focus groups

► Totals of yes or no responses for each question

► Totals of numbers circled for each scale question

► Number of similar comments, and those not shared by others

► Test results

Once the data have been collected and organized, information can be displayed using a variety of statistical methods and visual aids.

With this information in front of you, you can begin to analyze, organize, and display your data using a variety of statistical methods. Tables, bar graphs, pie charts, and other visual aids are among the clearest and most effective ways of presenting both the information you have gathered and the results of your investigation. These methods are presented in this section.

Frequency Distributions

When raw values are presented in no particular order, interpretation of the data is difficult. One way of organizing data into a usable format is through **frequency distribution**. Different types of distribution exist, but in each case, a distribution of data provides a quick indication of the values you are dealing with (Table 5.1).

Table 5.1 Frequency distributions of push-up scores for grade 11 students. **A.** Rank order. **B.** Simple frequency. **C.** Grouped frequency.

A

X (no. of push-ups)
24
22
20
18
18
18
17
15
13
13
13
5
5
4
2

N (number of scores) = 15
H (highest score) = 24
L (lowest score) = 2
R (range) = (24 − 2) = 22

B

X	f (frequency)
24	1
23	2
22	4
21	4
20	4
19	2
18	5
17	5
16	8
15	9
14	12
13	6
12	7
11	2
10	5
9	1
8	2

N (number of scores) = 79
H (highest score) = 24
L (lowest score) = 8
R (range) = (24 − 8) = 16

C

X	Tally	f	Relative Frequency (%)
21 − 25	HHT HHT I	11	14
16 − 20	HHT HHT HHT HHT IIII	24	30
11 − 15	HHT HHT HHT HHT HHT HHT HHT I	36	46
6 − 10	HHT III	8	10
1 − 5		0	0
		N = 79	100

Positive or negative reactions to the questions that surround your subject are of interest to you. Say you want to assess the interest in implementing a fitness program at your school. If you see high interest in such a program, you must cross-reference the interest with the age of the respondents that are in favour. Do all grades of students support this proposed program? Are the totals more in favour of the fitness program or opposed to it? Are the numbers close, or is there a clear preference?

Once you have determined that there is interest and a definite need for this program, move to the other questions you have asked.

- What types of strength training programs would you like to see? (could be a list of preselected programs or an open-ended question where the students list their preferred programs)

- How often (days per week) should this program take place?

- What time of day should the program take place?

From the totals of these sample questions, you can now summarize a clear picture of student preferences regarding the implementation of a school fitness program. You can display these results in a number of ways.

For example, if you are interested in the number of push-ups grade 11 students can perform during a fitness test, you may want to organize the data into a **rank order distribution** from highest to lowest for statistical analysis. The extreme scores (highest and lowest values) and variability in the scores can thus be easily identified (Table 5.1A).

If the number of students to be surveyed is relatively large (two or more grade 11 classes), their scores can be organized in a **simple frequency distribution** (Table 5.1B) or a **grouped frequency distribution** (Table 5.1C), where scores are arranged into nonoverlapping segments called **class intervals**. Intervals are equal in length, thereby aiding the comparison between the frequencies of any two intervals.

The number of observations falling into any interval is called the **class frequency (f)**. For the first interval, f is 11, obtained from the tally. The **tally** is a convenient way of keeping track of a set of observations (Table 5.1C).

Frequency tables often include other features, such as **relative frequency**, which represents the relative percentage of total cases falling within any class interval. It is obtained by dividing the number of cases in the class interval by the total number of cases and multiplying by 100. For example, in Table 5.1C, the relative frequency of the first class, 21 to 25 push-ups, is (11/79) x 100 = 13.9 percent (rounded to 14 percent). This value indicates the total percentage of total cases that fall into a given class interval.

Graphs

Although tables are useful tools for organizing data, particularly for determining the data's limits, **graphs** can provide distinct advantages when displaying information. Graphs are useful for making comparisons and identifying trends.

Basic line graphs and curves follow a simple form. All graphs show data along the x-axis (horizontal axis, abscissa) and the y-axis (vertical axis, ordinate) (Figure 5.1).

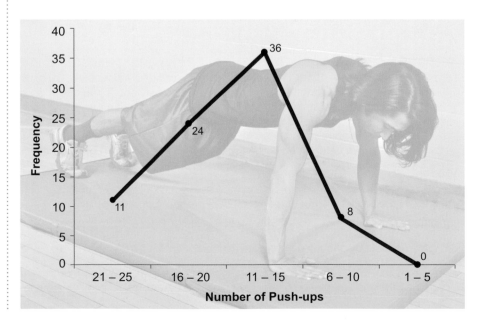

Figure 5.1 Graph of frequency polygon for push-up scores from Table 5.1C.

The World of Recreation and Fitness Leadership

A graph shows a relationship between values plotted on the vertical and horizontal axes. The dependent variable (e.g., performance), which changes in a way that is related to another variable, is normally plotted on the y-axis, while the independent variable (e.g., number of practice sessions), is plotted on the x-axis. Graphs allow us to quickly see trends in the data that may not have been apparent in a table, such as improved performance as a result of increased practice (Figure 5.2).

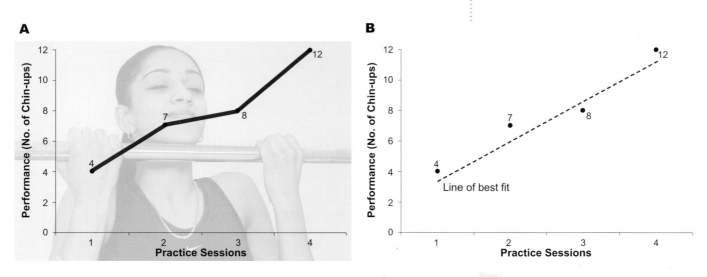

Figure 5.2 Number of chin-ups performed by four participants who trained once a week (participant 1), twice a week (participant 2), three times a week (participant 3), and four times a week (participant 4). **A.** Data points are connected with a line. **B.** A line of best fit is drawn through the points to indicate the general trend of the data.

Although data points are conventionally connected with a line, this is not necessarily the best way to illustrate a relationship. When a consistent relationship is suspected between variables, a **line of best fit** would be more appropriate (Figure 5.2B). This line travels through the data as close to most of the points as possible and allows predictions to be made about values that may be unknown. Although advanced statistical techniques exist for computing such lines, doing so by eye is often adequate.

Bar Graphs

Bar graphs, or histograms, are another simple but effective means of presenting similar data when comparison is desired. The bars on the x-axis represent the performance categories, groups, or participants, while the height of each bar is determined by the frequency of a particular group or participant (Figure 5.3).

If you want to graph the average height of 8th-grade students, you would label the various heights along the x-axis, with the frequency of these values placed along the y-axis, indicated by the height of the bars. The graph allows you to see the bars side by side so that you can easily visualize the comparisons.

Pie Charts

A popular way to display data arranged in categories is a **pie chart**, a circle divided into wedges that correspond to the percentage frequencies

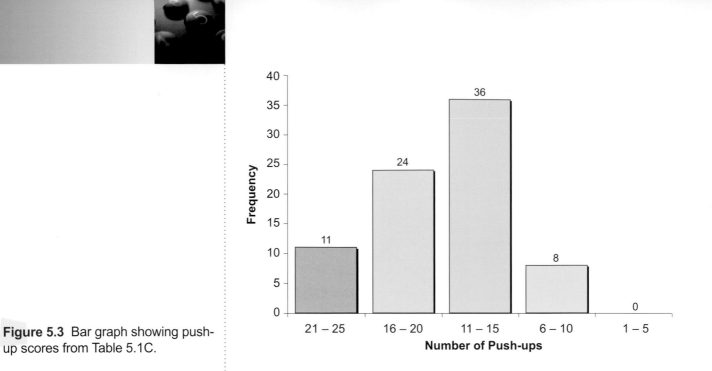

Figure 5.3 Bar graph showing push-up scores from Table 5.1C.

of the distribution (Figure 5.4). Pie charts are useful for conveying data across a small number of categories.

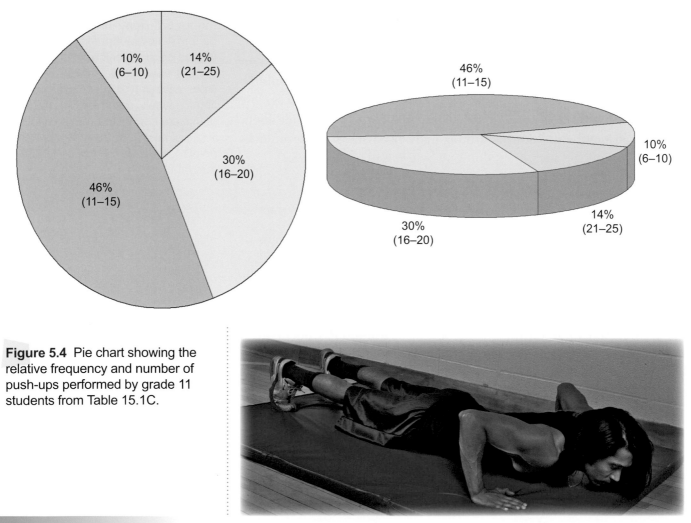

Figure 5.4 Pie chart showing the relative frequency and number of push-ups performed by grade 11 students from Table 15.1C.

Recreation and Fitness Leadership

Even this brief introduction to a complex subject will have served its purpose if it has demonstrated that raw data are of limited value – the significance of data emerges only through organization and display.

Analyzing Data

The raw data that have been collected must first be analyzed before any real conclusions can be drawn. Statistics is one way of collating the data to assess users' needs. Measures of central tendency, which allow single meaningful values to be extracted from a large amount of data, are the most common statistical measure. They describe the central characteristics of a set of data and are the most representative of all the values in a distribution. These measures allow a given score to be compared against those scores that typify the middle of a distribution of data.

Measuring central tendency shows us the middle scores from the needs assessment. This gives information about the positioning of the data and where most of the scores fall. The three statistical measures of central tendency are the mean, the median, and the mode.

The Mean

We are all familiar with the use of means in our everyday lives. The mean is the arithmetic *average* of a distribution of scores (the customary symbols are M or X); it is the most commonly used measure of central tendency.

The mean is calculated by adding all the observations (scores) in a sample and dividing by the number of observations. The calculated mean from Table 5.1A is 13.8.

The use of means in sports is obviously important for calculating baseball batting averages, basketball points-per-game averages, hockey goals-against averages, and so on. These calculations consider the number of scores involved as well as their value, giving each score weight relative to other scores in the data distribution.

The mean tends to be regarded as the most reliable of the three measures of central tendency when sample sizes are large. The mean, however, is vulnerable to extreme scores in a set of data. Scores that are *significantly* higher or lower than other scores will pull the mean towards that extreme, leading to potentially misleading average values.

Consider the following distribution of scores representing the total number of push-ups performed by a group of students: 18, 19, 20, 20, 22, 25, 100. Most individuals in the group scored in the same general range, but one student was able to do 100 push-ups; the mean here would be inflated by this one atypical score (M = 224/7 = 32).

The atypical low or high scores, called **outliers**, pull the average towards that extreme. In this case, the median would be of more value.

The most reliable of the measures of central tendency, the mean is used in sports to report statistics such as hockey goals-against averages.

 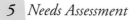

The Median

The median score in a distribution represents a middle point, with 50 percent of the scores being lower than the median and 50 percent of the scores being higher. When reporting the median (designated *MED*), you indicate that half the respondents scored higher than average and half the respondents scored lower than average. This popular measure of central tendency is often the best representation of a sample's responses.

Before determining the median for a set of data, the scores must be put in a rank order distribution (from lowest to highest, or ascending order). When the number of scores in a distribution is odd, the median is the exact middle score (15 in Table 5.1A), while the median for an even number of scores falls between two scores. For example, the odd number of scores in the distribution 2, 2, 3, 5, 6, 7, 7, 9, 11 gives a median of 6 (the middle score in the range); the even number of scores in the distribution 2, 3, 5, 6, 7, 7, 9, 11 has a median of 6.5 (falling between scores 6 and 7).

This method tends to be used when there are few tied scores or when a distribution has a small number of scores. Further, unlike the mean, the median is not affected by outliers (extreme atypical scores). For the example involving the number of push-ups performed by a group of students (18, 19, 20, 20, 22, 25, 100), the median value is 20, despite the outlying score of 100. Therefore, in this case the median more accurately represents the group's performance as a whole.

The Mode

The mode is simply the score that occurs most frequently in a distribution. It is the simplest of the three measures of central tendency and the roughest estimate of the middle score. Therefore, it is the least used of these measures because it does not take into account extreme scores, the number of scores, or their relationship to the middle of the set of data. When data have been arranged in a rank order distribution, the mode may be obtained by plain inspection, without any calculation. It is possible to have multiple modes within a distribution (18 and 13 in Table 5.1A); in this case, the distribution has more than one mode and is called **bimodal** or **multimodal**.

Percentiles

Percentiles are especially useful for interpreting data that may be difficult to appreciate in a raw form. Sportscasters commonly use percentages to describe data such as a team's free-throw shooting accuracy – this information in its raw form does not allow quick comparisons to be made with other teams. It is certainly more useful to know that a team is shooting 75 percent than to be told they have made 510 out of 680 attempted shots (Table 5.2).

The mode is the simplest – and least used – of the measures of central tendency because it does not take extreme scores into account. Can you think of specific situations when using the mode might be advantageous?

Recreation and Fitness Leadership

Table 5.2 Sample statistical scouting report on a visiting basketball team.

Statistics	Per Game Average
Points	74.5
Field goal percentage	.433
Three-point percentage	.386
Three pointers attempted	19.9
Free-throw percentage	.647
Total rebounds	37.7
Offensive rebounds	14.0
Assists	16.8
Steals	7.9
Turnovers	16.0
Blocks	2.2

In statistics, a percentile is defined as a standard score. It is a point or position on a continuous scale of 100 theoretical divisions such that a certain fraction of the population of raw scores lies at or below that point. In other words, the percentile rank of a score indicates the percentage of all scores that lie below a given score and, conversely, the percentage of all scores that lie above it.

We are often interested in how our scores rank relative to other individuals or groups. Your percentile score on a given test indicates how you compare with the other raw scores in the set of data.

For example, if you perform 50 sit-ups on a muscular endurance test, which we will assume is the 80th percentile, this means that 80 percent of the relevant comparison group performs 50 or fewer sit-ups, and only 20 percent perform more. This tells us that your level of muscular endurance is equal to or better than that of 80 percent of the individuals in the particular population. Therefore, percentile scores provide more information than do raw data alone.

The terms *percent* and *percentile* cannot be used interchangeably. For example, you may score 85 percent on an exam, but that doesn't necessarily equate to the 85th percentile. If your mark is equal to or greater than the marks attained by 95 percent of your classmates, your score is in the 95th percentile. Only 5 percent of your classmates scored higher than you.

If your performance on the sit-ups test puts you in the 80th percentile, this tells you that your level of muscular endurance is equal to or better than 80 percent of individuals in the relevant comparison group. It also tells you that only 20 percent scored better than you.

Sports pages and web pages dedicated to sports coverage offer good examples of how statistical data can be organized, analyzed, and presented in a form that is meaningful to the average reader.

Needs assessment is the most time-consuming step in the event planning process, but preparing and responsibly distributing, collecting, and analyzing data will ensure a popular and successful event or program in the long run. Conducting research and gathering relevant information answers questions and solves problems. The presented results of our research provide us with important insight into our questions. Assessing needs and gathering information are versatile in that you can pick and choose the tools you wish to use and that will suit your target group best.

Statistical tools allow us to analyze a large amount of data and extract a numerical value that reveals a characteristic or trait about the data under examination. Frequency distributions, graphs, and pie charts help us present collected data and their results in a meaningful way. Statistical techniques such as measures of central tendency and percentiles are precise, providing us with important insight into various investigations and inquiries.

Key Terms

bar graphs

bimodal

class frequency

class intervals

closed-ended questions

focus groups

frequency distribution

graphs

grouped frequency distribution

interest checklists

leading questions

line of best fit

mean

measures of central tendency

median

mode

multimodal

multiple choice

needs assessment

open-ended questions

outliers

percentile

pie chart

public meetings

questionnaire

random sample

rank order distribution

rating

relative frequency

simple frequency distribution

statistics

surveys

tally

target group

Review Questions

1. What is a needs assessment?

2. List the types of needs assessment tools that can be used.

3. What are the characteristics of a well-prepared survey/questionnaire?

4. What are the different information-gathering questions that can be used in a survey/questionnaire?

5. What is the difference between open-ended and closed-ended questions?

6. What are the steps you should take when conducting telephone interviews?

7. How do you plan for a focus group session?

8. List the pros and cons of using public meetings as needs assessment tools.

9. How can you display the results of your needs assessment information gathering?

10. Provide an example and calculate the three measures of central tendency. Which of the three is most accurate for your sample? Why?

In This Chapter:

CHAPTER 6
Event Coordination

In this chapter, you will learn about the following:

❶ Setting appropriate goals

❷ Planning a health and physical education event that reflects the needs and abilities of the participants

❸ Designing an action plan (i.e., a plan that specifies what, when, where, how, who) to implement the event

❹ Running effective meetings

❺ The various tournament formats and when they are suitable

"Would you tell me, please, which way I ought to go from here?" (Alice asked the Cheshire Cat.) "That depends a good deal on where you want to get to," said the Cat. "I don't care much where...," said Alice. "Then it doesn't matter which way you go," said the Cat.
Alice's Adventures in Wonderland
Lewis Carroll (1920, p. 81)

This chapter outlines the remaining steps of the event planning process, with an emphasis on setting goals and developing the event plan. In the previous chapter you learned how to complete the first step, performing a needs assessment. Now that the target group's needs have been identified, the next important step is to write the goals of the proposed event or project so that it may be structured to meet those needs. In coordinating any event, it is important to know the end result you want. Thus the starting point to consider is actually the desired end point – the goal of the entire process.

The event planning process involves several steps (Figure 6.1). Figure 6.1 shows how the needs of the group drive the goal-setting step, which drives step three (developing the event plan) – including coming up with the idea or concept. We first look at the importance of goals in the event planning process.

THE FLEXIBLE EVENT PLAN

▶ You must continually review and update the event plan.

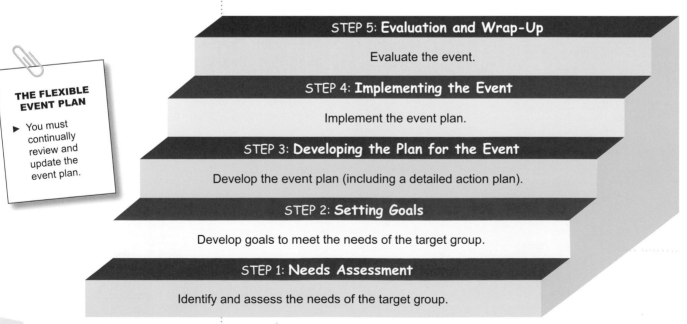

STEP 5: **Evaluation and Wrap-Up**
Evaluate the event.

STEP 4: **Implementing the Event**
Implement the event plan.

STEP 3: **Developing the Plan for the Event**
Develop the event plan (including a detailed action plan).

STEP 2: **Setting Goals**
Develop goals to meet the needs of the target group.

STEP 1: **Needs Assessment**
Identify and assess the needs of the target group.

Figure 6.1 An outline of the five-step event planning process.

Recreation and Fitness Leadership

Following the Event Planning Process

Needs Assessment
What do your potential participants want and/or need?

Setting Goals
What will your goals be?
Can you state your goals for the project in SMART terms?

Developing the Plan for the Event
Can you develop an idea
- using previous experiences?
- through brainstorming?

Can you select the best option
- after assessing possible problems and barriers?
- after considering alternatives?

Can you develop a detailed action plan
- stating who is responsible for what?
- that sets deadlines?

Implementing the Event
Can you run the event as planned?
Can you adjust your plan to handle unexpected changes?
Can you enjoy the experience?

Evaluation and Wrap-Up
Have you developed criteria to measure the success of the event?

Leave a report for future reference:
- Were there any areas that needed improvement?
- What unexpected things happened? Did you deal with them effectively?

Draw up a financial report. Pay bills.

WHO? WHAT? WHEN? WHERE? HOW?

Setting Goals

Becoming an effective fitness and recreation leader begins with setting goals and developing the sense of purpose that accompanies them. Setting goals is motivating because it directs our attention and action, increases our persistence, and encourages us to figure out ways to achieve those goals. The usefulness of goal setting for enhancing motivation has strong research support.

Goals protect us from aimless effort and point us in a positive direction. They are the building blocks of better time management. Therefore, fitness and recreation leaders are likely to find goal setting a helpful tool. Evaluation and feedback about how well we achieve our goals is also an essential element.

*R*esearch supports the notion that goal setting directs our attention and actions towards achieving our desired goals. Can you think of a time when setting a specific goal encouraged you to strive for and to achieve that goal?

SMART Goals

SPECIFIC

MEASURABLE

ATTAINABLE

RELEVANT

TIME FRAME

Goals, which are sometimes called targets, drive the planning process. Only a well-conceived action plan will help you attain goals. Determining what you want to accomplish is the starting point, but to reach your goal you need to write SMART goals. The mnemonic SMART is an aid for remembering the criteria for writing goals. Effective goals are specific, measurable, attainable, relevant, and completed within a certain time frame.

Specific

A goal must have one or at the most two intended results. The desired end product or behaviour must be stated and described unequivocally. The goal must be well defined and clear to anyone familiar with the project. For example, "The members of the salsa dance club will learn how to dance partner salsa."

Measurable

When setting goals, always make sure they are observable and measurable. It is of little value to use such general terms as "The dancers' ability will be greatly enhanced." In this case, you have no easy way of observing or measuring whether the desired goal has actually been achieved. On the other hand, if your goal is stated as "The dancers will be able to perform 10 different salsa steps in sequence," you can directly observe and measure if the club's members reach the desired criteria.

In summary, state the goal as a quantity whenever possible. Ideally, there will be an observable change in behaviour that can be measured. Select concrete methods and criteria for assessing progress towards the achievement of the goal. These methods should be reliable, valid, and objective.

Attainable

This criterion dictates that goals be achievable while presenting a realistic challenge. Writing goals with attainability in mind helps you identify barriers and thus focus on overcoming them. To set achievable goals, you must first consider your target group's characteristics and the physical, technical, and human resources available in your particular circumstances.

For instance, stating a goal that requires more money than your target population has or that requires growth and development that won't occur in the foreseeable future are examples of setting unattainable goals. You must make sure that physical resources – such as facilities, equipment, and space – are available. Before stating goals, take into account the quantity, quality, accessibility, and safety of these physical resources. The availability of technical and human resources also has an impact on attainability. For example, an adequate number

Recreation and Fitness Leadership

of volunteers, technical guides, progress charts, films and videos, technical manuals, and so on may be valuable in helping you create attainable goals.

Sometimes, with all good intentions, the standards of performance are set too high or unrealistically. When this happens, it is advisable to take another look at your determined performance standards. Going back to our earlier example, 10 different salsa steps may have been too difficult a standard to achieve within the relatively short period of six weeks, the length of the dance program. If at the midpoint of the program the dancers' progress is slower than you anticipated, modify the standard of performance to 6 steps, or make the change the next time you offer the program.

Relevant

Successful attainment of the goal should make a difference for the target group. Through needs assessment (Chapter 5), you become aware of the target population's feelings, beliefs, needs, and attitudes in order to identify the issues that are important to them.

The target group's needs become the central focus of your attention – they are the only valid criteria to use when assessing if your stated goals are relevant. In our example, the club members have paid a fee to attend, so it is clear that learning to dance the salsa is relevant to them for a number of personal reasons.

Can you identify the specific goal(s) of these activities?

Time Frame

The last element of a goal statement is the time frame for completion. This criterion is obviously stated as a length of time (e.g., days, weeks, months) or a specific completion date. For example, "The members of the salsa dance class will be able to perform 10 different steps in sequence by the end of the six-week session."

Outcomes

A concept related to goals is **outcomes**. Unlike goals, however, outcomes are more general statements of intent. They state desired results to which a fitness and recreation leader's effort is directed. Outcomes deal with abstract concepts and often sound lofty and idealistic. That is, the verbs in outcome statements tend to be vague and open to interpretation: appreciate, experience, understand, motivate, develop a positive attitude towards.

Goal Evaluation

In addition to the SMART guidelines provided in this section, the fitness leader should conduct periodic evaluation of planned goals.

Re-evaluation is vital to success. Fitness and recreation leaders may find that after they have fully committed and put all their efforts into a goal, that goal may be overambitious or unrealistic. If so, the goal should be re-assessed.

Fitness and recreation leaders should be able to recognize and face obstacles, realizing that they will not always be able to meet their goals. Successful leaders acknowledge and learn from their setbacks.

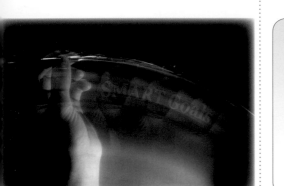

Set SMART Goals

To write SMART goals, ask yourself the following questions:

S   Exactly what is the end result I hope for?
M   What makes up a good job/event/performance?
A   Is my goal feasible?
R   Is my goal meaningful?
T   How much time do I have?

Examples of Setting Goals to Meet a Target Group's Needs

Note how each goal statement includes all five SMART principles.

Target Group 1

The 24 students in the recreation and fitness leadership class who have just begun the course

Needs
To experience plan coordination as a group, with a lot of guidance, as background to completing their own projects later in the semester. This need was identified by the teacher, who also determined the event.

Goals
1. The class will organize a pep rally the morning of the Fair Parade, with 95 percent of the school population attending. The students will learn/sing the school song, join in three cheers, and meet the members of the fall sports teams.

2. The class will sell out of promotional temporary mascot tattoos (300).

Outcome
The recreation and fitness leadership class will work as a group to plan an event that will boost the school population's school spirit and sense of belonging.

Target Group 2

The 18 members of the Outdoor Recreation Club, ranging in age from 15 to 17

Needs
To have a major outing as an end point of their season and an opportunity to test out the skills they have learned. A discussion led to consensus about the details of the trip.

Goal

The students will plan, prepare for, and complete an overnight canoe trip along the Goshecan River – including a 100-metre portage, campsite selection and set-up, and meal preparation – on the first weekend in June.

Outcome

The students will gain an appreciation of the skills required to enjoy a wilderness experience.

Target Group 3

The student population of Highlands Secondary School

Needs

The Parents' Council was concerned about student health issues such as obesity and substance abuse. A survey was developed and administered to a diverse group of 75 students to determine student concerns and preferences for delivery of information.

Goal

The recreation and fitness leadership class will organize a half-day Health Fair for the school community, bringing in at least eight organizations and agencies. Approximately 250 students will attend.

Outcome

The students will become more aware of healthy living strategies.

Target Group 4

The members of the Gateway Community Senior Citizens' Club

Needs
Social interaction, change of scenery, education

Goal
The group will take a "Fall Colours" bus tour, with a stop for lunch and a tour of the nature interpretation centre.

Outcome
The seniors group will enjoy a day-long outing.

Developing the Event Plan

With the goals defined, you can now begin planning an event or activity that will address them. In this initial stage, all ideas are generated, all decision making is done, and all details are organized. If all factors have been addressed and backup plans are in place to handle unforeseen situations, the event will go smoothly – and you may even have fun yourself.

How Are Events and Projects Conceived?

In many cases, an event that has historically served to meet specified needs and goals is already in place. This event will need to be re-assessed, with a view to

- keeping it up to date;

- making it more exciting and attractive to participants – it may have lost its appeal;

- tweaking it to make it more efficient; and

- using available resources, information, and equipment more effectively.

On the other hand, a session of **brainstorming** (see Chapter 3) may elicit several ideas for a new first-time event. A discussion balancing the pros and cons of each suggestion will eventually result in a final selection. Resources such as the Canadian Intramural Recreation Association also provide print and online suggestions and information about popular, innovative, and successful events.

Rules for Brainstorming

Allow enough time. "Let's spend the next 15 minutes coming up with all the ideas we can."

Encourage lateral "outside-the-box" thinking. "Let's be creative – anything goes."

Accept and record all suggestions without comment. "Don't react to any suggestions just yet."

The key thing to remember is that event planning starts with determining the needs of the group and setting goals. Just because an event seems easy to stage or looks like fun does not guarantee that it will be a hit with the target audience or that it will be worthwhile doing.

Writing the Proposal

It is a good idea to answer a uniform set of questions to describe the event. These questions will address the match between the event and the target group's identified needs and begin to set out the logistics of the event. In the real world, completing a proposal is a required step in the process of acquiring funding for an event (e.g., accessing budget funds or government grants).

Note that the question "How will participation in your event benefit the target group?" is, in fact, asking for information on needs and goals.

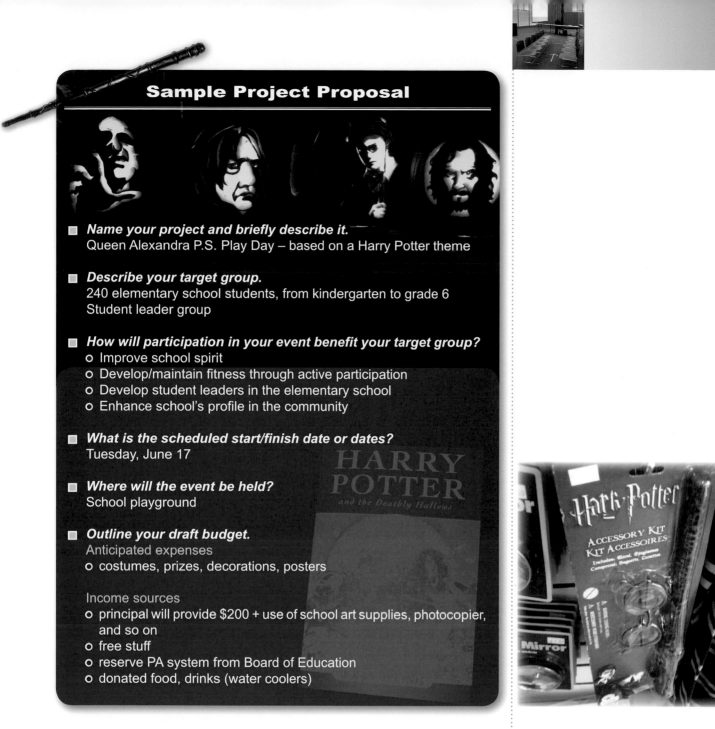

Sample Project Proposal

■ **Name your project and briefly describe it.**
Queen Alexandra P.S. Play Day – based on a Harry Potter theme

■ **Describe your target group.**
240 elementary school students, from kindergarten to grade 6
Student leader group

■ **How will participation in your event benefit your target group?**
o Improve school spirit
o Develop/maintain fitness through active participation
o Develop student leaders in the elementary school
o Enhance school's profile in the community

■ **What is the scheduled start/finish date or dates?**
Tuesday, June 17

■ **Where will the event be held?**
School playground

■ **Outline your draft budget.**
Anticipated expenses
o costumes, prizes, decorations, posters

Income sources
o principal will provide $200 + use of school art supplies, photocopier, and so on
o free stuff
o reserve PA system from Board of Education
o donated food, drinks (water coolers)

Staffing the Committee

Apart from identifying the target group, the other important people to be named are the people organizing the various aspects of the event. It takes thousands of volunteers to run a lengthy, complex event such as a world championship or an Olympic Games; it takes just a few people to organize an intramural tournament. The organizers of the larger event will have a long list of aspects to consider; the smaller event will have simpler requirements.

Identifying individuals or organizations that can assist with the event is a step that should not be overlooked. One strategy is to ask people you know who have the interest and expertise to help. You can also advertise for help through bulletin boards, school announcements, and so on.

If you need a lot of help, you may be able to enlist a group (e.g., a local service club, recreation department, or class of students) to organize a particular aspect of the event. Some municipalities have volunteer bureaus that link volunteers with organizations and events that need their assistance. Students and others who are required to complete volunteer service hours are another source of help.

Committee Structure

The tasks required for any major event can be categorized under standard headings, which may serve as either committee or individual designations. Subdividing the responsibilities makes the task less onerous. Most people are happy to have their areas of operation well defined and limited in scope and time frame.

Executive Committee When a large event requires many subcommittees, an executive committee consisting of the chairpersons of the individual subcommittees is formed. It is headed up by one of the subcommittee chairs or by another individual who takes on total responsibility. This arrangement ensures that all communication flows in two directions and that all volunteers are aware of the "big picture." Also, it provides a forum for sharing ideas and finding solutions for other committees' problems.

Putting together a competent group of individuals and forming designated committees are important steps to follow when organizing a successful event.

Recreation and Fitness Leadership

Finance Committee The finance committee develops a budget, establishes income sources, and predicts expenses. The treasurer makes bank deposits, writes cheques, and prepares interim and final financial reports.

Gate/Admissions/Registration Committee This may be a subcommittee of the finance committee or a separate entity. The person in charge of this aspect will need to obtain cash boxes, change, and tickets (or some other means of identifying paid participants/spectators); recruit volunteers to work; prepare signage; and ensure the security of the funds collected.

Program/Scheduling Committee This person or committee will produce a schedule of events by determining how, when, and where people will participate in the planned event.

Technical Committee Some events have complex technical requirements – such as bodies of rules and regulations – to be established, communicated, and enforced, requiring officials, equipment (e.g., stopwatches), forms (e.g., score sheets), and so on. Subcommittees may be placed in charge of

- the score room,
- volunteers (timers, scorers, pit crew), and
- equipment measurement.

Facility/Site/Equipment Committee This person or committee secures a facility and confirms its availability. In advance, the committee draws up a plan or map for the use of the facility and is responsible for securing all equipment (e.g., rental of bleachers, tables, water stations). **Security** may be considered a part of this portfolio or a separate one.

Public Relations/Communication Committee This group is in charge of all aspects of promoting the event to the public. This may include branding (logo design), media releases, press kits, signs, and advertising. Chapter 7 deals with this aspect in detail. In addition, this committee may be responsible for communicating information to the participants.

Protocol Committee This committee is in charge of obtaining and briefing announcers, writing the announcer's script, planning the opening and closing ceremonies, organizing awards ceremonies (all aspects: ordering awards, arranging presenters), arranging accommodations for special guests and dignitaries, and planning any related social events, such as receptions and banquets.

Souvenir Programs Committee Gathering information and formatting, editing, and publishing a program is a huge task. Obtaining advertising revenue may be assigned to a subcommittee under the program committee or the finance committee.

Concessions/Souvenirs Committee The organizing committee may decide to run a concession stand and/or a booth to sell souvenir clothing and other items. A committee is then needed to oversee this aspect of the event.

Accreditation/Registration Committee Athletes may need competitive numbers; athletes, officials, and volunteers may need identification badges, possibly even with photos. This committee may also be responsible for preparing and distributing information packages during registration.

Hosting Committee The hosting committee is responsible for accommodations and meals for participants, officials, and support personnel. It may be in contact with hotels, restaurants, and caterers or may even arrange billeting.

Medical Support Team This area of responsibility is key. Most organizations mandate a particular level of medical support, whether it is an individual qualified in first aid, a St. John Ambulance brigade, or a full-scale athletic therapy unit. Even for an informal event, someone must be prepared to handle medical emergencies. This aspect is presented in detail in Unit 4.

Transportation Committee This group organizes transportation to and from the venue(s). Volunteer drivers, shuttle buses, and public transportation all may need to be arranged.

Example of an Organizing Committee Structure

In the following example, a grade 12 leadership class was given the responsibility of running an event to give the incoming grade 9 students a fun introduction to the school (see the box *Frosh Olympics*). The 12th-graders decided to run a Sports Day with an Olympic theme. This was the first opportunity for the class to run an event on a large scale. The teacher guided the process, providing necessary information and tools. The students selected a chairperson (or two). The class brainstormed all the tasks that would need to be completed and grouped the tasks into four areas: public relations, program, protocol, and paperwork. Planning was done in class for a week prior to the event. At the end of each class, the subcommittees reported on their activities to keep everyone informed and to receive feedback and suggestions.

Frosh Olympics

- **Chairperson or Co-Chairs**
  - Lead brainstorming regarding activities at stations
  - Chair information-sharing wrap-up discussions at end of each class
  - Lead debriefing after the event

- **Staff Adviser**
  - Facilitates group process (provides materials, information)
  - Approves and signs posters, announcements

- **Subcommittee Chairpersons**
  - Coordinate the actions of the committee members
  - Report on progress

- **Subcommittee Responsibilities**

Program	Publicity	Paperwork	Protocol
• Select activities • Plan the schedule • Draw up facility map • Plan for safety • Recruit volunteers	Internal: • Design posters • Speak to grade 9 classes • Write PA announcements • Take photos • Create photo collage External: • Write media release • Assemble press packages • Meet and greet press	• Prepare station leaders' clipboards • Prepare/post team lists • Create signs and maps • Draw up score sheet	• Plan opening ceremonies • Recruit announcer • Write script • Book PA system • Form Spirit Squad • Arrange for refreshment station • Plan closing ceremonies • Purchase prizes

All committee members and volunteers are responsible for cleaning up their areas after the event.

Committee Checklist

No matter what the size of your organizing committee, you need to consider the following:

✔ What will this cost, and where will the money come from?

✔ Who will help?

✔ How will I generate enthusiasm for the event?

✔ What must be done in advance (e.g., site, paperwork, equipment)?

✔ How will I reward the participants?

✔ How will I deal with safety and risk management?

Action Planning

Establishing immediate and short-term plans is the last consideration when developing an event plan. Generally speaking, immediate plans cover day-to-day activities to ensure that goals for the day have been met, whereas short-term plans ensure completion of the stated goals on a weekly basis. The short-term plans are also designed to make sure the overall project is completed within the set time frame.

The immediate and short-term plans have a provision for an evaluation process. Because you have already established goals that are directly measurable, all that remains is to determine if the specific goals have been met. If the determined goals are not met, immediate correction is required. This corrective action can take one of two forms: You may need to restate your goal – it may not have been specific enough to be adequately measured or improved – or it may be best to redefine your standards of performance so that they are attainable.

An action plan is a detailed "to-do" list specifying who is responsible for each item and a target date for its completion. A well-constructed action plan will include all necessary details as well as backup plans in case of unforeseen complications. For instance, an outdoor activity may need an alternative location in case weather conditions are not ideal. In general, a detailed action plan includes the following:

▶ Name of event

▶ Description of event

▶ Specific tasks for event

▶ Specific timelines for completion of each task
  • leading up to the event
  • on the day of the event
  • following the event

Immediate and short-term goals must go through an evaluation process to determine if established goals have been met. Previous goals may need to be restated or redefined if specific goals have not been met.

- ► List of people assigned to each task
- ► Alternative plans (e.g., in case of bad weather, power failure)
- ► Promotion – examples of each
- ► Detailed safety check
- ► Supervision needs

Action plans must be updated and reviewed continually throughout the planning process. Make sure that what you are planning matches your goals. Action plans are useful tools for all events and projects. Figure 6.2 is a sample of a plan for a surprise birthday party. It was drafted two weeks ahead of the event.

Helpful Hints for Meetings

As soon as more than one person is involved in the organization of an event, meetings are a necessity. There is an art to efficiently and effectively chairing a meeting. Here are some hints on how to chair an effective meeting:

❶ Prepare your agenda well in advance of the meeting date. Ask group members if they have items that need to be included. Distribute the agenda before the meeting to allow members to prepare themselves (e.g., write reports).

❷ Keep the group on track during the meeting by following the agenda. Introduce the items for discussion in the order they are presented on the agenda.

❸ Keep things moving – don't let the group get "bogged down" in little items. Watch the group members to ensure that everyone has the opportunity to speak on an issue.

❹ Use your authority only when absolutely necessary (e.g., to keep the group on track or to facilitate conflict resolution).

❺ Handle all decisions by calling a group vote.

❻ Make sure that someone is taking the minutes for the meeting.

Once the agenda has been prepared and distributed, it is up to the person chairing the meeting to make sure the group stays on track and keeps things moving.

Item	Who's Responsible	Deadline
IDEA		
Set date, time	Jim	Today
Whose house?	Parents'	Today
Theme	Janey	Today
Guest list	Jim & Janey	Today
Budget	Jim & parents	Today
PROMOTION		
Invitations	Jim – phone, e-mail Janey – written	Next Monday
ORGANIZE		
Plan menu	Jim & parents	
Order cake	Jim	Mon June 15
Shop for food	Janey & C's mom	Fri June 19
Music: bring CDs	Charlie	
Extra lawn chairs	Include in invitation	
Pop & punch	Parents	
Decorations	Janey & Elaine	
Baby pix etc. on poster	Parents, Janey	
Outdoor games (horseshoes, lawn darts)	Charlie	
DO IT!		
Pick up cake	Jim	Sat June 20 by noon
Take Cathy shopping, arrive 30 minutes late	Janey	2:00–5:00 p.m.
Decorate	Elaine and Sherri	4:00 p.m.
Set out buffet	Everyone except Janey	4:00 p.m.
Set up chairs, games, etc.	Charlie	4:00 p.m.
Light candles and bring in cake	Jim	8:00 p.m.
CLEANUP		
Clean up all equipment, etc.	Parents, Charlie, Elaine, Sherri	
EVALUATE		
Listen for feedback		
From guests		
From Cathy		

Figure 6.2 Sample plan for a surface-16 birthday party for Cathy.

Figure 6.2 Sample plan for a surprise sweet-16 birthday party for Cathy.

The box *Sample Template for Organizing a Meeting Agenda* outlines a template for setting up an agenda for a meeting. Having an organized and itemized agenda helps to keep everyone in the meeting focused on the business at hand.

Recreation and Fitness Leadership

Sample Template for Organizing a Meeting Agenda

Name of Organization or Group

Day and Time _____   Location (e.g., which room) _____

<u>AGENDA</u>

1. **Call to order** – *The chairperson officially starts the meeting and the time is noted.*

2. **Roll call (attendance)** – *The secretary lists those present and those who sent regrets.*

3. **Appoint recording secretary** – *The recording secretary is officially named.*

4. **Minutes of previous meeting (review for errors and omissions)** – *Printed copies were distributed beforehand.*

5. **Revision of agenda** – *Review the prepared agenda, and add additional items under new business.*

6. **Information updates and correspondence** – *Only if the item does not fit under unfinished business.*

7. **Committee reports** – *Committee chairs present reports that ideally were written and distributed in advance.*

8. **Unfinished business arising from last meeting**
   8.1 (*list items*)
   8.2
   8.3 etc.

9. **New business**
   9.1 (*list items; new items may be added at any point*)
   9.2
   9.3 etc.

10. **Schedule next meeting**

11. **Adjournment**

Robert's Rules of Order

Most formal meetings are conducted according to a set of procedures called **Robert's Rules of Order**. Along with a group's constitution and bylaws, these rules form the "playing regulations." Some important considerations follow:

Quorum

How many members need to be present at the meeting in order to conduct official business? This number, known as a quorum, often represents 50 percent of the membership plus one additional person.

Voting

What issues need a 50 percent majority? A 90 percent majority? How are ties broken? Does the chairperson have a vote?

How to Make a Motion

A motion brings an item of business before the group for action. Gain the chairperson's attention and state, "I move that [the action you propose the group should take]." The chairperson will ask for someone to second the motion. Without a seconder, the motion cannot be discussed. If the motion is seconded, speak briefly in favour of it.

The chairperson opens the floor for discussion. Those who are against the motion and for the motion take turns presenting their views. When there is no further discussion, you may defend your motion one last time. The chairperson calls the vote and declares the motion "carried" or "defeated."

Recording the Minutes

Keeping an accurate record of meetings (i.e., the minutes) is essential. It will reduce confusion and provide documentation of what was decided and who is responsible for each task. The minutes also provide a historical record, helping a committee make consistent decisions based on past precedent (see the box *Sample Template for Recording Minutes of a Meeting*).

> "A meeting is an event where the minutes are kept and the hours are lost.
>
> *Anonymous*

The quotation above comments on the inefficiencies that can plague meetings. What strategies would you use to make sure a meeting runs as smoothly as possible?

Tournament Organization

One event that you may have the opportunity to organize is a sports tournament at your school. Because there are many types of tournaments, it is important to familiarize yourself with the proper techniques for organizing tournament draws and brackets. This information will also enable you to host your own tournament if the situation arises.

Three tournament types that are often used in high school intramural and inter-school competitions are round robin, elimination, and challenge. The format you select will depend on several factors:

▶ The type of activity/game

▶ The number of teams or players

▶ The amount of time available

▶ The facilities available

▶ The equipment available

Recreation and Fitness Leadership

Sample Template for Recording Minutes of a Meeting

1. **Meeting of the** _____ **committee**

2. Held on _____ at _____ a.m./p.m. in room #_____

3. Present: _____ (in the chair)

   _____ (recording secretary)

   _____

   _____

   _____

4. Minutes of last meeting (date: _____): Note amendments and approval

5. Agenda additions and approval

6. Correspondence

7. Reports

8. Business arising from the minutes

Discussion/Topic	Action	By whom?	By when?

9. New business

Discussion/Topic	Action	By whom?	By when?

10. Date and location of next meeting

11. Adjournment at _____ a.m./p.m.

Round-Robin Tournaments

In a round-robin tournament, each player or team gets to play every other player or team. In a single round robin, each entry plays every other entry once. In a double round robin, each competitor plays two games against every other entry.

When to Use This Type of Tournament

The round-robin tournament is the best competition format to use if sufficient time and facilities are available or if the number of competitors is small. If you want to determine a true winner and at the same time rank the other contestants in the best possible manner, a round-robin tournament is your best alternative. For example, to select a varsity badminton or table tennis team, simply have the athletes who attend tryouts compete in a round-robin tournament. The results can be one of the tools you use for selecting the team.

Procedures for Setting Up the Draw

Step 1

Assign numbers to the teams that have entered the tournament. If you have an even number of entries, arrange two vertical columns of numbers, representing the number of entries. This is done by listing the numbers consecutively down the first column and up the second. With each number representing a team, this provides the pairings for the first round.

To obtain the pairings for the subsequent rounds, rotate the numbers counter-clockwise around one number that remains fixed – usually the number in the top left position (e.g., 1 in Table 6.1). Continue this procedure until all the pairings have been determined (i.e., you arrive back at your original pairings of numbers). This process is illustrated in Table 6.1.

The procedure is the same for an uneven number of entries (e.g., seven teams entered the tournament). In this case, however, a **bye** should be placed in one of the positions (again, usually the top left), and the other numbers are rotated around it (in Table 6.1, 1 would be replaced with a bye).

The formula for determining the total number of games to be played in a round-robin tournament is $N(N-1)/2$, with N representing the number of teams or participating units in the tournament. Using our example in Table 6.1, a round-robin tournament with eight entries requires $8(8-1)/2$, or 28 games. This formula can be used with any number of entries.

A round-robin tournament can be used as an effective tool to help select a varsity table tennis team.

Table 6.1 The round-robin pairings for eight teams.

Round 1	Round 2	Round 3	Round 4	Round 5	Round 6	Round 7
1 vs. 8	**1** vs. 7	**1** vs. 6	**1** vs. 5	**1** vs. 4	**1** vs. 3	**1** vs. 2
2 vs. 7	8 vs. 6	7 vs. 5	6 vs. 4	5 vs. 3	4 vs. 2	3 vs. 8
3 vs. 6	2 vs. 5	8 vs. 4	7 vs. 3	6 vs. 2	5 vs. 8	4 vs. 7
4 vs. 5	3 vs. 4	2 vs. 3	8 vs. 2	7 vs. 8	6 vs. 7	5 vs. 6

Recreation and Fitness Leadership

Step 2

Draw up a schedule of the time and place for each game to be played. This page will be posted and/or included in the coaches' information packages.

Table 6.2 presents an example of eight teams playing on four courts, so no teams have a rest. All round-one games take place at 9:00 a.m. All round-two games take place at 10:00 a.m., and so on. Notice that the teams are placed on different courts as the tournament progresses.

Table 6.2 Huntsville High School Invitational Volleyball Tournament, Saturday, March 22, 2008.

ROUND	TIME	COURT A	COURT B	COURT C	COURT D
1	9:00	1 vs. 8	2 vs. 7	3 vs. 6	4 vs. 5
2	10:00	3 vs. 4	1 vs. 7	8 vs. 6	2 vs. 5
3	11:00	7 vs. 5	8 vs. 4	2 vs. 3	1 vs. 6
4	1:00	6 vs. 4	8 vs. 2	1 vs. 5	7 vs. 3
5	2:00	6 vs. 2	5 vs. 3	1 vs. 4	7 vs. 8
6	3:00	1 vs. 3	6 vs. 7	4 vs. 2	5 vs. 8
7	4:00	3 vs. 8	5 vs. 6	4 vs. 7	1 vs. 2

Step 3

Draw up and post the tournament score sheet as shown in Table 6.3.

Table 6.3 Tournament score sheet.

TEAM	1	2	3	4	5	6	7	8		Points	Place
1								W			
2											
3											
4											
5											
6											
7											
8	L										

Note 1: *The number of squares on one half of the sheet equals the number of games played in the tournament.*

Note 2: *Game results must be entered in two places (i.e., for each team playing the game). Example: In the first round, 1 beats 8. A **W** is placed on team one's line under column 8, and an **L** is placed on team eight's line in column 1. Alternatively, actual final scores may be entered (e.g., 25–19 for team one and 19–25 for team eight).*

Advantages and disadvantages of the round-robin tournament are included in Table 6.4. Consider them carefully before choosing this format.

Table 6.4 Advantages and disadvantages of the round-robin tournament.

Advantages
- All teams get to play to the end of the tournament.
- All teams play an equal number of games.
- It's the fairest way to determine a champion.
- All teams are ranked at the end of the tournament.
- It permits continuous play with maximum use of facilities.

Disadvantages
- Time consuming, especially if there are many teams or limited facilities.
- Can result in ties, necessitating tie-breaking procedures.
- More facilities are required.

When many teams have entered the tournament and limited time or facilities are available, the teams may be divided into pools of three, four, or five teams. The winners of the pools then play off to determine a champion. With two pools, have a **crossover semifinal**, with the winner of Pool A playing the second-place Pool B team and the winner of Pool B playing the second-place Pool A team. Then the winners play a final match. With three or four pools, have the winners play a round-robin tournament.

Tie-Breaking Procedures

The easiest tie-breaking procedure when two teams have earned the same number of win/loss/tie points is to declare the team with the most wins the champion. If this procedure does not break the tie, their head-to-head record could be used as the deciding factor. If they played each other twice and each team won once, other criteria need to be considered, such as the point spread of those two games. If the point spread is equal, then consider the total point spread over all games played. If all statistics are tied, the teams may need to play another short game (e.g., first team to 5 points), or a coin toss may be necessary.

When all tie-breaking statistics are tied between two teams, a coin toss can be used as a last resort to determine a winner.

Elimination Tournaments

In the elimination tournament structure, teams are eliminated after a set number of losses. We describe three kinds here: the single-elimination tournament, the consolation tournament, and the modified double-elimination tournament.

Single-Elimination Tournaments

One of the most common forms of athletic competition is the traditional **single-elimination tournament**, which emphasizes the elimination of teams and players. In this type of tournament, half the competitors are eliminated after the first contest. Often this type of competition is the least desirable, but in certain circumstances it is still valuable.

▶ 134

Recreation and Fitness Leadership

When to Use This Type of Tournament

You would probably choose the single-elimination format if you have limited time and facilities to run your competition (e.g., a weekend tennis tournament) or if you have many participants (e.g., 75 entries in the boys' darts competition). In many instances, a single-elimination tournament may be the only way you can accommodate all the competitors. Also, if the goal is to determine one champion only, the single-elimination tournament is an acceptable format.

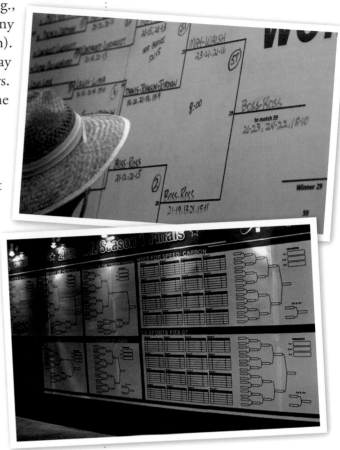

Procedures for Setting Up the Draw

The first step in arranging a single-elimination tournament is determining whether the number of entries is an even power of 2 (e.g., 4, 8, 16, 32, 64). If so, then proceed by drawing for position. For example, suppose you want to arrange a competition for eight teams. Because 8 is an even power of 2, you can set up the tournament as shown in Figure 6.3.

As you can see, the Angels were drawn for the first position, the Bobcats for the second, and so on. This procedure can be accomplished by either picking names or teams out of a hat or by having athletes draw numbers for positions.

Winning teams progress to the next round. Half the teams are eliminated in the first round and get to play only one game.

Figure 6.3 The bracket for a single elimination tournament with eight teams.

Byes If the number of teams entered is not a power of 2, you must arrange for byes. All "free matches" must be placed in the first round. This ensures that the number of contestants for the second round is an even power of 2. You can accomplish this by subtracting the total number of entrants from the next higher power of 2. For example, if you have 13 entrants, subtract 13 from the next higher power of 2, which in this case is 16. This leaves 3, which is the number of byes you need. The total number of entrants (13) minus 3 byes leaves 10 contestants to play each other in the first round. Five will lose, leaving 8 contestants in the second round. Because 8 is an even power of 2, 4 teams will reach the semifinals, and only 2 can now meet in the finals (Figure 6.4).

If there is an even number of byes, place half in the top and half in the bottom of the draw sheet. If there is an odd number of byes, put the larger number in the bottom half of the draw. Byes can be awarded on the basis of a random draw or by a process known as seeding.

Seeding is a technique used to keep the best players/teams from meeting until the end of the tournament. It prevents top players from being eliminated early, making the semifinal and final games more competitive. The two top-seeded, or top-skilled, players are placed one at the top and the other at the bottom of the draw in the first round. Other highly seeded players are placed towards the middle and evenly spaced.

Byes and Seeding If there are byes, seeded players should get them in order of their ranking (Figure 6.4). Thus, give the number-one seed the first bye, number two the second bye and so on. Remember, no player or team ever receives more than one bye, and seeding should be employed only when a competitor's previous record justifies it.

Notice in Figure 6.4 that there are 16 lines. The word *bye* is found on three of the lines (i.e., on lines 1, 9, and 16). The four highest seeded players have been inserted on lines 2, 8, 10, and 15.

The advantages and disadvantages of single-elimination tournaments are included in Table 6.5. Consider these pros and cons carefully before deciding on this tournament format.

A draw sheet is a schematic diagram that shows which teams play each other in a tournament.

Table 6.5 Advantages and disadvantages of the single-elimination tournament.

Advantages
- It takes a short time to determine a champion.
- It is a good option when facilities are limited.
- It is suitable for a large number of entries.
- It is easy to organize.

Disadvantages
- The eventual winner is not always the best entrant.
- The defeated finalist is not always second best.
- Teams/players who could benefit most from more playing experience don't get the opportunity to play.
- Except for the first game, players don't know their game times.
- It does not provide much competition for some teams.

Round 1	Round 2	Round 3	Round 4	Champion
bye				
	Almonte			
Almonte #1 seed				
		Cowie		
Benson				
	Cowie			
Cowie				
			Cowie	
Leith				
	Davidson			
Davidson				
		Davidson		
Everson				
	Everson			
Ford #4 seed				
				Kennedy
				Champion
bye				
	Galway			
Galway #3 seed				
		Galway		
Hughes				
	Isaac			
Isaac				
			Kennedy	
Larosse				
	Joyner			
Joyner				
		Kennedy		
Kennedy #2 seed				
	Kennedy			
bye				

Figure 6.4 The bracket for a single-elimination tournament for 13 entrants with four seeded entries. The top three seeded players have a bye in the first round.

Consolation Tournaments

A **consolation tournament** is an elimination tournament that provides each team with at least two games. No teams are eliminated in the first round; first-round winners move towards the right side of the draw and play other winners in the second round; first-round losers move towards the left side and play other first-round losing teams. Half the teams are eliminated in the second round. From the second round on, a loss eliminates the team. Both a tournament champion and a consolation champion are determined.

When to Use This Type of Tournament

Consolation tournaments are recommended when adequate time and facilities are available to accommodate the extra number of games. Also, when teams or players have to travel long distances to the competition site, it is a good idea to use a consolation format because each participant is guaranteed at least two contests, making the journey much more worthwhile.

Procedures for Setting Up the Draw

The procedure for this format is simply that all losers in the first round (as well as those who lose in the second round after receiving a first-round bye) play another single-elimination tournament. The person or team that wins this second tournament is deemed the consolation winner. Figure 6.5 illustrates how this competition would be arranged if there were no byes. Figure 6.6 illustrates how the tournament would be arranged if byes were necessary.

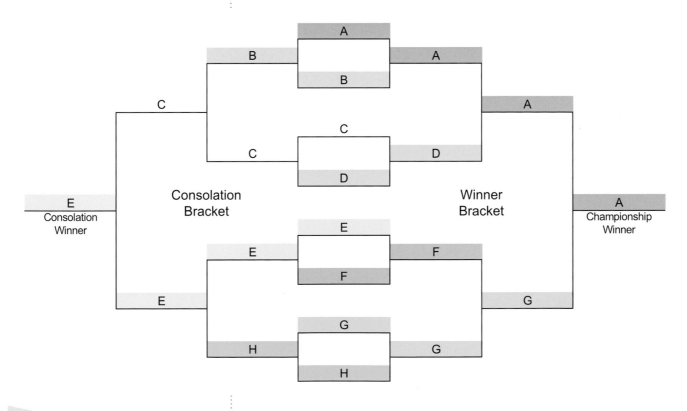

Figure 6.5 The bracket for a consolation tournament.

In Figure 6.6 you will notice that entry A goes into the consolation round after losing in the second round to entry C. This is because A

Recreation and Fitness Leadership

received a bye in the first round. The same procedure would have been followed had entry F lost to entry D. The easiest way to remember this is to place all losers of their first game in the consolation bracket, which is set up as any other single-elimination tournament.

The advantages and disadvantages of the consolation elimination format are summarized in Table 6.6. Use these pros and cons to determine if this format is best for your purposes.

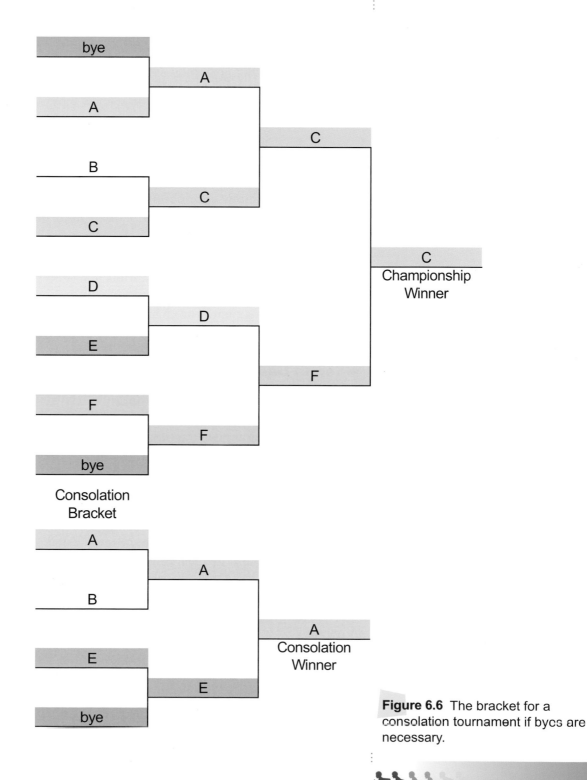

Figure 6.6 The bracket for a consolation tournament if byes are necessary.

Table 6.6 Advantages and disadvantages of the consolation elimination tournament.

Advantages
- Each entry plays at least twice before elimination.
- A strong entry eliminated by the champion early in the tournament may continue.
- It generates greater player interest.

Disadvantages
- Running the tournament is more time consuming.
- A first-round loss eliminates the opportunity to play in the tournament championship game.
- More games are involved, causing a potential space problem when there is a large number of entries.
- Except for the first game, teams don't know their game times.

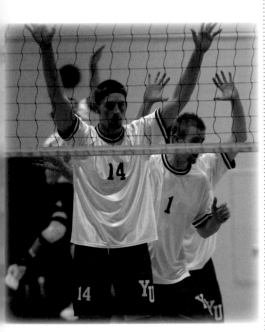

Modified double-elimination tournaments result in a more deserving winner by assuring all entries play at least two contests. These types of tournaments are well suited for most team sports.

Modified Double-Elimination Tournaments

In a modified **double-elimination tournament**, each entry is assured of playing at least two contests, as a first-round loss does not lead to elimination. This format results in the selection of a more deserving winner – a strong entry can play one bad game or match in the first round but still have the potential to win the championship. A loss in the second or any subsequent round results in elimination, similar to a single-elimination tournament. The championship game is played between the last remaining teams on the right and left sides of the draw (Figure 6.7).

When to Use This Type of Tournament

If you have lots of time available or not enough entries to warrant a single-elimination tournament, consider using a modified double-elimination format. When teams have travelled a great distance to compete, it makes the time and money spent more worthwhile.

Procedures for Setting Up the Draw

The brackets are arranged in the same way as for a single-elimination tournament, except they are placed in the middle of the page. Seeding is also performed in the same manner. After the first round, half the winning teams move to the right and half to the left; half the losing teams move to the right and half to the left. This is accomplished by moving the winners of games 1, 3, 5, 7, and so on to the right along with the losers of games 2, 4, 6, 8, and so on. The teams they met in the first round move in the opposite direction. The result is that each second-round game pits a winning team against a team with one loss. Teams losing in the second and subsequent rounds are eliminated. Two teams are left to meet in the championship game.

The advantages and disadvantages of the modified double-elimination tournament are summarized in Table 6.7. Consider these pros and cons carefully before deciding on this tournament format.

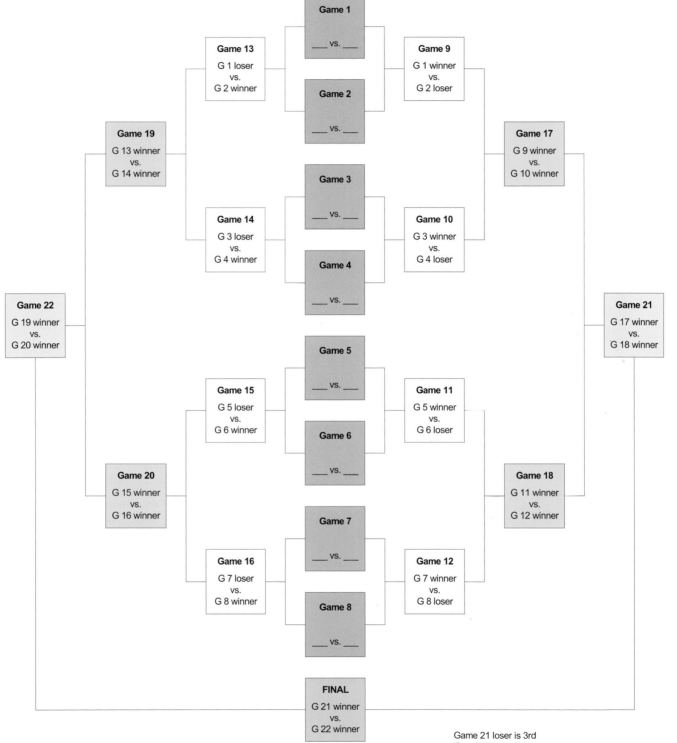

Game 1

___ vs. ___

Game 2

___ vs. ___

Game 3

___ vs. ___

Game 4

___ vs. ___

Game 5

___ vs. ___

Game 6

___ vs. ___

Game 7

___ vs. ___

Game 8

___ vs. ___

Game 13
G 1 loser
vs.
G 2 winner

Game 14
G 3 loser
vs.
G 4 winner

Game 15
G 5 loser
vs.
G 6 winner

Game 16
G 7 loser
vs.
G 8 winner

Game 9
G 1 winner
vs.
G 2 loser

Game 10
G 3 winner
vs.
G 4 loser

Game 11
G 5 winner
vs.
G 6 loser

Game 12
G 7 winner
vs.
G 8 loser

Game 19
G 13 winner
vs.
G 14 winner

Game 20
G 15 winner
vs.
G 16 winner

Game 17
G 9 winner
vs.
G 10 winner

Game 18
G 11 winner
vs.
G 12 winner

Game 22
G 19 winner
vs.
G 20 winner

Game 21
G 17 winner
vs.
G 18 winner

FINAL
G 21 winner
vs.
G 22 winner

Game 21 loser is 3rd
Game 22 loser is 4th

Figure 6.7 The bracket for a modified double-elimination tournament.

Table 6.7 Advantages and disadvantages of the modified double-elimination tournament.

Advantages
- A player or team is guaranteed two games.
- A team that gets off to a slow start is not immediately eliminated.
- It determines the most deserving winner. The final could be between two undefeated teams or between an undefeated team and a team that had one loss in the first round.

Disadvantages
- Except for the first game, teams don't know their game times.
- The tournament takes longer to run than does a single-elimination tournament.
- It emphasizes elimination.

Challenge Tournaments

The last type of organized competition that we present can be carried out by the players independently, without any formal schedules. Challenge tournaments are more often used for singles or doubles competitions than for team sports.

When to Use This Type of Tournament

Challenge, or ladder, tournaments work well for competitions that have no set schedule; that run over a lengthy time period; and that involve any number of players, some of whom may drop out, and some of whom are added partway through. Challenge tournaments are best suited to individual and partner activities, such as squash, racquetball, handball, table tennis, tennis, badminton, darts, and chess. This format maintains the players' interest in the activity throughout the season. The competition ends on a predetermined date, the winner being the person or team at the top on that date. Remember to provide a prize for the winner.

There are many varieties of challenge tournaments. We focus our attention on the traditional ladder tournament because of its expediency and simplicity. Other formats include the target, spiderweb, and pyramid.

Procedures for Setting Up the Draw

First, contestants' names are placed on cards that can be either put in slots or hung on hooks. Once you have all the names on the cards, initiate the tournament by drawing the cards out of a hat and placing them in the order drawn from the top of the ladder down to the last rung. Seeding is normally not used in challenge tournaments. At this point, your typical ladder tournament looks something like the one illustrated in Figure 6.8.

Once the ladder has been set up, the following rules govern the play:

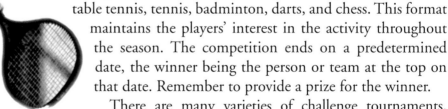

Challenge tournaments are best suited to individual and partner activities, such as tennis, badminton, darts, and chess.

Recreation and Fitness Leadership

- A standard criterion defines a win (e.g., one game, best two of three games).

- Players advance by challenging and defeating a competitor or by default if the challenge is not accepted.

- A competitor can challenge players only one or two places above himself or herself (e.g., in Figure 6.8, Julie can challenge only Linda or Sue).

- If a challenger wins, he or she trades card positions with the defeated contestant.

- Challenges must be played in the order they are made.

- After two contestants have played, they cannot play each other again until each has played another contestant at least once.

- A defender must play within three days (or whatever the administrator of the tournament deems appropriate) or default.

- The player at the top of the ladder at the end of a specified time period (e.g., 2 weeks, 10 days, 3 months) is the winner.

The advantages and disadvantages of the ladder challenge tournament are listed in Table 6.8. Consider them carefully before choosing this format.

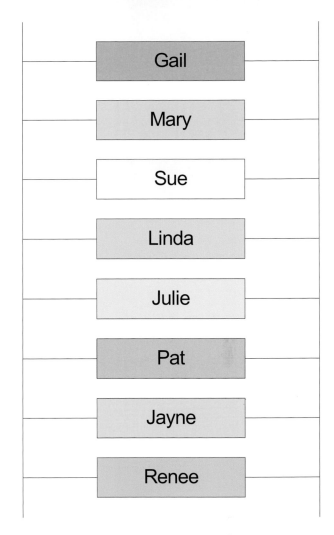

Figure 6.8 Singles tennis ladder tournament.

- *Hang cards with names on them.*
- *Challenge one or two levels higher.*
- *Winner takes higher spot.*
- *Arrange your own games.*
- *Person at the top at noon on June 30th wins a free dinner at Joel's Restaurant ($80 value).*

Table 6.8 Advantages and disadvantages of the ladder challenge tournament.

Advantages
- Competition can be carried out independently by the entrants without the presence of the tournament director or sports administrator.
- It affords competition between contestants of near-equal ability.
- No one is eliminated, thus play is continuous for all contestants.

Disadvantages
- Over a period of time, players often end up competing against the same people.
- Over a period of time, it can become less exciting.

Pyramid, spiderweb, and target tournaments follow the same rules as ladder tournaments. Examples are provided in Figures 6.9, 6.10, and 6.11.

- *Challenge anyone one or two levels above you. If you win, trade places.*

- *Play your way to the top of the pyramid!*

- *Prize: Free round for you and 10 friends*

- *Final day: May 1*

Figure 6.9 Pyramid legion darts tournament.

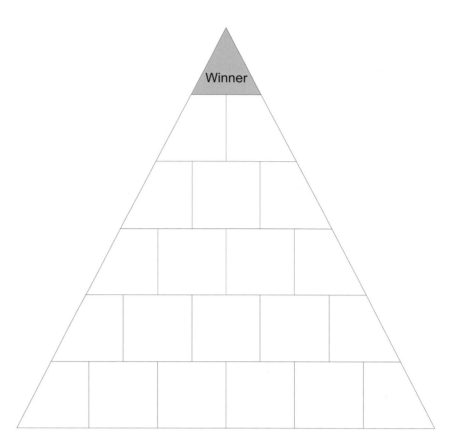

- *Challenge anyone closer to the centre of the web.*

- *Bouts must be performed at the special table at the bar and must be witnessed.*

- *Winner's name will be engraved on a plaque.*

- *Time limit: June 1*

Figure 6.10 Spiderweb arm wrestling tournament.

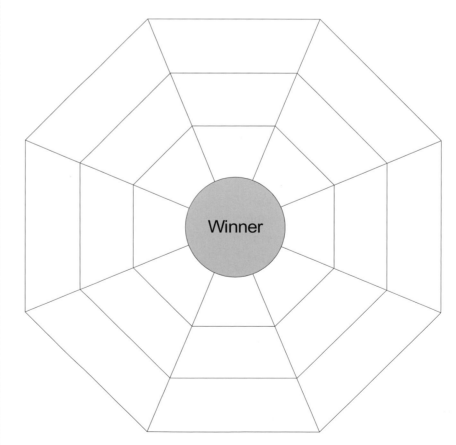

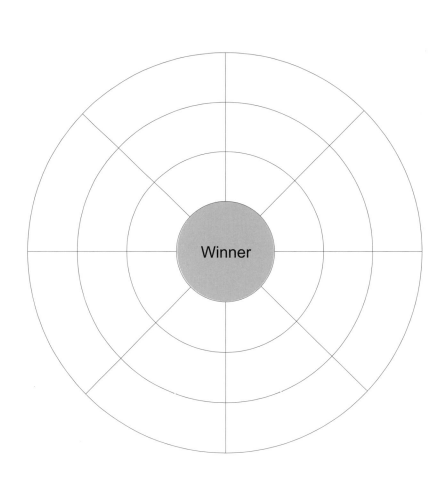

- *Sign up by Wednesday, April 7.*

- *Challenge anyone one ring closer to the bull's-eye.*

- *Prize: A Two Brothers' $40 gift certificate*

- *Closing date: April 30, 9:00 p.m.*

Figure 6.11 Target squash tournament.

Implementing the Event Plan

Now that your event plan is in place and you have chosen an appropriate tournament format, if necessary, it's time to put your plan into action. The hours leading up to the start of an event are busy ones. All equipment must be put in place, all signs need to be posted, and final safety checks must be carried out.

Once the event is under way, the organizers' task is to supervise all aspects of the event, troubleshooting any unforeseen situations that may arise. Risk management should continue to be foremost in the organizers' minds. Take the time to support and encourage your volunteers. If the action plan was correct and complete and all involved did/do their jobs, the organizers can relax and enjoy the event.

The final responsibility on the day of the event is cleaning up the facility, including taking down equipment and promotional material and disposing of any trash that has accumulated. Be sure to take cleanup into account as part of your event plan. Assign specific tasks as needed to make sure the job gets done.

Evaluating the Event

Ongoing evaluation can be critical to the success of an event. Organizers must be aware of how the planning is progressing. For instance, if timelines are not being met or if unforeseen barriers arise, these situations must be remedied immediately.

After the event, it is critical to evaluate whether or not your goals were met. Feedback, whether formal or informal, should be obtained. In addition, the process itself could be evaluated (e.g., what went smoothly as planned, what you would change for another time).

If a formal report is required, it could include the following:

❶ Action plan – with notations of work completed or not, on time or not

❷ Minutes of meetings held

❸ Copies of paperwork (e.g., schedules, results)

❹ Samples of promotional tools (e.g., announcements, posters)

❺ Financial report

❻ Feedback received from participants

❼ Recommendations regarding holding the event again and suggestions for improvement

❽ Notes highlighting what went very well

There is nothing like the satisfaction of running a successful event or tournament that leaves the participants satisfied regardless of the outcome. Whether they become better educated, more motivated, healthier – whatever the end result – it was because of your efforts and organizational ability. Give yourself a pat on the back!

Putting It All Together

Event coordination begins by assessing the needs of the people in the target group. The long process from this initial step to the finished project involves setting goals, developing an idea, setting out the details of an action plan, implementing the plan, and evaluating the resulting product. An important issue is determining what tasks need to be accomplished and then developing a committee structure to make sure they are completed.

This chapter provides the information you need in order to conduct effective committee meetings and run several different types of organized competitions. If you know the proper procedures, your meetings

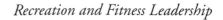

will proceed smoothly and effectively and your tournaments will run efficiently and fairly.

Key Terms

action plan	minutes
agenda	outcomes
brainstorming	quorum
bye	Robert's Rules of Order
challenge tournament	round-robin tournament
consolation tournament	security
crossover semifinal	seeding
double-elimination tournament	single-elimination tournament
draw sheet	SMART goals
elimination tournament	tournament

Review Questions

1. List the five stages of the event planning process.

2. What is the SMART principle?

3. Use examples to distinguish between an outcome and a goal.

4. Research a local event to discover its committee structure.

5. What is an action plan? Besides the name of the event, list three important elements that should be included in an action plan.

6. Define quorum. Do you think this regulation is necessary? Why?

7. When is it appropriate to follow a round-robin tournament format?

8. Name three types of elimination tournaments. Choose one format and describe it in more detail.

9. What are the advantages and disadvantages of challenge tournaments?

10. Discuss the following statement: The evaluation stage of the event planning process can be skipped if you are running short on time.

In This Chapter:

CHAPTER 7
Promoting Participation

In this chapter, you will learn about the following:

❶ The importance of promoting your recreation and leisure events

❷ The various methods of event promotion

❸ Effectively communicating information about an event to the target audience (e.g., through an oral or electronic presentation)

❹ The strategy of promoting recreation as an essential service

Who, what, when, where, and how are important criteria to consider when promoting an event. Do you know the difference between publicity and promotion? These terms are often used interchangeably but refer to slightly different concepts.

The many benefits of recreation were presented in Chapter 4, along with common barriers to participation. One significant barrier – and perhaps the easiest to remedy – is lack of knowledge about available programs and activities. How many times have you heard people say they just didn't know a program existed? Getting the message out about events and activities is termed publicity. Publicity lets people know the details about specific events and programs. The focus is on information required so that individuals can attend: what, when, where, the cost, how to register, and so on. Promotion, on the other hand, has been defined as "any form of communication used to inform, persuade, remind and/or educate people regarding the benefits offered through an organization's programs and services."

Other barriers to participation in recreation include lack of personal motivation, lack of facilities, insufficient time, and problems with affordability. The most important barrier may be ineffective promotion of the importance of recreation and fitness to the general population. We need to communicate more than just the name, time, and location of the activity – we must also show the reasons for taking part. The better we promote the many benefits of recreation to the general public and to identified target audiences, the more likely they are to be actively involved in our programs.

Event Promotion Criteria

WHO?
WHAT?
WHEN?
WHERE?
HOW MUCH?

Whether you are promoting an event for elementary students, high school students, a community group, or a group of elite international athletes, there are many important criteria that are similar. You need to consider questions with respect to who, what, when, where, and how (Table 7.1).

Who is your target audience? To effectively promote an event, you must be clear about the identity of your target audience, or target group. Knowledge of the target audience helps you select the most effective ways to get your message across. You need to think about how these people live their lives – where do they go, how do they get there, what do they like? Also, what type of media are they most likely to get information from? For example, consider the age group when deciding between print and electronic advertising (many young people don't read printed newspapers).

Table 7.1 Examples of events and promotional criteria.

Event	Who	What	When	Where
New mothers' support group	New mothers	Flyers	Ongoing	• Doctors' offices • Pharmacies • Children's clothing/toy stores
Card tournament	Seniors	Newsletter article	Three weeks before closing date for submitting entry	• Seniors clubs • Community centre bulletin boards
Fishing tournament	Avid fishers	Magazine ads Flyers	From end of previous season	• *Ontario Out of Doors* • *Outdoor Canada* • Sporting goods stores (bait and tackle shops)

What method will you use to promote the event? Your event may dictate the kind of promotion you want to use. For example, flyers in doctors' offices and pharmacies may be the most effective way to promote a health and wellness clinic.

When should you promote? The time frame for promotion depends on the type of promotion you are using. For example, if you are distributing brochures and flyers, your promotion time will be longer and include the set-up and printing time for your handouts. If you are using public service announcements on the radio, your promotion time will be shorter since you are preparing only a short promotional paragraph and do not have to worry about distribution. Ask the local radio stations for the lead-up time they require; often it is about two weeks to have a public service announcement read on a community bulletin board.

It may also be helpful to include a media release or to provide follow-up information upon completion of your event to keep the target audience informed and still involved afterwards. The format you use will depend on who your target audience is and what informational avenues they have access to.

Where will you promote? Where is the best place to catch your target audience? At the school? At a community centre? Advertising in more than one location is recommended to help you maximize the number of people you reach.

When promoting a specific product or event, select the most effective ways to get your message across. Know your target audience, and try to maximize the number of people you reach.

How much is your budget? Remember to include hidden costs such as staff time. If your budget is limited, using a low-cost or free publicity technique such as public service announcements can help save budget dollars for other areas of the event.

You can choose from a number of promotional strategies. Always make sure your strategies are sensitive to the cultural and ethnic diversity of the community you may be targeting. As well, when deciding what promotional strategies to use, you will need to evaluate which of your options will reach the largest audience and still work within your budget and timelines. Don't forget that you can use more than one promotional tool, and you can set up a sequence of promotions for your event using several different techniques to pique the interest of your audience.

Methods of Event Promotion

There are many options for promoting an event. The best option is dependent on your target audience and what informational avenues they have access to. When promoting events in a high school, PA announcements are frequently utilized, but other common options include posters, classroom chalkboards, and school websites. Word of mouth is also an important method of promotion, but make sure the details are available either electronically or on printed posters for later review.

Posters

Although placing flyers on car windows and doors can be an effective promotional strategy, it can also become a significant source of litter.

Posters are a simple promotional strategy, but they don't have to *be* simple – you can use unusual shapes and bright colours to attract attention. To increase the promotional exposure of your posters, place them in stairways, on access doors, in washroom stalls, above water fountains, and in other areas where they are most likely to be seen.

Other promotional ideas for schools or communities include footprints placed on the floor or ceiling (to focus attention, with information provided at the end), flyers placed on car windshields (cause litter), advertising printed on bookmarks and handed out in your school or town library, and doorknob hangers. If you are selling tickets to your Spring Fling dance, you could hold contests at lunch in the cafeteria to promote the event and give out free tickets to the dance as prizes.

Broadcast Media

Broadcast media (community radio stations or local cable television channels) often run **public service announcements**, which are free paragraph-long advertisements for upcoming community events. You prepare the paragraph and send it to the local television and radio stations to be reviewed and run. Some communities have a local channel that offers opportunities for community organizers to chat on the air about upcoming events. Radio stations often go to local community events and broadcast "live on location." Figure 7.1 shows the format and text of a public service announcement.

Another popular promotion option involves "roving musicians" handing out information or giving away free promotional T-shirts. Information can also be distributed through community websites and local bulletin boards such as those at grocery stores. An informative article in the local newspaper (e.g., the *Mississauga News* rather than the *Toronto Star*) is often an effective way to promote your event.

Online Advertising

Online advertising may also be used to promote your events. Add information directly to your website, then post on other web pages, providing a link to your site. You can even use a counter to track how many visitors you have. If resources are available, you can also e-mail your target audiences with important information about your event if they consent to being on a mailing list.

Figure 7.1 Sample press release.

123 Dance Street
Calgary, Alberta T3G 1P5

CONTACT: Jane Doe
Phone: 403-555-2345
Fax: 403-555-4567
E-mail: jdoe@hotmail.com

NEWS RELEASE

FOR IMMEDIATE RELEASE
JANUARY 6, 2014

Dance the Night Away with the Jane Doe Dance Studio

CALGARY, AB – Jane Doe Dance Studio will be presenting its annual gala on Thursday, January 30, at Vertigo Theatre. The performance will feature students of JDDS as well as a special appearance by a guest hip hop choreographer and producer, Mandy Miltown. Curtain time is 8:00 p.m.

The cost of admission is $5.00, and profits will be donated to the Red Cross for Hurricane Sandy disaster relief.

END

Display Media

Display media – another method of promoting your event – include billboards, bulletin boards, display booths, posters, and signs. Billboards should use about seven words or fewer to describe your event. They must be easy to read at fast speeds and be visually appealing to the eye. Bulletin boards need to be placed in high-traffic locations and should be changed periodically to keep the observers' interest. Posters can be either professionally done or handmade by committee members. The poster itself must catch the eye while conveying the intended message to the target audience. Use colour and catchy pictures and sayings to get your message across.

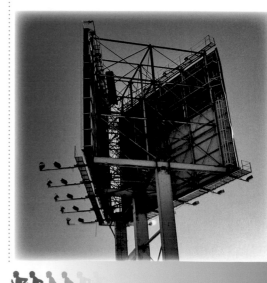

...ation

Promotional Ideas

- Posters cut in fun shapes and colours and placed in areas where they will be read
- Footprints that focus attention and lead readers to promotional information
- Chalkboards in classrooms
- Promotional messages written on bathroom mirrors with erasable markers
- Flyers on windshields of cars in parking lots
- School or community web page
- School or network home page
- Doorknob hangers
- Roving musicians handing out material
- Promotional T-shirts, bookmarks, pens, key chains, and so on
- Local bulletin boards

- T-shirts, buttons, water bottles as promotional "give-aways"
- Network classified ads
- Portable signs
- Public service announcements on the local radio station or TV channel
- Articles in local newspapers and follow-up media reports after event
- Promotion through related organizations or web links such as OFSAA, OPHEA, and CAHPERD
- An "Everybody's doing it" promotion to encourage participation
- An exclusivity theme with individual invitations
- Personal endorsements by significant role models or key figures in the community

Printed Media

Brochures and flyers constitute **printed media**. A brochure is like a business card, letting the public know what your event is all about. Recurring events could be promoted with a generic brochure. Information in the brochure should include a description of the event, where and when it will be held, a registration form if needed, and a phone number or e-mail address. Include a brief description of your organization and a mission statement if you have one.

A flyer is more specific than a brochure and is used for a targeted event. Flyers should include a short message with all pertinent information. They can be posted on bulletin boards, in hallways, and on telephone poles, as well as many other places.

Presentations

Presentations are another promotional tool. They include public speaking and can incorporate PowerPoint, slides, or videos. This provides variety using audio and visual presentation techniques. See the box *Sport Promotion Ideas* for some ways to combine school sports, student participation, and school spirit.

Sport Promotion Ideas

- *Beat the Pro Community Event* – A "field day" in which local sports celebrities set standards at activity stations.

- *Favourite Team Day* – A special day on which students and staff wear clothing that shows off the logo or team colours of their favourite sports team.

- *Game-and-Dance Promotion* – Increase fan support by combining a game with a school dance.

- *Halftime Games* – Promote your school by having elementary school students play in a brief competition during the halftime of your games.

- *Crazy Name Contest* – Crazy team names will give prospective participants the correct impression that your intramural program is all about fun.

- *Jumbo Sports Night* – Fill your stands with an event comprising several different sports on the same evening.

- *Intramural Championships Before Varsity Games* – Scheduling intramural championships before varsity games offers many benefits for both programs.

- *School Spirit Poster Contest* – A poster contest will promote school spirit in your school.

- *Name the Mascot Contest* – Ask students to submit suggestions, then take a vote.

- *Special Invitations* – Increase attendance at competitions by sending a formal invitation to each athlete's parents.

- *Student Council Initiatives* – Have fourth-period buyouts for sporting events or guest speakers.

- *Students vs. Teachers* – Play games such as dodgeball or basketball, or participate in activities that are just plain fun, such as an obstacle course.

- *Students vs. Police or Community Organizations* – These events are great for school spirit.

Event Promotion Considerations

There are many things to consider when planning your event promotions. First of all, the learning styles and preferences of your audience will often dictate the strategy that is most likely to be effective. Drawing up a schedule, or timeline, will help you organize and implement your plan more efficiently, and don't forget to monitor the plan to make sure everything is moving along as intended. There are many potential barriers to participation, and being aware of them allows you to plan accordingly. When developing promotional materials, keep other cultures and ethnic groups in mind, and always be sensitive to the customs and religious beliefs of others. Finally, public speaking presents a challenge for many people. This section concludes by offering some tips for making announcements and giving presentations.

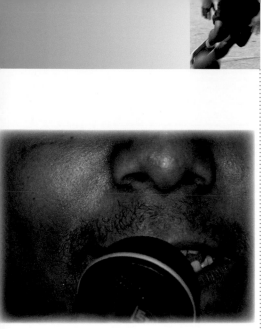

Learning Styles and Preferences of the Audience

When developing promotional strategies, it's a good idea to consider the learning styles of the audience. How a person learns greatly affects how he best absorbs information, and this will impact the effectiveness of your promotions. For example, if the person is an auditory learner (i.e., he learns best by listening), he will grasp information well when someone speaks to him. This means that public announcements in school, personal visits to the target audience, and radio announcements would be very effective for this type of person.

Someone who is more of a visual learner may respond better to promotions that involve print media (press releases, newspaper articles or ads), display media (banners, billboards, Internet ads, electronic bulletin boards, flyers), and concrete items with messages (buttons, T-shirts, water bottles, bookmarks). A kinesthetic learner will absorb information best if she has an opportunity to actually try the activity. She needs to touch and manipulate information, so mini introductory clinics and displays that allow for interaction will be most effective for this person.

Some people respond better to one style of promotion than to another. For some, advertising that incorporates a personal endorsement by an authority figure or a popular hero appeals to them and is more likely to get them interested in the event. For others, emphasizing the exclusivity of an event (e.g., by issuing personal invitations or limiting the number of participants) is an important strategy to consider. And the message that "everybody's doing it" is the key to getting yet another group of individuals involved. All these factors must be considered when planning your promotional campaign, once again demonstrating the importance of knowing your potential audience.

Promotional strategies must be adjusted to reflect the specific learning styles and preferences of the target audience. While auditory learners may respond well to radio announcements or personal visits (above), visual learners may respond better to print and display media (below).

Promotional Timelines

Once you have determined the promotional method you plan to use, set promotional timelines for the various stages, prepare the material, and review your deadlines to ensure completion. To make the greatest impact, incorporate a number of phases in your promotions. For example, in the initial phase of promotion, you need to create a general awareness of the event that reaches as many potential participants as possible. The second phase of event promotion is more focused, reminding the target audience that this is an event they won't want to miss while still trying to attract more participants. The last phase involves a final push to draw in the undecided while still outlining important information for anyone already committed to the event or planning to get involved.

Timing is everything when it comes to promotions. If you are promoting on a community cable station or in a community newspaper, there will be specific timelines for submission. Publicity posters need to be in place long enough to give the target audience time to read them,

Recreation and Fitness Leadership

but if posters are up too early, they might be pulled down or destroyed, or the information could be attended to and then forgotten. However, if they are not in place early enough, your group will not have time to evaluate the effectiveness of the poster campaign and still have time to try alternative methods or make revisions.

Monitoring the Plan's Success

As in all parts of the event planning cycle, it is important to evaluate the success of your promotional plan. Evaluation should occur on an ongoing basis, not just after the event is over. Measuring the effectiveness of a promotion throughout the campaign allows for adjustment of the current plan in addition to providing information to improve future campaigns. Have "backup material" ready in case your original campaign is not reaching your target audience. At the very least, you should be prepared for some "last-minute blitzing" if you are not satisfied with the response to your original promotional plan. A last-minute blitz will also maximize the exposure of your event to the target audience.

Barriers to Participation

When marketing or promoting recreational activities, there are many barriers that can interfere with the success of your event. It is important to address these issues in the event planning process. Try to make the community aware of the potential benefits of participation, while at the same time try to overcome or at least minimize the barriers.

What can you do to overcome the barriers to recreation? If expense is a barrier for a particular group, make the event affordable and then promote the low cost as part of your marketing plan. If accessibility or transportation is a problem, find a sponsor to pay for a bus ride to the site, then include transportation as a major part of your promotional strategy.

Potential barriers to participation must be identified and addressed during the event planning stage to maximize the success of your event.

Cultural or Ethnic Diversity of the Audience

Promotions must be sensitive to the diversity of your target audience, and the larger your audience, the more diverse and "broad" your message must be. Unless you have a very specific target audience, you should feature a broad range of people from a variety of ethnic backgrounds and religious beliefs in all your print and display media.

When you are producing promotional material, it is important that your message be in a form that your target audience will easily identify with. For example, if you are trying to reach teenagers, use bright colours on posters and include pictures and graphics they can identify with. Also, consider using an electronic medium since many teenagers are comfortable with and have wide access to computers and smartphones. On the other hand, some seniors may prefer posters or word of mouth, but they will

Although you should be careful to avoid stereotypes when dealing with any group, understanding your target group is critical. For example, electronic promotions may be effective with teenagers, since they tend to be more comfortable with computers and technology.

not all have this preference. Be careful to avoid stereotypes in any promotional material when dealing with any group. In addition, be sensitive to ethnic customs and religious beliefs when planning your events and promotions.

Dos and Don'ts of Public Speaking

When you are making a presentation or announcement to a target audience, there are a number of things to remember. It is always important to present yourself so you look and feel confident. Dress in a manner that is similar to your audience if possible, but avoid distracting accessories or flashy colours. Ensure your equipment is working before the presentation, and practice your announcement so you are comfortable with the content.

Keep the announcement or presentation as short and simple as possible. State the information clearly, and make sure your listeners can understand and relate to the information and language used. Sensitivity to any ethnic or cultural differences is always important when making announcements. You also need to be aware of potential communication barriers (see Chapter 2) and attempt to minimize their impact.

Keep your announcement or presentation short, simple, and concise. Confidence, tone of voice, and poise can go a long way in holding the attention of the audience. But before you begin, make sure the equipment is in good working order.

Recreation and Fitness Leadership

When making your announcement, be sure your tone of voice is enthusiastic and "upbeat," and try to sound confident. You have to believe in the product or event you are promoting in order for others to believe in it as well. Keep your body language neutral and calm. Do not cross your arms or put your hands in your pockets. Take slow, relaxed breaths. Avoid holding anything in your hand that might encourage you to fidget and distract your audience. Be sure the microphone is positioned properly so that you can be heard easily, but don't let the mike hide your face. Avoid holding on to the microphone if you can because it may make distracting background noise. Always make eye contact; don't ever look down or into space. State the important information early, then repeat all the "key information" just before you finish.

Memorable catchphrases or slogans can help promote a specific brand or event. Can you identify the brands associated with the slogans below?

Just do it!
Is it in you?
Impossible is nothing.
It's fun to play together.
Life is short. Play hard.
Live in your world. Play in ours.

Important Things to Remember about Event Promotion

- Keep material simple, and focus mainly on the "who, what, when, where, and how."

- Consider using a "focal point" or slogan.

- Check all information thoroughly to avoid errors.

- Make posters or written materials colourful, and consider pictures to attract attention.

- The best font colours for attracting attention are red, orange, and yellow.

- The best background colour is blue for the general public, but orange appeals to youth.

- Don't rely entirely on posters to promote your event because not everyone reads posters.

- Establish timelines for all phases of your promotion.

- Make sure your promotional plans fit your timelines and your budget.

- Outline the action plan, and make sure all members of your group know their responsibilities.

- Review the deadlines of your action plan, and ensure completion of all steps.

- Determine a way to measure the effectiveness of your promotions (e.g., how many have signed up for the program), and be prepared to make adjustments if needed.

- Have follow-up material ready if necessary.

- Make sure your promotions are sensitive to the cultural and ethnic diversity of your target audience.

Promoting Recreation as an Essential Service

As discussed in Chapter 4, recreation and leisure offer numerous personal, social, economic, and environmental benefits. As a result, governments fund agencies or pass laws to promote campaigns involving recreation and fitness.

Many government-funded agencies try to promote recreation as an essential service. Examples of these agencies include Own the Podium (Olympic and Paralympic campaign) and ParticipACTION. Some provincial governments (e.g., Ontario) have made funding available to

increase community access to the affordable recreation traditionally offered in schools.

The government also gives money to educational agencies such as Physical and Health Education Canada (PHE Canada), the Canadian Colleges Athletic Association (CCAA), and the Canadian Fitness and Lifestyle Research Institute (CFLRI) as well as to recreational associations such as the Canadian Parks and Recreation Association (CPRA). These organizations are primarily involved in promoting the importance of physical and recreational activities or providing structure or funding so that recreational or sporting activities take place.

Most levels of government recognize the important relationship between recreation and leisure opportunities and a healthy society. That is why there are government-funded agencies that promote and help finance amateur sporting events such as the Canada Games and the 2010 Vancouver Olympics. Also, local tax bases are largely responsible for facilities such as arenas, skateboard parks, and swimming pools in many towns and cities.

See the box *Agencies Promoting Sport and Recreation* for a brief outline of some of the organizations supporting fitness and recreation in Canada.

Since recreation and leisure opportunities are linked to a healthy society, most levels of government are willing to fund and support local recreational facilities and infrastructure.

Recreation and Fitness Leadership

Agencies Promoting Sport and Recreation

- Active Healthy Kids Canada – a national charitable organization whose mission is to inspire all Canadian children and youth to engage in physical activity

- Active Living Alliance for Canadians with a Disability – an alliance that promotes, supports, and enables Canadians with disabilities to lead active, healthy lives

- Canadian Fitness and Lifestyle Research Institute – a national research agency that conducts research, monitors trends, and makes recommendations to increase physical activity levels across all populations and improve the health of all Canadians

- Canadian Parks and Recreation Association – an organization advocating that parks and recreation are essential to individual, family, and community health and well-being

- Canadian Sport for Life – a movement to improve the quality of sport and physical activity in Canada

- KidSport Canada – a not-for-profit organization that provides financial assistance so that underprivileged kids can play sports

- Leisure Information Network – a national knowledge base for sharing information about recreation, parks, and healthy living

- Own the Podium – a government-funded agency whose vision is for Canada to be a world leader in high-performance sport

- ParticipACTION – a long-running program dedicated to making active living a priority for all Canadians

- Physical and Health Education Canada – a professional organization for physical and health educators that advocates for quality programs to give students the opportunity to develop the knowledge, skills, and attitudes to lead physically active and healthy lives

- Sport Canada – a government agency whose mission is to enhance opportunities for all Canadians to participate and excel in sport

Putting It All Together

You can spend countless hours planning and organizing an event, but unless people know about the event and attend, your efforts will be wasted. The questions who, what, when, where, and how guide you as you formulate your promotional plan. Event promotion can be as simple as hanging a poster or as complex as designing a website. The method you use will depend on your target audience, but it is a good idea to use more than one approach so that you reach the largest possible audience.

Our governments fund many agencies to promote recreation and fitness as an essential service. Amateur athletes from the grassroots level to the Olympic level receive financial support in the form of facilities.

Governments also fund various educational agencies to promote the importance of physical and recreational activities for all members of the community. It is important that we continue to work towards reducing the barriers to recreation and fitness if we want a vibrant and healthy society now and in the future.

Key Terms

broadcast media

display media

diversity

essential service

online advertising

posters

presentations

printed media

promotion

promotional timeline

public service announcements

publicity

target audience

Recreation and Fitness Leadership

Review Questions

1. Discuss the difference between promotion and publicity.

2. Outline five important criteria that you should consider before designing a promotional plan for an upcoming event.

3. Choose three methods of event promotion, and give one example of when each would be useful.

4. Discuss the following statement: It doesn't matter which promotional strategy you use. Everyone will get the message.

5. Why are promotional timelines so important?

6. Should you consider ethnic and cultural diversity in all your promotional material or event planning?

7. List five ways you can improve your public speaking.

8. List eight important points to remember about event promotion.

9. Do you think the government should help fund amateur sporting events such as the Olympics?

10. Using the Internet, research two of the websites provided in this chapter. What is the mandate of each organization? Were the websites easy to navigate? Did their websites contain useful information? Compare both. What are the best components of each site?

UNIT 3

PHYSICAL FITNESS AND WELL-BEING

Ultimately we make the decisions about our own health and how we choose to live our lives, but many people need support to help them achieve their goals. Lifestyle coaches and personal trainers are professionals that work with people one on one to help them lead healthier lives. With a population that is becoming more and more aware of the importance of health and has the finances to do something about it, career opportunities in this field are increasing rapidly.

Unit 3 examines how you as an individual can influence others to live longer and healthier lives. And although the information can and should be applied in your personal life, our focus will be on the effect you can have on others through the helping relationship we call "mentoring."

First you will learn about different aspects of mentoring, in particular the stages of the relationship between a mentor and client and the actions the mentor can take to bring about behaviour change. You will also receive the basic information you will need to advise a client about nutrition and healthy food choices and to assess a client's current level of physical fitness.

Personal health can be improved through even very small lifestyle changes, changes that reflect Health Canada's vitality message about healthy eating, active living, and satisfaction with one's body image. You will learn about the essentials of physical fitness that enable a lifestyle coach or personal trainer to plan and implement fitness programs for clients.

You might assume that everyone who seeks out a lifestyle coach or personal trainer is ready and willing to make lifestyle changes, but this isn't necessarily so. Overcoming resistance to change is particularly challenging, but it can reap incredible rewards.

> The best six doctors anywhere
> And no one can deny it
> Are sunshine, water, rest, and air
> Exercise and diet.
> These six will gladly you attend
> If only you are willing.
> Your mind they'll ease
> Your will they'll mend
> And charge you not a shilling.
> *Nursery rhyme*

In This Chapter:

CHAPTER 8
Mentoring

In this chapter, you will learn about the following:

❶ The role of mentors in the health and fitness environment

❷ Practical applications of behaviour change theories

❸ The steps in the lifestyle mentoring process

❹ Supporting others in setting, following, and revising personal fitness and nutrition plans

> "If you want one year of prosperity, grow grain.
> If you want ten years of prosperity, grow trees.
> If you want one hundred years of prosperity, grow people."
> Chinese proverb

We all know special people who have had a major influence on our lives – advising and supporting us in our attempts to achieve our dreams and aspirations. These special people are called **mentors**. Mentors can be relatives, co-workers, bosses, teachers, or friends. Most often they are more experienced or older persons whom we look up to. A mentor may act as a role model and may make important contributions to our values, moral development, and understanding of the world.

This chapter focuses on mentoring in the area of personal fitness and well-being. You will learn how to support others in setting short-term and long-term goals and in setting and following personal health improvement plans. The attributes of an effective mentor are explored, the benefits of mentoring are discussed, and leadership and mentoring are compared and contrasted. Various career opportunities in mentoring, such as personal training and lifestyle coaching, are also explored.

What Is Mentoring?

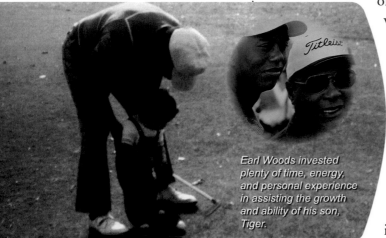

Earl Woods invested plenty of time, energy, and personal experience in assisting the growth and ability of his son, Tiger.

"Mentorship is a fundamental form of human development where one person invests time, energy, and personal know-how in assisting the growth and ability of another person." It is believed that the word *mentor* is derived from the story of Homer's *Odyssey*. When Odysseus, king of Ithaca, went off to fight in the Trojan War, he entrusted the care of his home to Mentor. Mentor became synonymous with trusted adviser, friend, teacher, and wise person. History offers many examples of helpful mentoring relationships, such as Plato and Socrates, Beethoven and Haydn, and Jung and Freud. Modern sporting examples include Tiger Woods and his father Earl; Jimmy Connors and his grandmother Bertha; Wayne Gretzky and his father Walter; and Michael Jordan and his coaching mentor Phil Jackson. Mentoring is one of the oldest forms of influence, and most people can identify a person who, at some time in their lives, has had a significant and positive impact on them.

The Importance of Mentoring

Mentoring is a powerful tool in the shaping of young people's lives. Successful mentoring programs can have profound positive impacts on both individuals involved. Foremost is the boost to a person's self-esteem as a result of receiving positive attention from someone perceived as superior and a role model. In the fitness and health context, the client gains knowledge and strategies to make adjustments to his or her lifestyle that can result in better health. Ideally, the client also learns self-motivation in order to be able to continue making healthy choices.

The benefits to the mentor include improved leadership and communication skills as well as personal satisfaction. Lasting friendships have developed from what started out as formal mentoring relationships. The mentoring experience can be included on a resume for employment or admission to postsecondary institutions. However, mentoring takes time and commitment, and success is not guaranteed.

Leaders versus Mentors

Leaders and mentors share many similar characteristics. The main difference is that leaders influence groups, while mentors influence individuals. Leaders need to communicate effectively with both groups of people and individuals, and mentors need to excel in one-on-one situations. Mentors often adopt a democratic style, acting as a guide, while leaders can choose from a variety of styles (democratic, autocratic, laissez-faire) depending on the circumstances and the stage of group development (see Chapter 1).

Attributes of an Effective Mentor

Research has shown that mentors are committed individuals with finely developed listening skills, a warm personal style, and a positive outlook. They neither dictate nor abdicate but rather facilitate a person's decision-making processes. Successful mentors possess all or most of the following personal qualities and abilities:

▶ Personal commitment to be involved with another person for an extended period of time

▶ Respect for individuals, their abilities, and their right to make their own choices in life

▶ Ability to listen and accept different points of view

▶ Ability to empathize with another person's struggles

▶ Ability to see solutions and opportunities as well as barriers

▶ Flexibility and openness

▶ Skill in motivating others

> "I believe some of us must assume leadership. I believe young people thirst to be led to better themselves. Life is hard and success is survival. Leaders inspire us. Leaders show us the way."
> *Frank Leahy*

Although mentors and leaders share many characteristics, the former tend to adopt a democratic style and influence individuals, while the latter adopt a variety of styles and tend to influence groups.

Examples of Mentoring Relationships

There are many examples of mentoring relationships. The following is a brief introduction to a few:

Advising – **Advising** is a simple form of mentorship. It is the backbone of the education and career planning process in secondary and postsecondary institutions. Students are connected with staff members who help them set and revise plans to achieve their long-term goals. Advisers provide career information and act as a sounding board and resource.

Peer counselling – In a **peer counselling** program, students selected on the basis of their interest, maturity, and interpersonal skills are trained in listening and mediation techniques. They advise their peers on personal problems, help them explore problem-solving techniques, and mediate disputes between other students.

Job shadowing – A somewhat limited short-term form of mentoring is **job shadowing**. A student follows a selected adult for a day or two, learning about all aspects of a particular career.

Co-operative education – **Co-operative education** programs at the high school and postsecondary level involve semester-long placements in a job situation. The student's immediate supervisor plays a major mentorship role, assisted by the staff member who monitors the program.

Internships – An intern is an advanced student undergoing supervised practical training. **Internships** are commonly part of professional preparation programs.

Lifestyle coach/personal trainer – Personal trainers and **lifestyle coaches** are hired professionals trained to assist individuals with their fitness and lifestyle goals. Usually they meet with their clients on a regular basis (e.g., weekly), initially to gather information and lead goal setting, then to develop courses of action and to monitor progress, and finally to continue to create new fitness goals.

Lifestyle Mentoring

Personal trainers and lifestyle coaches help clients set attainable fitness and lifestyle goals and help them develop courses of action to monitor progress and to achieve those goals.

Lifestyle coaches and personal trainers guide clients in addressing the root causes of their poor health habits rather than simply prescribing exercises and providing dietary advice. They help participants gain insight into the factors that have a negative impact on their ability to become and stay physically active and healthy. These factors include the following:

▶ Perceived and real barriers

▶ Negative feelings about the desired behaviour

▶ Lack of confidence in their ability to make changes

▶ Unrealistic goals

▶ Insufficient rewards for the behaviour change

▶ Lack of a support system

▶ Lapses from the desired behaviour

Recreation and Fitness Leadership

- ▶ Being unaware of the many misconceptions in the health, fitness, and nutrition fields

- ▶ Lack of motivation

- ▶ Being a victim of fad diets and fitness gimmicks

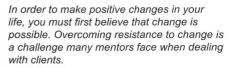

In order to make positive changes in your life, you must first believe that change is possible. Overcoming resistance to change is a challenge many mentors face when dealing with clients.

The underlying principle of mentoring is that people are capable of changing their behavioural patterns, beliefs, and values. If you believe the adage "you can't teach an old dog new tricks," studying personal influence is a waste of time. As long as the client accepts the concept that change is possible, great strides can be made.

Occasionally a client does not share this belief that change is possible, whether out of previous failed attempts to change or a generally pessimistic attitude. Overcoming a client's resistance to change is particularly challenging for a mentor.

Behaviour Change Theories

Extensive research has provided us with theories and models of human behaviour that can guide the development and refinement of health promotion efforts. Each has its practical applications. The successful mentor is adept at employing a wide range of well-tested strategies that have proven effective in changing lifestyle behaviours.

Transtheoretical Model: Stages of Readiness for Change

In the **transtheoretical model**, behaviour change is conceptualized as a five-stage process: precontemplation, contemplation, preparation, action, and maintenance (Figure 8.1). People are thought to progress through these stages at varying rates, often moving back and forth along the continuum a number of times before attaining the ultimate goal of maintenance – the point where the new healthy habit has been acquired and committed to. According to this theory, tailoring interventions to match a person's readiness or stage of change is essential. For example, for people who are not yet considering becoming more active, encouraging a step-by-step movement along the continuum of change may be more effective than encouraging them to move directly into action.

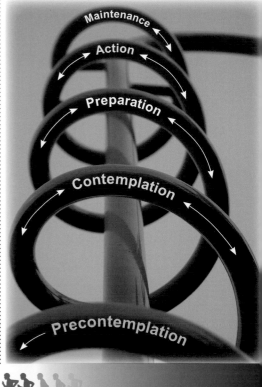

Figure 8.1 The transtheoretical model conceptualizes behaviour change as a five-stage process progressing along a dynamic continuum.

When the seasons change, which makes participation outdoors difficult, clients must be prepared to take their activities indoors.

Relapse Prevention Model

In the proactive **relapse prevention model**, the lifestyle coach helps new clients anticipate problems of adherence before they happen. Principles of relapse prevention include identifying high-risk situations for relapse (e.g., change in season) and providing appropriate solutions (e.g., finding a place to walk inside during the winter). Helping people distinguish between a lapse (i.e., a few days of not participating in their planned activity) and a relapse (i.e., an extended period of not participating) is thought to improve adherence. Simply encourage the person not to dwell on the lapse but to get back on the program.

Social Cognitive Theory

Central to the **social cognitive theory** is the concept of **self-efficacy**, or the belief in one's power to act. A person must believe in his or her capability to perform the behaviour (i.e., the person must possess self-efficacy) and must perceive an incentive to do so (i.e., the person's positive expectations from performing the behaviour must outweigh the negative expectations). Additionally, a person must value the outcomes or consequences that he or she believes will occur as a result of performing a specific behaviour or action. Outcomes may be classified as having immediate benefits (e.g., feeling energized after physical activity) or long-term benefits (e.g., experiencing improvements in cardiovascular health as a result of physical activity). Self-efficacy is believed to be the single most important characteristic that determines a person's behaviour change. Another factor in social cognitive theory is **modelling** – that is, learning from an example provided by another person, such as the mentor.

Self-efficacy is believed to be the most important characteristic affecting an individual's behaviour change. Can you think of a specific situation where self-efficacy had a positive or negative impact on a change in your behaviour?

Social Support

Social support must not be underrated as a tool for bringing about health behaviour changes. Social support for physical activity can

Recreation and Fitness Leadership

be *instrumental*, as in giving a nondriver a ride to an exercise class; *informational*, as in telling someone about a walking program in the neighbourhood; *emotional*, as in calling to see how someone is faring with a new walking program; or *appraising*, as in providing feedback and reinforcement in learning a new skill. Similar examples can be found for quitting smoking and changing eating habits. Sources of support include family members, friends, neighbours, co-workers, and exercise program leaders and participants. The mentor provides support directly and facilitates the development of a social support network for the client.

Having a trusted source of social support can help you stay on track with your exercise program.

Health Belief Model

The **health belief model** stipulates that a person's health-related behaviours depend on the person's perception of four critical areas: the severity of a potential illness, the person's susceptibility to that illness, the benefits of taking preventive action, and the barriers to taking that action. The model also incorporates cues to action (e.g., leaving written reminders to oneself to walk) as important elements in eliciting or maintaining patterns of behaviour.

Don't forget to call Jill tonight to set up a time to go walking.

Ecological Approach

The **ecological approach** places the creation of supportive environments on par with the development of personal skills. Physical activity could be promoted by providing facilities, such as bike paths, parks, and playgrounds, and by offering incentives, such as free pedometers and instructional workshops. Better nutrition is promoted by, for instance, replacing junk food and soft drinks in school vending machines with healthy snacks and beverages.

Physical activity can be promoted by providing facilities such as public parks, playgrounds, and designated bike paths and cycling lanes.

Theory into Action: How the Theory Guides the Mentor

Transtheoretical Model

In the *precontemplation stage*, the client is not aware of a problem situation. This may be brought to light in the assessments done by the lifestyle coach and by laboratory test results.

In the *contemplation stage*, the client knows there is a problem but has done nothing to address it. The lifestyle coach's task is to encourage the client to deal with the problem and set goals.

In the *preparation stage*, the lifestyle coach helps the client make plans to change the behaviour. This may involve setting a date to stop smoking, signing up for an aqua fitness class, buying running shoes, or making an appointment with a registered dietitian to obtain information about a diabetic diet.

In the *action stage*, the lifestyle coach keeps the client on track with the new behaviour. The coach monitors adherence and provides advice, support, and rewards. The personal trainer takes the client through the program.

In the *maintenance stage*, the new behaviour has become an established habit. The coach can help the client set new goals, avoid situations that might lead to lapses, and counsel through relapses.

Relapse Prevention Model

The mentor helps the client identify high-risk situations for relapse (e.g., change in season, extended business absence, or holiday) and develop appropriate solutions ahead of time.

Social Cognitive Theory

The mentor builds the client's sense of self-efficacy. Self-efficacy can be increased in several ways, among them by providing clear instructions, providing the opportunity for skill development or training, and modelling the desired behaviour. To be effective, models must evoke trust, admiration, and respect from the observer; models must not, however, appear to represent a level of behaviour that the observer is unable to visualize attaining.

Social Support

The lifestyle coach provides encouragement, feedback, and information. The support can be very practical (e.g., supplying transportation, equipment, or clothing). The trainer helps the client build a personal support network of friends, family, co-workers, and so on.

Health Belief Model

The lifestyle coach provides and explains factual information about the severity of an illness, a person's susceptibility to the illness, and the benefits of taking preventive action. He also helps identify barriers to improved health behaviours and encourages the use of cues to action.

Ecological Approach

Personal trainers provide in-home sessions and bring their equipment with them.

Stages and Strategies of the Mentoring Process

The mentoring process starts with assignment of mentors to clients. The introductory meeting is crucial in setting the tone for a positive relationship. The initial assessment of a client's attitudes and behaviours along with formal diagnostic tests lead to goal setting. From here, a program is designed for the client. Maintenance of the program and the mentoring relationship includes many factors. Throughout the pairing, monitoring and record keeping enable the program to stay up to date and relevant. Subsequent assessments and goal setting also help maintain continuity in the program. Finally, at some point, the relationship ends in parting, with the client hopefully having the knowledge and motivation to sustain the program on her own.

The introductory meeting between mentors and clients is crucial in setting the tone for a positive relationship.

Assignment

The pairing of client and mentor can take many forms. The relationship may develop informally and spontaneously, or the matching of mentors with clients may be a formal hiring process. Some thought may go into appropriately matching mentors and clients, but assignment can also be random.

Introductory Meeting

In the first meeting, the main tasks of the mentor are to make the client feel at ease and to set parameters regarding each person's roles and responsibilities. Choosing a nonthreatening environment, using welcoming body language, or telling a joke can make the client comfortable. Assure the client about the confidentiality of the relationship in order to build trust. Set guidelines regarding making contact with each other. For instance, the mentor may agree to be available at any time to lend assistance or may set specific times for meetings and consultations. The mentor may also set boundaries about the range of topics or issues to be dealt with. Answer any questions the client may have.

Initial Assessments

As a starting point, it is important to gain information about the client's attitudes and behaviours. This can be accomplished in three ways: structured interviews, questionnaires, and journals.

Prepare your interview questions ahead of time. Be sure to present them as open-ended questions to encourage detailed responses (see Chapter 5).

Several questionnaires are readily available, or you can create your own. See Figures 8.2 and 8.3. To get pertinent and helpful information, attempt to individualize the questionnaire to your client.

The final way to gather information is to ask the client to keep a one-week record of the behaviour being focused on (e.g., exercise, eating habits, smoking habits). This journal should include how the client feels, not just facts.

The second step of assessment is to administer physical fitness tests (e.g., cardiorespiratory tests, muscular strength tests, muscular endurance tests, flexibility tests) and complete a nutrition evaluation program. These topics are addressed in the chapters that follow.

Your family plays a crucial role in influencing your decisions and attitudes about physical activity and sport.

Figure 8.2 Personal fitness profile for a student entering high school.

Personal Fitness Profile

In this log, you will recollect your physical activities through your childhood up to the present. You will reflect on how your parents and peers influenced your attitudes and participation in physical activities.

1. List all the activities you have ever tried. Include school activities (teams and intramurals), community leagues, and classes or lessons you have been enrolled in. Include recreational activities you have done with your family.

2. Your parents have the greatest influence on your activity level when you are a child. Would you describe your family as an active one? Explain.

3. Who is the most physically active person in your immediate family? Why did you select this person? Who is the most fit person?

4. Are your parents proud of their children's accomplishments in sports and other active pursuits? How do they show this?

5. Your peer group also plays a crucial role in your decision about physical activity. Have you ever tried an activity because your friends were doing it? Or avoided an activity because you didn't know anyone else who was joining up? Give examples.

6. Do you have a sports hero? Whom do you admire and why?

7. Do you participate in more or less physical activity now compared with when you were younger? Account for the difference.

8. List all the physical activities you are currently doing or plan to do in the near future.

9. What has been your greatest physical accomplishment?

10. What is one thing you would like to change about your lifestyle? Explain.

Recreation and Fitness Leadership

Figure 8.3 Do you have a fantastic lifestyle?

The Fantastic Lifestyle Checklist (CPAFLA)

INSTRUCTIONS: Unless otherwise specified, place an "X" beside the box that best describes your behaviour or situation **in the past month**. The explanation for scoring is provided on the next page.

FAMILY FRIENDS	I have someone to talk to about things that are important to me	Almost never	Seldom	Some of the time	Fairly often	Almost always
	I give and receive affection	Almost never	Seldom	Some of the time	Fairly often	Almost always
ACTIVITY	I am vigorously active for at least 30 min per day (e.g., running, cycling, etc.)	Less than once/week	1 – 2 times/week	3 times/week	4 times/week	5 or more times/week
	I am moderately active (gardening, climbing stairs, walking, housework)	Less than once/week	1 – 2 times/week	3 times/week	4 times/week	5 or more times/week
NUTRITION	I eat a balanced diet	Almost never	Seldom	Some of the time	Fairly often	Almost always
	I often eat excess: (1) sugar, (2) salt, (3) animal fats, or (4) junk food	Four of these	Three of these	Two of these	One of these	None of these
	I am within _____ kg of my healthy weight	Not within 8 kg (20 lb)	8 kg (20 lb)	6 kg (15 lb)	4 kg (10 lb)	2 kg (5 lb)
TOBACCO TOXICS	I smoke tobacco	More than 10 times/week	1 – 10 times/week	None in the past 6 months	None in the past year	None in the past 5 years
	I use drugs such as marijuana, cocaine	Sometimes				Never
	I overuse prescribed or over-the-counter drugs	Almost daily	Fairly often	Only occasionally	Almost never	Never
	I drink caffeine-containing coffee, tea, or cola	More than 10/day	7 – 10/day	3 – 6/day	1 – 2/day	Never
ALCOHOL	My average alcohol intake per week is _____	More than 20 drinks	13 – 20 drinks	11 – 12 drinks	8 – 10 drinks	0 – 7 drinks
	I drink more than four drinks on an occasion	Almost daily	Fairly often	Only occasionally	Almost never	Never
	I drive after drinking	Sometimes				Never
SLEEP SEATBELT STRESS SAFE SEX	I sleep well and feel rested	Almost never	Seldom	Some of the time	Fairly often	Almost always
	I use seatbelts	Never	Seldom	Some of the time	Most of the time	Always
	I am able to cope with the stresses in my life	Almost never	Seldom	Some of the time	Fairly often	Almost always
	I relax and enjoy leisure time	Almost never	Seldom	Some of the time	Fairly often	Almost always
	I practice safe sex	Almost never	Seldom	Some of the time	Fairly often	Always
TYPE OF BEHAVIOUR	I seem to be in a hurry	Almost always	Fairly often	Some of the time	Seldom	Almost never
	I feel angry or hostile	Almost always	Fairly often	Some of the time	Seldom	Almost never
INSIGHT	I am a positive or optimistic thinker	Almost never	Seldom	Some of the time	Fairly often	Almost always
	I feel tense or uptight	Almost always	Fairly often	Some of the time	Seldom	Almost never
	I feel sad or depressed	Almost always	Fairly often	Some of the time	Seldom	Almost never
SCHOOL JOB	I am satisfied in my role as a student	Almost never	Seldom	Some of the time	Fairly often	Almost always
	I am satisfied with my part-time job	Almost never	Seldom	Some of the time	Fairly often	Almost always
STEP 1	Total the X's in each column →					
STEP 2	Multiply the totals by the numbers indicated (write your answer in the box below) →	0	X 1	X 2	X 3	X 4
STEP 3	Add your scores across the bottom for your grand total →	0				=

Adapted from the "Fantastic Lifestyle Assessment" © 1985 Dr. Douglas Wilson, Department of Family Medicine, McMaster University, Hamilton, Ontario, Canada L8N 3Z5

Figure 8.3 Do you have a fantastic lifestyle? *contd.*

WHAT DOES THE SCORE MEAN?

→	85 – 100	70 – 84	55 – 69	35 – 54	0 – 34
	EXCELLENT	**VERY GOOD**	**GOOD**	**FAIR**	**NEEDS IMPROVEMENT**

NOTE: A low total score does not mean that you have failed. There is always the chance to change your lifestyle – starting now. Look at the areas where you scored a 0 or 1 and decide which areas you want to work on first.

TIPS:
1 Don't try to change all the areas at once. This will be too overwhelming for you.
2 Writing down your proposed changes and your overall goal will help you to succeed.
3 Make changes in small steps towards the overall goal.
4 Enlist the help of a friend to make similar changes and/or to support you in your attempts.
5 Congratulate yourself for achieving each step. Give yourself appropriate rewards.
6 Ask your personal trainer, coach, family physician, nurse, or health department for more information on any of these areas.

Adapted from the "Fantastic Lifestyle Assessment" © 1985 Dr. Douglas Wilson, Department of Family Medicine, McMaster University, Hamilton, Ontario, Canada L8N 3Z5

Facilitating Goal Setting

In Chapter 6 you learned about setting goals and memorized a mnemonic for them. Remember SMART? Goal statements should be specific, measurable, achievable, relevant, and completed within a certain time frame. This applies just as surely for setting individual lifestyle goals as it does for event or program goals. Thus, one of the mentor's responsibilities is helping the client establish short-term, intermediate, and long-term goals. Generally speaking, short-term goals cover a period of one month or less; intermediate goals or plans cover up to a year; and long-term goals range from one to four years. Only mentors who utilize all three types of goal plans will help their clients reach and maintain the desired outcome.

Designing the Program

The personal trainer or lifestyle counsellor develops an individualized program for the client based on the initial assessments and the client's goals. The next two chapters supply the information you need to perform this part of the mentorship. Goals should be reassessed and modified at regular times during the program (e.g., every four to six weeks).

Maintenance

The relationship between a mentor and client needs to be developed and nurtured over time. A good relationship doesn't just happen automatically – it requires a conscious effort on the part of both persons. Here are some things a mentor should keep in mind when working with a client.

Build Self-Esteem

Closely related to self-efficacy, self-esteem refers to how people see themselves. It is moulded by the reactions of others and further shaped by experiences in life. People's views of themselves strongly affect their motivation, learning, performance, and personal relationships. The two

Do you remember how to set SMART goals? They should be specific, measurable, achievable, relevant, and completed within a certain time frame.

Recreation and Fitness Leadership

most important ways to help clients is to show an interest in them and to manage them positively (see the box *Fostering a Positive Self-image*).

Fostering a Positive Self-image

As a mentor, show that you have a personal interest in your clients by doing the following:

- Call your clients by name. Greet them when passing in the hall. Don't ignore them outside of the gym!

- Ask clients about themselves, their families and friends, and their outside interests.

- Point out successes in an especially warm way.

- Praise good effort and behaviour – not just good performance.

- Use nonverbal gestures of approval: thumbs up, high-fives.

- Encourage them after a mistake or failure.

- Listen attentively.

- Do not indicate that you are disinterested or bored while working with them.

Adopt a Positive Management Style

Manage your clients positively by emphasizing self-responsibility. Let them make their own decisions and draw their own conclusions. Show confidence in their ability to take on and master challenges. Encourage them to ask questions, make suggestions, and be reflective.

Foster Positive Thinking

From the previous information, it is obvious that the mentor needs to exude positive expectations about the client and the program. It is absolutely essential that the client share those positive expectations. The concept of **self-fulfilling prophecy** is at work here. If the client makes negative statements about herself or expresses doubt regarding a possible outcome, the mentor needs to educate the client about replacing these

The self-fulfilling prophecy:
Whether you think you can or think you can't, you're right.
Henry Ford

negative thoughts with positive self-talk. Suggest a mantra, or motto, that is very positive, such as "If it is to be, it is up to me" or "Success comes in *cans*," or have the client make up her own mantra. This positive statement should be dramatically highlighted and obvious: a poster in the bedroom, a note on the fridge door, or even a card in a pocket or wallet.

Employ Motivational Strategies

There are many ways to motivate people, but to select the best motivational strategies, you need to know something about your clients and what they value. Structured discussions and questionnaires are two ways to obtain this information. Armed with this knowledge, the mentor can select and develop effective tools to motivate the client and to reward

Common Motivations

Achievement – The achievement-motivated client finds it easy to set tangible goals and likes to keep track of progress towards them. Keeping a journal of fitness test results in order to see written records of progress is an example of a motivational technique. Tangible rewards such as stars and stickers may motivate. The individual may also select his own rewards (e.g., new clothes, a new piece of equipment, a night out with friends, a holiday). He likes to discuss progress and re-evaluate goals, and he often enjoys competition as a proving ground. In the fitness setting, this may be hazardous. Discourage comparing fitness gains or goals with others.

Affiliation – Many people join a particular program or gym because their friends have signed up or work out there. They enjoy the personal interactions of the activity and often like to extend these social contacts outside the gym. This type of person wants to have a positive and friendly relationship with the mentor. She thinks it's great to have a senior student take an interest in her. Return the friendship. Perhaps do things together outside of the gym (e.g., discuss progress over lunch). You will likely become a role model for this person, so be a good one!

Sensation – The sensation-motivated person likes the feelings generated by a workout. Exertion, sweat, tension, and release are some of the internal feelings relished by this client. The activity itself and the environment in which the activity occurs also produce the desired sensations. A skateboarder may enjoy the feeling of the wind in his face, the sound of the board on the concrete, and the sense of weightlessness as he goes airborne. Help the client identify all the feelings that are part of the experience. Discuss all the senses that can be explored through the activity – sight, sound, smell, touch, or taste. Does the jogger enjoy the scenery? Is it the music that keeps the person active beyond fatigue? Are the smells of the horses and stable part of the allure of horseback riding? Does the equipment have an interesting texture or shape? Is the taste of salty sweat appealing? The sensation-motivated participant often enjoys variety, so introduce different ways of working out.

Self-direction – The self-directed client likes making personal decisions and enjoys the whole process of planning, executing, and evaluating the program. This person will be interested in doing personal research to find better ways to develop fitness or skills. Taking a leadership role on a team, such as a catcher in baseball or a quarterback in football, provides the opportunity for the self-directed participant to extend decision-making responsibilities in a group setting. It is particularly important that the mentor allow this client to make her own decisions.

Recreation and Fitness Leadership

progress. Common motivations for physical activity include achievement, affiliation, sensation, and self-direction.

Needless to say, the motivation for health habit changes for many people is simply to achieve better health, to lose weight, or to improve overall fitness. For these people, lower total cholesterol levels, the weight shown on the scale, or the ability to walk or work out longer without getting out of breath are rewards in themselves.

Behaviour Modification

Changing a health habit, whether it be quitting smoking or changing from a sedentary to an active lifestyle, requires **behaviour modification**, which involves modifying many of the small behaviours that make up a more complex behaviour. For example, principles of behaviour modification suggest that a complex behaviour pattern, such as walking continuously for 30 minutes daily, can be learned by first breaking the task into smaller segments (e.g., walking for 10 minutes daily). Behaviours that are steps towards a final goal need to be reinforced and established first, with rewards given for partial accomplishment if needed. Incremental increases, such as adding 5 minutes to the daily walking time each week, are then made, as the complex pattern of behaviour is "shaped" towards the target goal.

Challenges arise when new patterns of behaviour must compete with former patterns of behaviour that are often cued by the environment.

Challenges arise when new patterns of behaviours must replace or compete with former patterns of behaviours that are often satisfying (e.g., sitting and watching television), habitual (e.g., parking close to the door), or cued by the external environment (e.g., the presence of an elevator or an escalator).

The principle behind behaviour modification is that people will most likely engage in a desired behaviour if they are rewarded for doing so. These rewards are most effective if they immediately follow the desired response. Behaviour that is not rewarded, or that is punished, is less likely to be repeated. Similarly, a lifestyle coach or personal trainer should never assign laps or push-ups as punishment (e.g., for being late). Clients may then associate these beneficial exercises with punishment and in turn not feel motivated to do them in their programs.

Offer Feedback

In your role as a mentor, **feedback** serves as a prime motivator and educational tool. Providing effective feedback requires skill and talent. The mentor needs to know what to look for, needs to have acutely developed observation and listening skills, and needs to use a proven format for giving the critique (see the box *The Feedback Sandwich*).

It is also important that feedback occur in a timely manner. Feedback is more meaningful when it is immediate and the client can apply corrections sooner rather than continuing an incorrect action or behaviour. Limit the number of suggestions to one or two, depending on the client's age, maturity, and ability to focus. Realistically, most people can effectively apply only one correction at a time.

Use language the client understands. To check that the feedback has been understood, ask the client to repeat your suggestions in his own words. Listen and watch to see if the client understands and makes the correction you suggested.

The Feedback Sandwich

Effective feedback begins with a positive statement. Find something to congratulate the client about. Follow up with information about the improvement or accomplishment that you chose to reward. Feedback that is always positive, without being informative, soon grows stale. Next is the constructive part of the feedback, a suggestion for improvement or correction. The final "slice" is again positive, a prediction for success.

Here are two examples:

"Way to go, Jeremy! You bent your elbows to exactly 90 degrees that time. If you keep your head in line with your spine, you'll find the push-ups are even easier to do."

"That's quite an improvement, Sally! Your dietary record shows you ate breakfast five days last week. You chose multigrain and whole wheat bagels, which are a great way to get good carbs. How about drinking a cup of milk or juice instead of or in addition to your coffee so that you get more nourishment and another food group in your meal? I think you will like the variety."

Layer 1: Praise the client with a positive statement.

Layer 2: Follow up with information about the improvement or accomplishment.

Layer 3: Provide a constructive suggestion for improvement or correction.

Layer 4: Offer another positive statement with a prediction for success.

The First Layer of the Feedback Sandwich: 24 Ways to Say "Good Job!"

1. That's the best you've ever done!
2. You're on the right track.
3. Sensational!
4. I knew you could do it.
5. Perfect!
6. Best yet.
7. You've mastered that.
8. You've got that down pat.
9. Superb!
10. Good thinking!
11. I've never seen anyone do it better.
12. I'm very proud of you.

13. Way to go.
14. Now you have the hang of it.
15. Congratulations, you got it right.
16. That's quite an improvement.
17. Fantastic!
18. You're learning fast.
19. You haven't missed a thing.
20. I couldn't have done it better myself.
21. Now that's what I call a fine job.
22. Right on!
23. Terrific!
24. You outdid yourself today.

Monitoring Lifestyle Changes

Keeping a diary or journal is an effective way to monitor how a person is progressing towards the accomplishment of her personal fitness and lifestyle goals. Personal reflections on current lifestyle habits and how past history has been an influence is a good starting point and reference for future comparison. Many people never consider the factors that contribute to their attitudes, beliefs, and behaviours about physical activity and healthy eating.

If physical fitness has been identified as the main goal, recording initial fitness test scores provides a base point for measuring improvement. This kind of record is highly motivating for achievement-oriented individuals. Completing line graphs and colouring in bar graphs are very meaningful activities for them.

If weight loss is the main goal, it is important to keep track of how many kilograms (or pounds) have been lost rather than keeping a weight chart; its fluctuations (e.g., varying levels of hydration) can be demotivating. Keeping an intake record is the most effective way to keep track of nutrition choices.

Discussing the journal can be the starting point of each meeting between a client and lifestyle coach. An insightful coach will use the diary as a means to delve further into the client's perceptions of the progress he is making and his changing attitudes.

Journals, diaries, and training logs can be very effective ways to monitor your progress towards achieving personal fitness and lifestyle goals.

If the mentor is successful, the client should be prepared to proceed independently by the end of the mentoring relationship.

Parting

All good things come to an end, and at some point the mentoring relationship will conclude. This is a time for evaluation of what has transpired. It is also a time to make plans that the client can carry out on his own. The commitment to a healthy lifestyle requires ongoing attention. The goal of the mentor should be to prepare the client to proceed independently. If this goal is achieved successfully, the mentor will have had a rewarding experience as a change agent.

Putting It All Together

Mentoring is a powerful support tool that can have a profound influence on people's lives. Successful mentors are committed, positive individuals who are good listeners and effective motivators. Lifestyle coaching and personal training are two career paths that require mentoring skills to help others improve their health habits.

Several theories of behaviour change have been proposed to guide the development and refinement of health promotion. Strategies such as building self-esteem, fostering positive thinking, and offering feedback can be adopted throughout the stages of the mentoring process. Ideally, the mentoring assignment will be positive and rewarding for both the mentor and the client.

Key Terms

advising
behaviour modification
co-operative education
ecological approach
feedback
health belief model
internship
job shadowing
lifestyle coaches
mentor

mentoring
modelling
peer counselling
relapse prevention model
self-efficacy
self-fulfilling prophecy
social cognitive theory
social support
transtheoretical model

Review Questions

1. Define mentoring. What is the difference between leading and mentoring?

2. List six attributes of an effective mentor.

3. Describe three examples of mentoring relationships.

4. List six theories of behaviour change. For each theory, provide one strategy a lifestyle coach could use to influence a client.

5. List the steps in the mentoring process.

6. What are the goals of the introductory meeting?

7. What should be assessed at the beginning of the mentoring process, and how is this assessment carried out?

8. What are four common motivations for physical activity? How would you use each one to motivate a client?

9. What is the purpose of keeping a journal or diary?

10. What takes place at the conclusion of the mentoring process?

In This Chapter:

CHAPTER 9
Nutrition Guidelines

In this chapter, you will learn about the following:

❶ The nutrition requirements and components of a healthy diet

❷ The official nutrition advice provided to Canadians

❸ The unique nutrition needs of various populations

❹ The facts on supplements, ergogenic aids, vegetarianism, and fast food

> "To eat is a necessity, but to eat intelligently is an art."
> François de La Rochefoucauld

Not all factors associated with health can be controlled, but your clients' attitudes and habits related to diet can influence their health in a positive way. The role of diet in overall health is significant and has profound effects on general well-being. Poor diets are often associated with disease and illness, but healthy diets can be sources of energy and vigour. Choosing foods that provide the necessary nutrients, while limiting those associated with disease, can therefore significantly affect the course a person's life and health will take.

The purpose of this chapter is to make you well informed so that you can advise your clients about nutrition and the importance of a healthy diet. Use this factual information as the benchmark for evaluating your clients' current status and to help your clients identify problem areas and set goals for improvement.

Along the way you will probably need to debunk a number of myths. Advice abounds in the media. We are bombarded with headlines about the latest findings, which are often refuted months later by other research. The food industry advertises a plethora of products appealing to our appetites and allegedly offering simple solutions to our dietary concerns. All these facts and opinions can be confusing and overwhelming. This chapter presents current information on which to base decisions about nutrition.

Nutrition Requirements: Types and Sources of Nutrients

The term **nutrition**, the science of food and how the body uses it in health and disease, encompasses a wide variety of topics and issues. When you consider what your diet is composed of, you probably think about the foods you eat. Really, what is important is what nutrients they contain. The nutrients are obtained when the foods we eat are digested (broken down) into compounds that can be absorbed and used by the body. It is vital to consume a diet containing adequate amounts of all essential nutrients, which provide energy as well as the materials to build and maintain tissues and regulate body functions. The body requires three **macronutrients** (proteins, fats, and carbohydrates) and a long list of **micronutrients** (vitamins and minerals). Water and fibre complete the picture of a healthy diet.

There are three nutrients that provide the body with energy, namely carbohydrates, fats, and proteins. Fats are the most calorie dense, providing nine calories per gram. In contrast, proteins and carbohydrates each provide four calories per gram. Another source of energy (though not an essential nutrient) is alcohol, which provides seven calories per gram. Alcohol has no nutritional value, but its high caloric content creates the problem of excess calories being consumed (which in heavy drinkers replace calories from nutritional sources).

Calorie Density

A kilocalorie (commonly called a calorie) is the amount of energy that is required to raise 1 kg of water 1 degree Celsius.

- 1 gram of **CARBOHYDRATE** provides ④ calories of energy.

- 1 gram of **FAT** provides ⑨ calories of energy.

- 1 gram of **PROTEIN** can provide ④ calories of energy if it is not used for tissue building and repair.

- 1 gram of **ALCOHOL** provides ⑦ calories of energy.

Macronutrients

Carbohydrates

Carbohydrates are the primary source of energy in our diets and should make up 55 to 60 percent of our daily caloric intake. The body can use carbohydrates easily and quickly. They are used first, before fats and proteins. Carbohydrates are commonly called sugars and starches.

Sugars The simplest of **sugars** (also known as monosaccharides and disaccharides) include glucose, fructose, lactose, and sucrose. Glucose, also known as dextrose, is a single sugar that makes up the body's primary source of energy (blood sugar). Fructose, also a single sugar, is known as *fruit sugar*. Glucose tends to be found in foods such as vegetables, fruit, and honey, whereas fructose is often found in fruits and berries.

Lactose and sucrose are double sugars. Lactose, also known as *milk sugar*, is made by animals and is found in milk products. Sucrose, known as *table sugar*, is refined from sugar beets or sugar cane. Sucrose is used as a table sweetener and is found in candies and baked goods.

Starches Starches are complex carbohydrates (also called polysaccharides).

*E*ating breakfast is very important to kick-start brain function in the morning. If you skip breakfast, you starve your brain. Encourage your clients to eat a healthy breakfast every day, and don't forget to follow your own advice!

They are found in vegetables, fruits, and grains (e.g., pasta, bread, and rice). Starches are the recommended form of carbohydrate to eat because in addition to energy, these foods provide numerous vitamins, minerals, water, and protein and are also a good source of dietary fibre.

Before starches and double sugars can be taken up and used for energy, the body must digest them (break them down) into single sugar molecules (such as glucose) for absorption. Once in the bloodstream, glucose is able to provide cells with an energy source. The liver and muscles also store glucose in the form of **glycogen**. When glycogen stores are full, any carbohydrates consumed beyond the body's needs are synthesized into fat and stored.

Did You Know?

Unlike muscles, which have three sources of energy for contraction, the brain and nervous system have only one source of fuel – the glucose that circulates through the bloodstream. Roughly 50 percent of the food energy we ingest is used to fuel the brain's activities.

What's the Word on Glycemic Index?

Glycemic index (GI) ranks carbohydrates according to their effect on blood glucose. Low-GI carbohydrates are absorbed slowly and produce only small fluctuations in blood glucose and insulin levels. Low-GI foods have many health benefits, including control of diabetes and blood cholesterol and reduction of heart attack risk factors. Switching to eating mainly low-GI carbohydrates that slowly trickle glucose into your blood stream keeps your energy levels balanced and helps you feel fuller for a longer time between meals. Eating a lot of high-GI foods can be detrimental to your health because it pushes your body to extremes. This is especially true if you are overweight and sedentary. However, high-GI foods play an important role in refuelling carbohydrate stores after strenuous exercise.

Examples of foods that have a high GI are carbohydrates that have been processed (i.e., have had their natural nutrients and fibre removed) and many "starchy" foods. These foods include white bread, white rice, French fries, potatoes, white pasta, refined breakfast cereals, soft drinks, and sugar. Examples of low-GI foods include whole wheat bread, oats, bran, couscous, whole wheat pasta, converted or parboiled rice, and sweet potatoes. Most fruits, vegetables, and milk products have a low glycemic index. Legumes such as chick peas, beans, and lentils have a low glycemic index and are an excellent source of fibre. Meat and fish are also low-GI foods.

Fats

Fats (also known as lipids and fatty acids) are very important nutrients in our diets for many reasons. Fat is a source of usable energy. It insulates our bodies, cushions our organs, is involved in the synthesis of many hormones, and aids in the absorption of the fat-soluble vitamins A, D, E, and K (which would otherwise pass through our bodies). Further, the presence of fat in foods adds important flavour and texture (palatability), which is one reason many people find it difficult to cut down on some of their favourite foods. Still, because it is the most concentrated source of energy, fat consumption should be closely monitored. The main factor that determines the healthfulness of a fat is its effect on blood cholesterol, a high level of which is a precursor of cardiovascular diseases. Table 9.1 at the end of this section presents the common properties, sources, and health impacts of the various kinds of fats.

Saturated and Unsaturated Fats Fats are large molecules made up of two kinds of smaller molecules – fatty acids and glycerol (an alcohol). Three fatty acids are linked to one glycerol, which is why fats are also called *triglycerides*. Fats that naturally occur in foods can be classified as saturated, monounsaturated, and polyunsaturated, based on the number of double bonds between the carbon atoms of the fatty acid molecules. If no double bonds exist, these are **saturated fats**. When one double bond exists, the fatty acids are called monounsaturated fats, while those with two or more double bonds are called polyunsaturated fats. Monounsaturated and polyunsaturated fats are classified as **unsaturated fats**.

Although most foods contain some combination of these fats, the dominant type of fatty acid determines the characteristics of the fat. Foods that contain an abundance of saturated fat are usually solid at room temperature. Saturated fats are commonly found in animal products such as meats, dairy products, eggs, and many baked products. Since this type of fat is most closely associated with numerous cardiovascular diseases such as heart disease, it should be eaten less often.

Foods that contain large amounts of unsaturated fats usually come from plant sources and are liquid at room temperature (so-called oils). These unsaturated fats come in two forms, monounsaturated and polyunsaturated. These fats are deemed more desirable because they are not linked to cardiovascular disease; in fact, monounsaturated and polyunsaturated fats may lower blood cholesterol levels and reduce the risk of heart disease. Monounsaturated fats are found in large amounts in olive, canola, sesame, and peanut oils. Sunflower, safflower, and corn oils contain mostly polyunsaturated fats (Figure 9.1).

Since foods containing high levels of saturated fat have been linked to numerous cardiovascular diseases, these foods should be eaten less often.

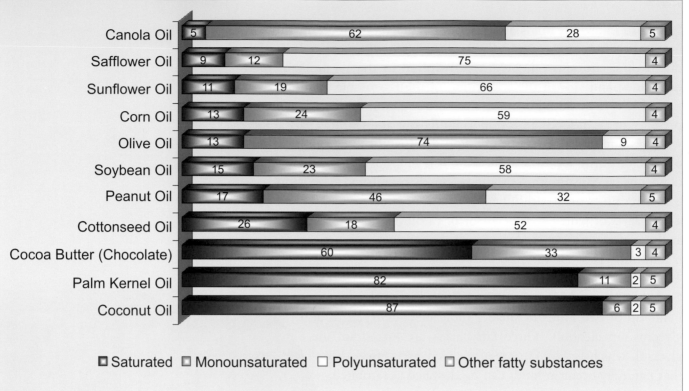

Figure 9.1 chart — percentages of fats in common oils:

Oil	Saturated	Monounsaturated	Polyunsaturated	Other fatty substances
Canola Oil	5	62	28	5
Safflower Oil	9	12	75	4
Sunflower Oil	11	19	66	4
Corn Oil	13	24	59	4
Olive Oil	13	74	9	4
Soybean Oil	15	23	58	4
Peanut Oil	17	46	32	5
Cottonseed Oil	26	18	52	4
Cocoa Butter (Chocolate)	60	33	3	4
Palm Kernel Oil	82	11	2	5
Coconut Oil	87	6	2	5

☐ Saturated ☐ Monounsaturated ☐ Polyunsaturated ☐ Other fatty substances

Figure 9.1 Percentages of saturated, monounsaturated, and polyunsaturated fats in some common oils.

Trans Fat To extend the shelf life of fats (i.e., to keep them from breaking down or turning rancid), a process called **hydrogenation** was invented. It turns what were double bonds in unsaturated fats to single bonds, yielding a more solid product. Until recently most packaged and mass-produced baked goods (cakes, cookies, pies, crackers, snack foods) contained partially hydrogenated vegetable oils. Another name for this manufactured product is **trans fat**. The dangers of trans fats are now well known, and many food companies have removed trans fats from their products. In fact, legislation may be passed to ban the use of partially hydrogenated vegetable oils. Hydrogenated oils and fats should be consumed sparingly. When counselling your clients, stress the importance of reading labels and avoiding foods that contain palm, coconut, palm kernel, or tropical oil; these cheaper oils are most likely to have undergone hydrogenation.

Cholesterol Another type of lipid that circulates in the blood is **cholesterol**, an essential component of all human and animal tissues. Cholesterol acts like a sort of cement, or mortar, strengthening and fortifying the walls of the cells. It is also needed to make vitamin D, the coverings of nerve fibres, and certain hormones. In healthy people, the body produces all the cholesterol it needs.

When foods with high cholesterol content are consumed, additional cholesterol enters the bloodstream. Excessive amounts of cholesterol in the bloodstream have been implicated in the development of cardiovascular disease.

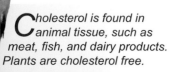

Cholesterol is found in animal tissue, such as meat, fish, and dairy products. Plants are cholesterol free.

HDL and LDL Two protein particles called lipoproteins act as cholesterol carriers: **low-density lipoprotein (LDL)** and **high-density lipoprotein (HDL)**. The responsibility of LDL is to carry cholesterol to the body's cells. However, any excess cholesterol in the bloodstream is deposited in the blood vessels, eventually causing artery clots and a narrowing and hardening of the arteries (i.e., the arteriosclerosis that can lead to heart attacks and strokes). Therefore, LDL is known as the "bad" cholesterol.

On the other hand, HDL delivers cholesterol back to the liver, where it is removed from the blood. Therefore, HDL is known as the "good" cholesterol and is not linked to cardiovascular disease. Important facts about HDL and LDL follow:

▶ Males before puberty and females before menopause have a high HDL level, after which the level drops and they become susceptible to heart disease.

▶ Smokers, people with diabetes, and people who are obese have low HDL levels.

▶ Dietary habits can raise or lower LDL and HDL.

▶ Participation in regular vigorous exercise increases levels of HDL.

Triglycerides Free fatty acids, or **triglycerides**, make up most of the fat in our diets and most of the fat that circulates in the blood. In combination with cholesterol, triglycerides speed up formation of plaque in the arteries. Triglycerides are carried in the bloodstream primarily by **very low-density lipoproteins (VLDL)**.

> "Take good care of your body – there is no spare in the trunk."
> *Anonymous*

From Your Doctor's Files:
Optimal Cholesterol Levels

Researchers believe that the best predictor of a future heart attack is the ratio of total cholesterol to HDL. This ratio should be as close to 3.5 as possible. A ratio of 5 for men and 4.5 for women represents average risk.

	Amount mmol/L (mg/dl)	Rating
Total Cholesterol (TC)	≤ 5.2 (200) 5.2 – 6.2 (200 – 239) ≥ 6.2 (240)	Desirable Borderline high High risk
Bad Cholesterol (LDL)	≤ 2.6 (100) 3.4 – 4.1 (130 – 159) ≥ 4.9 (190)	Optimal Borderline high High risk
Good Cholesterol (HDL)	≤ 1.0 (40) ≥ 1.5 (60)	High risk Low risk
Triglycerides	≤ 3.3 (125)	Desirable

Table 9.1 Properties, sources, and health impacts of the various kinds of fats.

Type of Fat	Source	Characteristics	Total Cholesterol	HDL (the healthy stuff)	LDL (the lousy stuff)	Triglycerides
Trans fats (partially hydrogenated vegetable oils)	• Processed foods: cookies, cakes, muffins, crackers, potato chips, fried fast foods	• Manufactured for longer shelf life	↑	↓	↑	↑
Saturated fats	• Fatty meat and dairy products • Baked goods made with butter or lard • Tropical oils: coconut, palm, palm kernel	• Solid at room temperature	↑		↑	
Polyunsaturated fats	• Vegetable oils: corn, soybean, safflower • Walnuts, pecans	• Liquid at room temperature	↓	↓	↓	
Monounsaturated fats	• Olive oil • Canola oil • Avocados • Nuts, seeds	• Liquid at room temperature • Cloudy when refrigerated	↓	↑?	↓	
Essential fatty acids (EFAs) Omega-3 Omega-6	• Coldwater fish (salmon, herring, mackerel, tuna, trout, sardines, char) • Enriched eggs • Flaxseed oil	• Reduce heart attack risk • Alleviate arthritis symptoms • Improve immune system	↑		↓	↓

Because of the health benefits of monounsaturated fats, the new Canada's Food Guide recommends eating two to three tablespoons of olive, canola, sesame, or peanut oils each day. Similarly, it recommends eating two servings of fish each week.

Go for QUANTITY and QUALITY!

Some Healthy Food, Fatty Food Equivalents

- You'd have to eat 30 kiwi fruit to consume the 15 grams of fat found in 1 package of Reese's Peanut Butter Cups.

 vs.

- If you eat a single restaurant-style egg roll, you're choosing 6 grams of fat, the equivalent of eating 60 fresh peaches.

 vs.

Recreation and Fitness Leadership

Did You Know?

All vegetable oils, butter, and regular margarine are 100 percent fat and contain up to 15 grams of fat (up to 135 calories) per tablespoon, equivalent to the fat in one scoop of ice cream. Look for the Health Check symbol on tubs of soft margarine. The Heart and Stroke Foundation awards this symbol to brands that have no trans fat, are nonhydrogenated, and are low in saturated fat. For a lower-calorie spread, try the calorie-reduced versions with half the fat and half the calories.

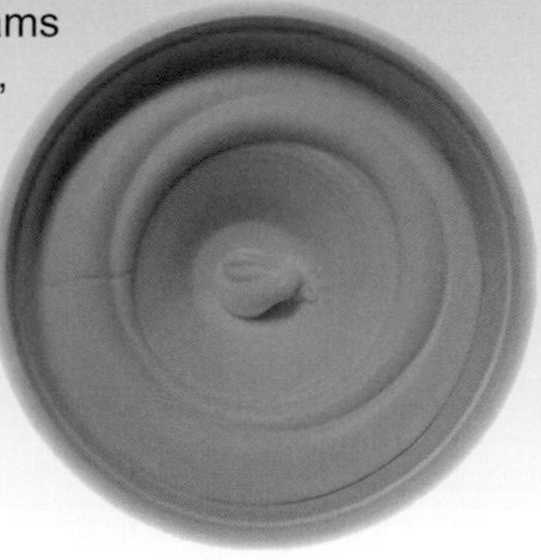

Proteins

Found in every living cell, **proteins** provide important structural components for building and repairing muscles, bones, blood, enzymes, some hormones, and cell membranes. Proteins themselves are composed of chains of **amino acids**, the building blocks of life. There are 20 commonly recognized, naturally occurring amino acids; of these, the body can synthesize all but 9 – the so-called essential amino acids – which must be supplied by the food we eat. Because amino acids are the building blocks of proteins, they are essential for our existence.

Some sources of protein are better than others at providing these essential amino acids. Individual protein sources are "complete" if they supply all 9 essential amino acids. Such **complete proteins** are animal products, such as meat, fish, poultry, eggs, milk, and cheese. Sources of food that do not contain all the essential amino acids are called **incomplete proteins.** These usually come from plant sources such as grains, beans, peas, and nuts. Although these foods are usually low in 1 or 2 amino acids, they are still good sources of essential amino acids.

Although incomplete protein sources on their own will not provide the appropriate complement of amino acids, various sources may be combined to achieve the full range and make a meal complete (Figure 9.2). This is particularly important for vegetarians, who must combine plant foods to account for the essential amino acids missing in some foods. Some common combinations include peanut butter and bread, rice and beans, milk and cereal, and macaroni and cheese.

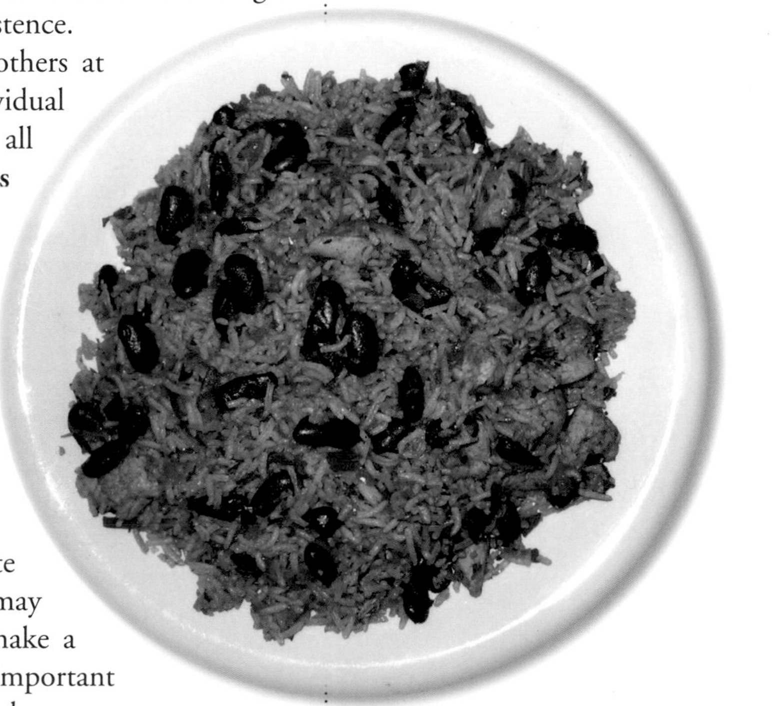

Figure 9.2 Rice and beans are examples of complementary protein sources.

One serving of meat is about the size of a deck of playing cards or the palm of your hand. A small cooked chicken breast (75 grams) is equivalent to one serving.

Meat = Protein?

Question: Meats are considered protein foods, but is there anything else in them? A boneless, skinless chicken breast is only 23 percent protein, so what makes up the rest of it?

Answer: Chicken is 75 percent water. The other 2 percent provides vitamins, minerals, and a tiny amount of saturated fat. The same is true of other lean meats. This is why Inuit people can eat a diet consisting almost entirely of meat and fish and still get the nutrients they need.

Any protein consumed beyond the body's needs is synthesized into storage fat for future use as a source of energy. Nutritionists recommend that the amount of protein we eat should not exceed 15 percent of our total daily caloric intake. North American diets usually contain an overabundance of protein, and only the destitute consume too little, as protein foods tend to be expensive.

On the other end of the spectrum, after all stored fat has been metabolized, protein from muscles and organs is used to sustain life. We see this in images of starving children, emaciated persons with anorexia nervosa, and World War II concentration camp prisoners.

Relative Percentages of Proteins, Fats, and Carbohydrates

How much of each of the three macronutrients should we eat? The best current advice suggests that caloric intake should be distributed as 55 percent carbohydrates, 15 percent proteins, and no more than 30 percent fats, with no more than one-third being saturated fats. Table 9.2 gives a rough approximation of how this would be calculated for a person who is vigorously active 40 minutes a day. The most important numbers to make note of are the ones for fat. Nutrition labels provide the total fat, saturated fat, and trans fat content in grams. Encourage your clients to stay under their ceiling numbers for fat and saturated fat.

Recreation and Fitness Leadership

Table 9.2 Total caloric needs based on 40 minutes of vigorous activity each day; guidelines for carbohydrate, protein, and fat consumption.

Weight in kg (lb)	Total calorie needs	Carbohydrates 55%	Proteins 15%	Fats 30%	Total fat grams Fat cal/9	Max saturated fat grams Total fat/3
45.5 (100)	1,800	990	270	540	60	20
50.0 (110)	1,900	1,045	285	570	63	21
54.5 (120)	2,000	1,100	300	600	67	22
59.0 (130)	2,100	1,155	315	630	70	23
63.5 (140)	2,200	1,210	330	660	73	24
68.2 (150)	2,300	1,265	345	690	77	26
72.7 (160)	2,400	1,320	362	720	80	27
77.3 (170)	2,500	1,375	375	750	83	28
81.8 (180)	2,600	1,430	390	780	87	29
86.4 (190)	2,700	1,485	405	810	90	30
90.9 (200)	2,800	1,540	420	840	93	31

Micronutrients

Vitamins

Vitamins are organic (carbon-containing) substances that are required in small amounts for normal growth, reproduction, and maintenance of health. Unlike the nutrients discussed thus far, vitamins do not provide calories; instead, they serve as **coenzymes**, facilitating the action of enzymes in a variety of responses and chemical reactions.

A distinction can be made between two broad classifications of vitamins: **water-soluble** (able to dissolve in water) and **fat-soluble** (able to dissolve in fat or lipid tissue). The water-soluble vitamins (including vitamin C and the B-complex vitamins) are not readily stored, so any excess is usually eliminated from the body during urination (Table 9.3). The fat-soluble vitamins (A, D, E, and K), taken in excess, are stored in fat (adipose) tissue in the body (Table 9.4). Consuming and retaining too many of these particular vitamins (especially A and E) may lead to toxicity. Obviously, a diet lacking adequate amounts of a particular vitamin will lead to characteristic symptoms of a deficiency.

Table 9.3 The major water-soluble vitamins.

Vitamin	Physiological Functions	Vitamin Food Sources	Deficiency Effects
Thiamin (B$_1$)	Glucose metabolism; nervous system synaptic functioning	Enriched breads and cereals; pork, kidney; peas; pecans	Constipation; nausea; depression, fatigue, irritability; loss of hand–eye coordination; gait changes; often seen with anorexics
Riboflavin (B$_2$)	Red blood cell formation; glycogen synthesis; energy release from glucose and fatty acids; growth; adrenal cortex activity	Beef, liver, heart; yogurt, milk, cheese; almonds, broccoli, asparagus; produced by intestinal flora	Personality shifts, depression; cracked mouth and lips; purplish-red tongue; dry skin; fetal development effects
Niacin (B$_3$)	Protein and fat synthesis; energy release from all nutrient forms	Meat, poultry, liver; peanut butter	Diarrhea; depression, irritability, headaches; sleeplessness; personality disorientation; pellagra-dermatitis; death
Pyridoxine (B$_6$)	Protein, lipid, and carbohydrate metabolism; neurotransmitter synthesis; hemoglobin synthesis; antibody production; fetal nervous system function; synthesis/breakdown of amino acids	Chicken, fish; egg yolk; bananas, avocados; whole-grain cereal	No known deficiency in adults; poor growth; anemia; skin lesions; decreased niacin production, convulsions; decreased antibody production
Cobalamin (B$_{12}$)	Red blood cell formation; metabolism of folacin; growth and function of nervous system	Meat, liver, kidney; eggs; dairy products	Pernicious anemia in adults; however, caused by lack of absorption rather than lack of B12
Folacin (folic acid)	Red blood cell formation; fetal development; DNA synthesis required for rapid cell division	Bread; oranges and orange juice; meat, poultry, fish, eggs; broccoli, lima beans, asparagus, spinach	Infections; rheumatoid arthritis; chronic alcohol use leads to inadequate absorption; toxemia of pregnancy
Ascorbic acid (vitamin C)	Tooth development; maintenance of scar tissue; folic acid formation; absorption of iron and calcium; neurotransmitter synthesis	Peppers, broccoli, kale, cauliflower, strawberries, lemons, papayas, spinach, asparagus; liver	Scurvy; fatigue, shortness of breath, muscle cramps, skeletal pain; dry skin; anorexia; bleeding gums; depressed glucose tolerance; personality disorders

Recreation and Fitness Leadership

Table 9.4 The major fat-soluble vitamins.

Vitamin	Physiological Functions	Vitamin Food Sources	Deficiency Effects
A	Bone growth; night vision; sperm production; growth of epithelial cells; estrogen synthesis; mucus gland secretion	Eggs, cheese, milk, liver; fruits and vegetables that contain beta carotene, which is converted to vitamin A in the intestine; yellow, orange, and dark green vegetables, cantaloupe, mangoes, pink grapefruit	Night blindness, corneal deterioration; skin changes; enamel alteration; diarrhea; respiratory infections
D	Bone growth; calcium and phosphorus absorption; kidney resorption of calcium and phosphorus; neuromuscular activity	Egg yolk; fortified milk; fish-liver oil, tuna; sunlight stimulates the body's production of the vitamin	Osteomalacia; osteoporosis; tooth malformation; rickets
E	Vitamin A absorption; antioxidation of unsaturated fatty acids and tissue lipids; heme synthesis for red blood cell function	Wheat germ, whole-grain cereal; vegetable oils; liver; leafy green vegetables	Deficiency rarely seen in humans; destruction of red blood cell membrane
K	Synthesis of clotting factors in the liver	Dark green leafy vegetables, cabbage, cauliflower, tomatoes; eggs; liver; produced by intestinal flora	Prolonged coagulation time, bleeding, bruising

Too Much of a Good Thing?

If a little is good, more is better. Right?

Not so in the case of the following vitamins and minerals:

- Too much vitamin A acetate or palmitate (more than 10,000 IU a day) raises the risk of hip fractures.

- Too much vitamin E (more than 400 IU a day) increases the risk of death.

- Too much iron (the highest safe level is 45 mg per day from all sources) can cause constipation and iron overload.

- Too much zinc (men need 11 mg, women need 8 mg) can make it hard to absorb or retain copper. Megadoses of 300 mg a day can impair the immune system.

DANGER

Minerals

Minerals are inorganic (non-carbon-containing) materials needed in small amounts to perform numerous functions in the body. Minerals function as structural elements (e.g., in teeth, muscles, hormones), regulate body functions (e.g., muscle contraction, blood clotting, heart function), aid in the growth and maintenance of body tissues, and act as catalysts in the release of energy. There are approximately 17 to 21 identified essential minerals for human health; the major minerals found in relatively large amounts in our bodies include calcium, phosphorus, magnesium, sulphur, sodium, and potassium (Table 9.5). Other micronutrients (also known as **trace elements**) that are needed in relatively small amounts include chromium, iodine, zinc, iron, copper, fluoride, and selenium (Table 9.6).

Table 9.5 Major minerals and their roles.

Mineral	Physiological Functions	Mineral Food Sources	Deficiency Effects
Calcium	Bone ossification; tooth formation; general body growth; cell membrane maintenance; neuromuscular function	Milk and milk products; turnip greens, collards; broccoli; shellfish; soy products; molasses	Osteoporosis (not due to deficiency, but caused by calcium reabsorption); osteomalacia; tetany
Phosphorus	Tooth and bone development; energy release (ADP/ATP); fat transport; acid–base balance; synthesis of proteins, enzymes, and DNA/RNA	Meat, poultry, fish; eggs; cereal products; peanuts; cheddar cheese; carbonated soft drinks	Fatigue; demineralization of bone occurs in people taking high doses of antacids; often seen with anorexics
Potassium	Protein synthesis; fluid balance; acid–base balance; nerve transmission; energy release	Potatoes; bananas; liver; milk; apricots, cantaloupe, avocados; lima beans	Abdominal bloating; muscle weakness; heart abnormalities; respiratory distress; most often seen in infants with vomiting and diarrhea
Sulphur	Metabolism; blood clotting; collagen synthesis; detoxification of body fluids	Protein foods	Not clearly established
Sodium	Nerve transmission; acid–base balance; formation of digestive secretions	Bacon; olives; table salt; processed cheese; sauerkraut	Unlikely to occur; vomiting or extreme sweating in children could reduce sodium
Chloride	Acid–base balance; carbon dioxide transport; acidity of stomach	Table salt	Unlikely to occur; may be lost as a result of vomiting
Magnesium	Protein, lipid, and carbohydrate metabolism; energy production; protein synthesis; nerve transmission; tooth enamel stability	Nuts; soy beans; whole grains; spinach; green leafy vegetables; clams; cocoa	Uncertain effects; nervousness, irritability, convulsions; skin changes; vasodilation; related to vomiting

Table 9.6 Micronutrients and their roles.

Mineral	Physiological Functions	Mineral Food Sources	Deficiency Effects
Iron	Oxygen and carbon dioxide transport; red blood cell formation; vitamin A synthesis; antibody production; collagen synthesis; removal of lipids from the blood	Spinach, peas, greens, asparagus; liver; enriched breads and cereals; clams; beans	Anemia and fatigue
Zinc	DNA/RNA synthesis; enzyme formation; acid–base balance; collagen production; fetal development; wound healing; HCl production; enhanced appetite and taste	Meats, seafood; whole-grain bread, whole wheat; cashew nuts	N/A
Copper	Hemoglobin, protein, and cholesterol synthesis; energy release; enzyme formation; myelin sheath development	Liver; oysters; cherries; mushrooms; whole-grain cereal; nuts; cocoa	N/A
Iodine	Protein, thyroxine, cholesterol, and vitamin A synthesis; cell metabolism	Water supply (depending on location); seafood; dairy products; iodized salt; spinach	Goiter (mainly in developing nations)
Fluoride	Skeletal stability; prevention of osteoporosis, dental caries, and periodontal disease	Water supply; tea; rice; spinach; soy beans; mackerel, salmon	N/A
Selenium	Antioxidation; energy release; heart muscle function; regulates thyroid function; immune system role	Meats, organ meats, seafood; eggs; nuts; cereal; milk and dairy products; fruits; plant sources depend on soil concentrations	N/A

Although needed only in small quantities, trace elements are nonetheless essential for good health. Mineral intake is like the intake of vitamins. Any essential mineral taken in an amount that is either too small or too large can lead to harmful symptoms.

Water

Water is a vital nutrient that is often ignored, but it is perhaps the most essential nutrient for life. Water makes up such a large percentage of our bodies and the food we eat that its importance cannot be overstated. How can we overlook a substance that provides the medium for nutrient and waste transport, assists digestion and absorption, helps regulate body temperature, forms the base of fluids that serve as lubricants (e.g., synovial fluid within joints), and plays a key role in the majority of the chemical reactions that take place within our bodies?

Dehydration is more of a problem than many acknowledge. Although thirst alerts us to consume more water, it is not always a reliable indicator of dehydration. For example, during an illness or during intense exercise, you may not feel the urge to drink, but that does not mean your body is fully hydrated. When a person feels uncharacteristically weak or fatigued, it just may be that he is slightly dehydrated and needs to take in more fluids. An extreme bout of dehydration can cause severe weakness and hospitalization, or even lead to death.

Encourage your clients to take in the equivalent of eight glasses of water a day. Juices, tea, coffee, soup, gelatin desserts, and milk all contain large proportions of water and can be included in the total.

Fibre

By definition **fibre** is not a nutrient, but it is still a very important element in our diets. For the most part, fibre includes plant substances that cannot be digested; as a result, they pass through the digestive tract relatively unchanged, adding bulk to facilitate elimination.

Fibre can be classified as soluble or insoluble, and each has significant physiological effects on the body. **Soluble fibre** has the ability to bind cholesterol-containing compounds in the intestines, thus lowering blood cholesterol levels by clearing cholesterol from the intestinal tract. Soluble fibre has also been shown to slow the body's absorption of glucose, having potential implications for the treatment of diabetes.

Fibre that is classified as insoluble also offers important benefits for good health. Its main function is to absorb water from the intestinal tract, thereby preventing constipation. Research on the effect of **insoluble fibre** in preventing cancer of the lower intestinal tract is inconclusive.

All plant foods contain some dietary fibre, although some more than others. Some rich sources of soluble fibre include fruits, legumes (e.g., beans, peas, lentils), oats, and barley. Sources of insoluble dietary fibre are wheat, grains, vegetables, and cereals. Since the processing of foods can remove some of their valuable fibre content, it is always a good idea to eat fresh fruits and vegetables and whole grain foods.

To enjoy all the benefits of fibre, aim to ingest 32 grams each day.

Nutrition Recommendations and Guidelines

Nutrition recommendations provide information to guide us in following a dietary pattern that supplies everything we need for health. However, we eat food, not nutrients. That's where **Canada's Food Guide** comes in. The six-page handbook on healthy eating effectively translates nutrient recommendations into a food group plan that is easy to understand and apply. *Eating Well with Canada's Food Guide* (Figure 9.3) takes Canada's Guidelines for Healthy Eating one step further by helping Canadians evaluate their eating habits and plan healthy meals through a daily selection of food.

Canada's Food Guide to Healthy Eating

A new version of Canada's Food Guide was released in early 2007 – the first revision of the Guide in 15 years. For the first time, the Food Guide is gender- and age-specific for Canadians over the age of two, offering tailored dietary advice for three different age groups of children, teens, and two different age groups of adults. And also for the first time, a national food guide for First Nations, Inuit, and Métis – *Eating Well with Canada's Food Guide: First Nations, Inuit and Métis* – has been developed to reflect the unique values, traditions, and food choices of aboriginal populations.

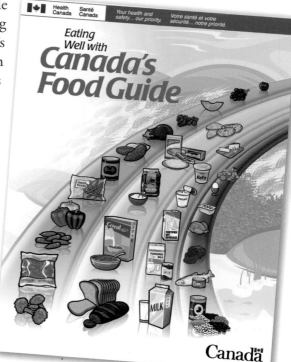

Just as no two people are exactly alike in appearance, personality, or interests, the same holds true when it comes to food and nutrition needs – different people need different amounts and types of food. The amount of food a person needs each day from the various food groups differs according to age (e.g., teenagers have higher energy needs), body size (e.g., nutrient and energy needs are greater for those with a larger body size), sex (e.g., men generally have higher nutrient and energy needs), activity level (e.g., the greater the activity, the higher the energy and nutrient needs), and whether the person is pregnant or breastfeeding. The Food Guide accounts for these differences and makes daily planning easier for all individuals.

> One should eat to live, not live to eat.
> *Cicero*

The Food Groups

Most of us have heard and learned about food groups. These groups are created to help us choose foods that will lead to a healthy diet, emphasizing the ideas of balance, variety, and moderation. Choosing foods from each group in appropriate amounts will improve your chances of having a healthy diet. The Guide presents a recommended number of servings from four food groups: vegetables and fruit; grain products; milk and alternatives; and meat and alternatives. A small amount (30 to 45 ml) of

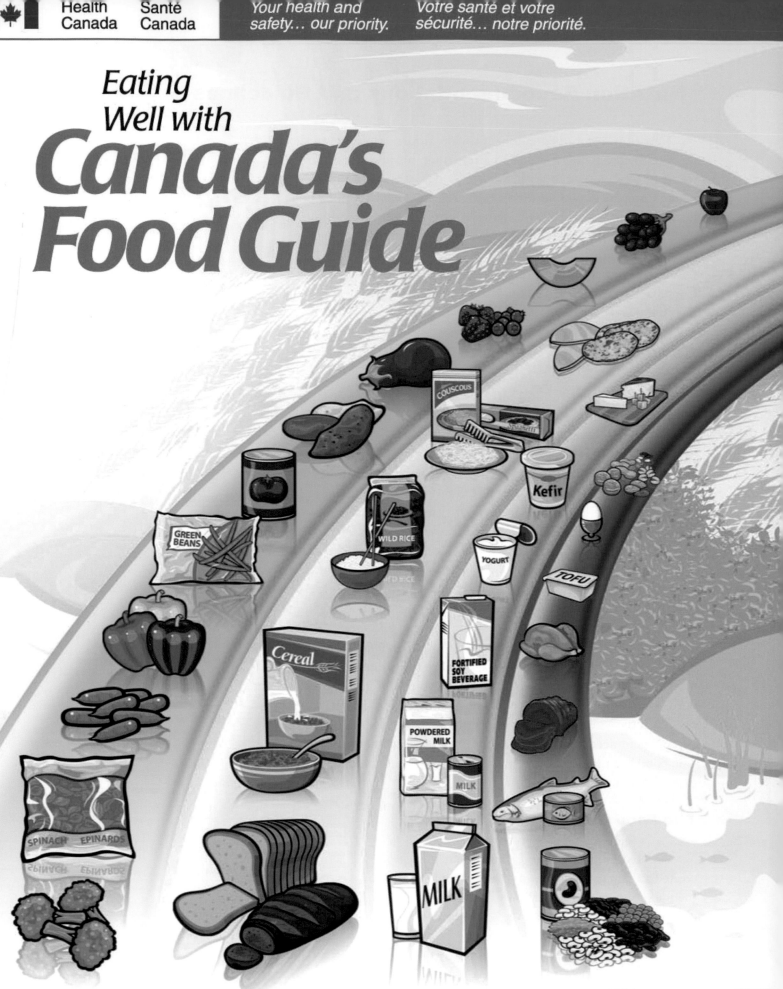

Eating
Well with
Canada's
Food Guide

Canada

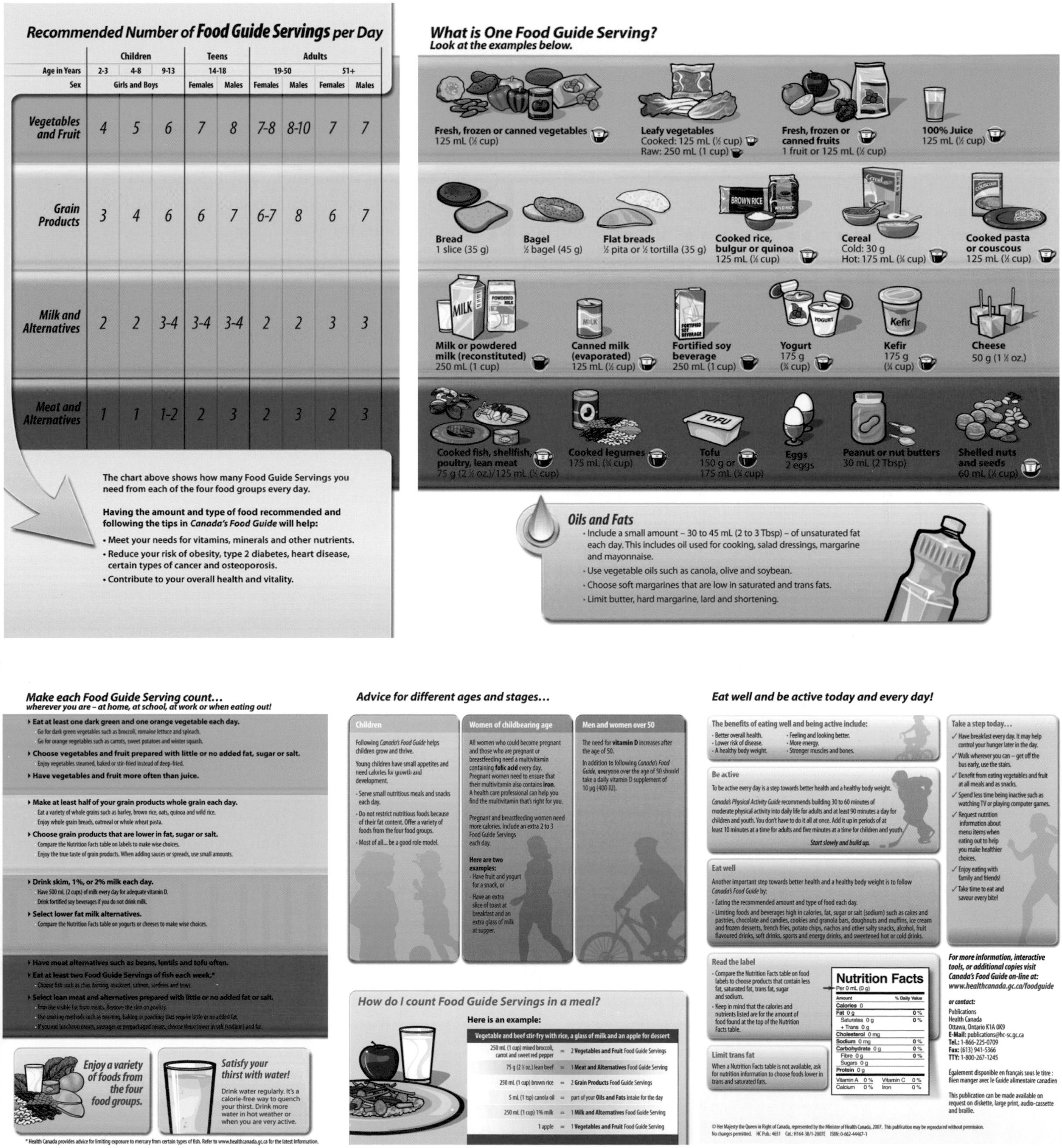

Recommended Number of Food Guide Servings per Day

	Children			Teens		Adults			
Age in Years	2-3	4-8	9-13	14-18		19-50		51+	
Sex	Girls and Boys			Females	Males	Females	Males	Females	Males
Vegetables and Fruit	4	5	6	7	8	7-8	8-10	7	7
Grain Products	3	4	6	6	7	6-7	8	6	7
Milk and Alternatives	2	2	3-4	3-4	3-4	2	2	3	3
Meat and Alternatives	1	1	1-2	2	3	2	3	2	3

The chart above shows how many Food Guide Servings you need from each of the four food groups every day.

Having the amount and type of food recommended and following the tips in *Canada's Food Guide* will help:

- Meet your needs for vitamins, minerals and other nutrients.
- Reduce your risk of obesity, type 2 diabetes, heart disease, certain types of cancer and osteoporosis.
- Contribute to your overall health and vitality.

What is One Food Guide Serving?
Look at the examples below.

Fresh, frozen or canned vegetables 125 mL (½ cup)

Leafy vegetables Cooked: 125 mL (½ cup) Raw: 250 mL (1 cup)

Fresh, frozen or canned fruits 1 fruit or 125 mL (½ cup)

100% Juice 125 mL (½ cup)

Bread 1 slice (35 g)

Bagel ½ bagel (45 g)

Flat breads ½ pita or ½ tortilla (35 g)

Cooked rice, bulgur or quinoa 125 mL (½ cup)

Cereal Cold: 30 g Hot: 175 mL (¾ cup)

Cooked pasta or couscous 125 mL (½ cup)

Milk or powdered milk (reconstituted) 250 mL (1 cup)

Canned milk (evaporated) 125 mL (½ cup)

Fortified soy beverage 250 mL (1 cup)

Yogurt 175 g (¾ cup)

Kefir 175 g (¾ cup)

Cheese 50 g (1 ½ oz.)

Cooked fish, shellfish, poultry, lean meat 75 g (2 ½ oz.)/125 mL (½ cup)

Cooked legumes 175 mL (¾ cup)

Tofu 150 g or 175 mL (¾ cup)

Eggs 2 eggs

Peanut or nut butters 30 mL (2 Tbsp)

Shelled nuts and seeds 60 mL (¼ cup)

Oils and Fats
- Include a small amount – 30 to 45 mL (2 to 3 Tbsp) – of unsaturated fat each day. This includes oil used for cooking, salad dressings, margarine and mayonnaise.
- Use vegetable oils such as canola, olive and soybean.
- Choose soft margarines that are low in saturated and trans fats.
- Limit butter, hard margarine, lard and shortening.

Make each Food Guide Serving count...
wherever you are – at home, at school, at work or when eating out!

▶ **Eat at least one dark green and one orange vegetable each day.**
Go for dark green vegetables such as broccoli, romaine lettuce and spinach.
Go for orange vegetables such as carrots, sweet potatoes and winter squash.

▶ **Choose vegetables and fruit prepared with little or no added fat, sugar or salt.**
Enjoy vegetables steamed, baked or stir-fried instead of deep-fried.

▶ **Have vegetables and fruit more often than juice.**

▶ **Make at least half of your grain products whole grain each day.**
Eat a variety of whole grains such as barley, brown rice, oats, quinoa and wild rice.
Enjoy whole grain breads, oatmeal or whole wheat pasta.

▶ **Choose grain products that are lower in fat, sugar or salt.**
Compare the Nutrition Facts table on labels to make wise choices.
Enjoy the true taste of grain products. When adding sauces or spreads, use small amounts.

▶ **Drink skim, 1%, or 2% milk each day.**
Have 500 mL (2 cups) of milk every day for adequate vitamin D.
Drink fortified soy beverages if you do not drink milk.

▶ **Select lower fat milk alternatives.**
Compare the Nutrition Facts table on yogurts or cheeses to make wise choices.

▶ **Have meat alternatives such as beans, lentils and tofu often.**

▶ **Eat at least two Food Guide Servings of fish each week.***
Choose fish such as char, herring, mackerel, salmon, sardines and trout.

▶ **Select lean meat and alternatives prepared with little or no added fat or salt.**
Trim the visible fat from meats. Remove the skin on poultry.
Use cooking methods such as roasting, baking or poaching that require little or no added fat.
If you eat luncheon meats, sausages or prepackaged meats, choose those lower in salt (sodium) and fat.

Enjoy a variety of foods from the four food groups.

Satisfy your thirst with water!
Drink water regularly. It's a calorie-free way to quench your thirst. Drink more water in hot weather or when you are very active.

* Health Canada provides advice for limiting exposure to mercury from certain types of fish. Refer to www.healthcanada.gc.ca for the latest information.

Advice for different ages and stages...

Children
Following *Canada's Food Guide* helps children grow and thrive.
Young children have small appetites and need calories for growth and development.
- Serve small nutritious meals and snacks each day.
- Do not restrict nutritious foods because of their fat content. Offer a variety of foods from the four food groups.
- Most of all... be a good role model.

Women of childbearing age
All women who could become pregnant and those who are pregnant or breastfeeding need a multivitamin containing **folic acid** every day. Pregnant women need to ensure that their multivitamin also contains **iron**. A health care professional can help you find the multivitamin that's right for you.
Pregnant and breastfeeding women need more calories. Include an extra 2 to 3 Food Guide Servings each day.
Here are two examples:
- Have fruit and yogurt for a snack, or
- Have an extra slice of toast at breakfast and an extra glass of milk at supper.

Men and women over 50
The need for **vitamin D** increases after the age of 50.
In addition to following *Canada's Food Guide*, everyone over the age of 50 should take a daily vitamin D supplement of 10 μg (400 IU).

How do I count Food Guide Servings in a meal?
Here is an example:

Vegetable and beef stir-fry with rice, a glass of milk and an apple for dessert		
250 mL (1 cup) mixed broccoli, carrot and sweet red pepper	=	2 Vegetables and Fruit Food Guide Servings
75 g (2 ½ oz.) lean beef	=	1 Meat and Alternatives Food Guide Serving
250 mL (1 cup) brown rice	=	2 Grain Products Food Guide Servings
5 mL (1 tsp) canola oil	=	part of your Oils and Fats intake for the day
250 mL (1 cup) 1% milk	=	1 Milk and Alternatives Food Guide Serving
1 apple	=	1 Vegetables and Fruit Food Guide Serving

Eat well and be active today and every day!

The benefits of eating well and being active include:
- Better overall health.
- Lower risk of disease.
- A healthy body weight.
- Feeling and looking better.
- More energy.
- Stronger muscles and bones.

Be active
To be active every day is a step towards better health and a healthy body weight.
Canada's Physical Activity Guide recommends building 30 to 60 minutes of moderate physical activity into daily life for adults and at least 90 minutes a day for children and youth. You don't have to do it all at once. Add it up in periods of at least 10 minutes at a time for adults and five minutes at a time for children and youth.
Start slowly and build up.

Eat well
Another important step towards better health and a healthy body weight is to follow *Canada's Food Guide* by:
- Eating the recommended amount and type of food each day.
- Limiting foods and beverages high in calories, fat, sugar or salt (sodium) such as cakes and pastries, chocolate and candies, cookies and granola bars, doughnuts and muffins, ice cream and frozen desserts, french fries, potato chips, nachos and other salty snacks, alcohol, fruit flavoured drinks, soft drinks, sports and energy drinks, and sweetened hot or cold drinks.

Read the label
- Compare the Nutrition Facts table on food labels to choose products that contain less fat, saturated fat, trans fat, sugar and sodium.
- Keep in mind that the calories and nutrients listed are for the amount of food found at the top of the Nutrition Facts table.

Limit trans fat
When a Nutrition Facts table is not available, ask for nutrition information to choose foods lower in trans and saturated fats.

Nutrition Facts	
Per 0 mL (0 g)	
Amount	**% Daily Value**
Calories 0	
Fat 0 g	0 %
Saturates 0 g	0 %
+ Trans 0 g	
Cholesterol 0 mg	
Sodium 0 mg	0 %
Carbohydrate 0 g	0 %
Fibre 0 g	0 %
Sugars 0 g	
Protein 0 g	
Vitamin A 0 %	Vitamin C 0 %
Calcium 0 %	Iron 0 %

Take a step today...
✓ Have breakfast every day. It may help control your hunger later in the day.
✓ Walk wherever you can – get off the bus early, use the stairs.
✓ Benefit from eating vegetables and fruit at all meals and as snacks.
✓ Spend less time being inactive such as watching TV or playing computer games.
✓ Request nutrition information about menu items when eating out to help you make healthier choices.
✓ Enjoy eating with family and friends!
✓ Take time to eat and savour every bite!

For more information, interactive tools, or additional copies visit Canada's Food Guide on-line at: www.healthcanada.gc.ca/foodguide

or contact:
Publications
Health Canada
Ottawa, Ontario K1A 0K9
E-Mail: publications@hc-sc.gc.ca
Tel.: 1-866-225-0709
Fax: (613) 941-5366
TTY: 1-800-267-1245

Également disponible en français sous le titre :
Bien manger avec le Guide alimentaire canadien

This publication can be made available on request on diskette, large print, audio-cassette and braille.

Figure 9.3 *Eating Well with Canada's Food Guide*. For more information on Eating Well with Canada's Food Guide, visit the Food & Nutrition section of Health Canada's website at www.hc-sc.gc.ca/fn-an/food-guide-aliment/index_e.html.

healthy monounsaturated oils or fats is also recommended daily for optimal health. All foods can be a part of a healthy eating pattern.

Although all the food groups in Canada's Food Guide are vital to a healthy diet, you will notice that the amounts required from each group vary — the rainbow design depicting the food groups provides a visual representation of this idea. The vegetables and fruit arc occupies the largest (outer) portion of the rainbow, while the meat and alternatives arc occupies the smallest (inner) portion of the rainbow. Notice also the directional statements that offer key points for choosing appropriate foods within each food group.

Vegetables and fruit:

▶ Eat at least one dark green and one orange vegetable each day.
▶ Choose vegetables and fruit prepared with little or no added fat, sugar, or salt.
▶ Have vegetables and fruit more often than juice.

Grain products:

▶ Make at least half of your grain products whole grain each day.
▶ Choose grain products that are lower in fat, sugar, or salt.

Milk and alternatives:

▶ Drink skim, 1 percent, or 2 percent milk each day.
▶ Select lower-fat milk alternatives.

Meat and alternatives:

▶ Have meat alternatives such as beans, lentils, and tofu often.
▶ Eat at least two Food Guide servings of fish each week.
▶ Select lean meat and alternatives prepared with little or no added fat or salt.

The revamped Guide provides more details than ever on how to choose foods within the four food groups, and a wider variety of foods (e.g., couscous, flatbreads, tofu, and bok choy) are included to reflect the ethnic and cultural diversity of the population. To help you understand how much food from a specific food group makes up a Food Guide serving, more detailed information is also provided on serving sizes and food portions. For example, one slice of whole wheat bread, half a bagel, and half a cup of cooked pasta are each considered one serving from the Grain Products food group.

Canada's Food Guide also highlights the importance of physical activity in maintaining a healthy body and mind. Eating well and being active work together to help people achieve better overall health, including a healthy body weight, stronger muscles and bones, and a reduced risk of various cardiovascular and other diseases. The Guide not only tells you and your clients to eat well and be active but also offers practical tips and guidelines on how to get there.

How much food from the Grain Products food group makes up a serving? Half a cup of cooked rice or pasta are each considered one serving. Half a cup is about the size of a hockey puck; one cup is about the size of a baseball.

Recreation and Fitness Leadership

What Food Labels Tell You

To make intelligent choices about what you eat, and to counsel your clients about their dietary habits, you must know how to read and understand food labels. Nutrition labels are standardized presentations of the nutrient content of food (Figure 9.4). Each label consists of a heading, a serving size, and values for energy (calories). A % Daily Value is given for essential nutrients, including fat (total, saturated, and trans fat), cholesterol, sodium, carbohydrate (total, fibre, and sugars), protein, vitamin A, vitamin C, calcium, and iron. These % Daily Values are based on a 2,000 calorie per day diet. Always check the serving size carefully, as subsequent values on the label are calculated based on this amount of the product. Be aware that serving size often differs from the actual contents of the package (i.e., a package may contain two or more of the servings that the values are based on).

Serving Size

Are you eating the serving size indicated on the label? If not, you must adjust the nutrient and calorie values accordingly.

Calories

Are you watching your weight? This value tells you how many calories are contained in a single serving of the product.

Protein

Where are you getting your protein? Animal proteins are usually higher in fat and cholesterol. Emphasize low-fat milk, yogurt, and cheeses, and try vegetable proteins such as beans and cereals, as well as nuts and seeds.

Total Carbohydrate

Need a boost of energy? Carbohydrates provide a major source of energy and are found in foods such as breads, cereals, and fruit. But watch out for foods high in simple sugars.

Total Fat

It's a good idea to cut back on fat for heart health and general well-being. Look for products with low-fat alternatives.

Dietary Fibre

Soluble and insoluble sources of fibre help prevent heart disease and cancer, as well as keep you regular.

Vitamins and Minerals

Eat a variety of foods daily to ensure an adequate intake of vitamins and minerals needed for vital body functions.

Sodium

You know it better as salt. High sodium consumption is associated with hypertension (or high blood pressure) in some individuals, so keep your intake low.

Daily Value

What percentage of your Recommended Nutrient Intake (RNI) does a serving of this product give you? Use these numbers as a guide.

Nutrition Facts

Per 0 mL (0 g)

Amount	% Daily Value*
Calories 0 g	
Fat 0 g	0 %
Saturates 0 g	0 %
+ Trans 0 g	
Cholesterol 0 mg	
Sodium 0 mg	0 %
Carbohydrate 0 g	0 %
Fibre 0 g	0 %
Sugars 0 g	
Protein 0 g	

Vitamin A	0%	Vitamin C	0 %
Calcium	0%	Iron	0 %

*% Daily Values are based on a 2,000 calorie per day diet.

Figure 9.4 Sample nutrition label.

Nutrition Claims and What They Mean

Often presented in a bold banner format on the product package, nutrition claims highlight a nutritional feature of a product. Since these claims must always be backed up by detailed facts relating to the claim, look for more information on the label.

- **LOW** is always associated with a very small amount.

- **LESS** is used to compare one product with another. A bag of chips claiming to contain "50 percent less salt" means it has half the salt of the food to which it was compared.

- **LIGHT** or **LITE** may refer to anything about the product including taste, texture, colour, or fat content. Look further to find out which feature of the product is "light."

- **LOW IN SATURATED FAT** or **CHOLESTEROL** may lead you to believe the product is low in fat. Not necessarily so. Vegetable oils may be low in saturated fat and contain no cholesterol, but may still be high in total fat.

- **FAT FREE** indicates the product contains less than 0.5 grams of fat per serving.

- **LOW FAT** indicates the product contains 3 grams of fat or less per serving and no more than 15 percent fat on a dry basis.

- **FAT REDUCED** indicates at least 25 percent less fat than the original product.

- **% M.F.** or **% B.F.** listed on most dairy products indicates percentage of milk fat or butter fat, respectively. This information can be used to choose lower-fat dairy products.

Do We Need a Nutrition Traffic Light System in Canada?

In 2001, the U.K. Food Standards Agency proposed a traffic light system for food labelling and encouraged its adoption throughout the European Union. In this system, total fat, saturated fat, sugar, and salt contents of a food product are indicated by green, amber, and red "traffic lights" on the front of the package. This system has been found easier for consumers than text-based information. Many food producers and grocery chains opposed this educational tool.

Example:

(red dot)	(green dot)	(amber dot)	(green dot)
FAT	SAT FAT	SUGAR	SALT
15 g	1.5 g	20 g	0.6 g

This food has high levels of fat, moderate levels of sugar, and acceptable levels of saturated fat and salt.

Does All Food Fit?

Until recently, one of the healthy eating mottos was All Food Fits. With our current level of knowledge, is this still the case? Labelling foods as good or bad sends a negative message about eating that should be avoided. An overall pattern of healthy eating should be our practical goal. So it is better to classify foods as anytime, sometimes, and seldom. In Table 9.7, foods are classified based on their fat and calorie content.

Table 9.7 Healthy eating guidelines based on the fat and calorie content of food.

Food Group	Anytime	Sometimes	Seldom
Fruits and vegetables	• Fruit: fresh, frozen, dried, canned (in juice) • Fruit and vegetable juices • Beans, peas, lentils • Vegetables: fresh, frozen, canned • Baked French fries and potato chips • Soy or veggie burgers and hot dogs	• Fruit canned in syrup • Fruit "cocktails" • Avocado • Guacamole • Mashed potatoes • Potato salad • Canned tomato and vegetable juices • Coleslaw	• French fries • Hash browns • Onion rings • Potatoes au gratin • Vegetables in rich sauces • Coconut
Grain products	• 100% whole wheat bread, bagels, pitas, crackers, pasta, couscous, and so on • Tortillas • Popcorn (air-popped) • Brown rice • Baked tortilla chips • Breakfast cereals: whole grain, low sugar (hot or cold)	• Angel food cake • All other bread products • Plain biscuits • Fig bars • Low-fat cakes, cookies, and muffins • Pretzels, corn chips • Pancakes • White rice • Breakfast cereals: not whole grain, heavily sugared • Cereal bars	• Belgian waffles • Butter tarts • Cake with frosting • Chocolate chip or sandwich cookies • Cinnamon rolls • Coffee cake • Croissants • Danishes • Doughnuts • Dipped granola bars • Pie (except pumpkin) • Tiramisu • French toast with syrup
Milk and alternatives	• Buttermilk • Skim or 1% milk • Low-fat cheese, sour cream, plain yogurt, and cottage cheese • Ultra-low-fat cream cheese	• 2% milk • Fat-free ice cream • Frozen yogurt • Low-fat fruit yogurt	• Cheese (e.g., cheddar, Swiss, processed) • Cheesecake • Cream cheese • Full-fat yogurt • Ice cream • Whole milk
Meat and alternatives	• Skinless chicken or turkey • Fat-free hot dogs and cold cuts • Egg whites, egg substitutes • Lean cuts of pork or beef • Lobster, clams, shrimp • Tuna canned in water • Fish (broiled, steamed, poached, not breaded)	• Fatter cuts of beef and pork, trimmed • Low-fat chicken bologna, bacon • Ground chicken or turkey • Eggs • Chicken or turkey breast or thigh with skin • Nuts, peanut butter • Tuna canned in oil • Turkey or chicken hot dogs	• Untrimmed beef, pork, or lamb • Beef or pork ribs • Beef steaks and roasts • Chicken wings or thighs with skin • Fried chicken or seafood • Ground beef, regular or lean • Ham, hot dogs, bologna, salami, liver • Pork chops and roasts
Fats, sweets, condiments	• Ketchup • Fat-free mayonnaise • Mustard • Olives • Fat-free salad dressings	• Hard candies, jam, syrup, sherbet • Light tub margarine • Mayonnaise • Pickles • Regular salad dressing • Soya sauce • Vegetable oils	• Butter • Candy bars • Chocolate • Lard • Stick margarine
Restaurant fare	• Bean burritos • Bean salad • Chicken or vegetable fajitas • Spaghetti with tomato sauce • Turkey, vegetable, or chicken sandwich • Stir-fried vegetables or chicken with rice • Perogies • Garden salad with chicken chunks and light dressing • Pizza, cheeseless • Hummus with pita	• Beef or chicken burritos • Chicken Caesar salad • Chicken chow mein • Chicken taco • Ham or roast beef sandwich • Peanut butter and jam sandwich • Spaghetti with meatballs • Garlic shrimp • Tuna or chicken salad sandwich • Club sandwich	• Beef taco • BLT sandwich • Chicken pot pie • Chili • Croissant sandwich • Fettuccini Alfredo • Grilled cheese sandwich • Hamburger or cheeseburger • Hot dog on a bun • Lasagna with meat • Macaroni and cheese • Pizza, except cheeseless • Shepherd's pie • Taco salad • Nachos with cheese • Poutine • King Pao chicken

Nutrition Questions and Answers

There are several issues to consider when choosing which foods to eat and when making decisions that apply to your own nutrition needs and the needs of your clients. This section attempts to highlight some of these issues, now that you understand the basis of good nutrition and a healthy diet.

Are there foods that boost our health?

Functional foods offer unique health benefits that go beyond simply meeting basic nutrient needs by helping reduce the risk of chronic disease. Foods containing antioxidants are one example of functional foods. They help protect the body from cell damage and may help repair cells if damage occurs. Antioxidants aid in preventing cell damage from such diseases as prostate cancer, heart disease, and macular degeneration (a serious eye disease). Foods containing vitamin C, vitamin E, and beta carotene (such as dark green, orange, and red vegetables) are the best examples of antioxidants.

Foods containing antioxidants, such as tomatoes, pomegranates, and blueberries, help protect the body from cell damage and may help repair cells if damage occurs.

Free Radicals and Antioxidants

Free radicals are formed as natural by-products of the conversion of oxygen into energy in the human body. Free radicals have an unpaired electron, and they try to find a match for this electron by stealing one from another molecule. This process, which is known as oxidation, causes harm to cells and literally makes our bodies rust and rot. In addition to the free radicals produced by the body's metabolism, exposure to various environmental factors such as pollution, smoke, and pesticides causes damage to our cells as well. Many foods are alleged to counteract this process. They are called **antioxidants**.

To get the best benefit of functional foods, encourage your clients to choose at least the minimum number of servings recommended for their age and gender from each of the four food groups of Canada's Food Guide. Aim for a wide variety of vegetables, fruits, whole grains, milk products, and meats and meat alternatives. By taking this approach, both you and your clients will enjoy foods that taste great, meet basic nutrient needs, and offer a supply of the bioactive compounds that promote health.

Recreation and Fitness Leadership

What are nutraceuticals?

Advances in food science now make it possible to break foods into their nutritional building blocks or parts. As a result, the health-promoting bioactive compounds found in some foods can be extracted, refined, and then sold as purified preparations, or what food scientists call **nutraceuticals**, a take-off on the word *pharmaceutical*.

Bioactive compounds can also be added to foods to enhance health. Breads, pastas, and cereals made using flax seeds or flax meal are one example of this approach to food production. Flax is a source of omega-3 fatty acids, a type of fat that may contribute to maintenance of heart health as well as brain development and vision.

Probiotics are an example of a nutraceutical. Probiotics are health-promoting micro-organisms, similar to those that are normally found in the intestines. Probiotic supplements are concentrated preparations of these micro-organisms that are taken to help prevent or treat disease. They are available in liquid and capsule form, may be added to foods, and in many parts of the world are routinely used as remedies for problems such as diarrhea. Probiotics have also been linked to enhanced immunity.

It is expected that interest in nutraceuticals will continue to grow. Although more research is needed to fully explain the role of foods or food components in preventing and treating disease, it is clear that what we eat affects our health.

Probiotics are health-promoting micro-organisms that may be added to foods to help strengthen the immune system.

Are vitamin or mineral supplements necessary?

If a person's diet is balanced and has adequate variety, most nutritionists agree that the need for supplements is low or nonexistent. A pill cannot turn a deficient diet into a healthy one. Many people use supplements as nutritional insurance to make sure they get all the nutrients they need, but there is no reason why most people can't obtain the vitamins and minerals they need from a healthy, balanced diet.

Yet the supplement industry would have us believe that their products are absolutely essential and offer incredible benefits. Here are some of the claims made by supplement manufacturers that are meaningless and in some cases illegal: weight control, high potency, more antioxidants, diabetic formula, active formula, stress formula. There is no solid evidence that any vitamin or herb makes you more energetic or boosts athletic performance.

That being said, there are several special cases where vitamin and mineral supplementation should be considered:

▶ Women with excessive bleeding during menstruation may need iron.

▶ Pregnant or breastfeeding women require iron, folate (also known as folic acid or folacin), and calcium (inadequate amounts of folate during pregnancy have been linked to birth defects called neural tube defects).

*Most people have heard about the importance of adequate **folate** intake for pregnant women. What they might not know is that folate is known by a few other names, including **folic acid** and **folacin**.*

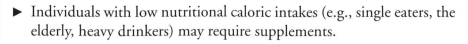

► Individuals with low nutritional caloric intakes (e.g., single eaters, the elderly, heavy drinkers) may require supplements.

► Some vegetarians may need calcium, iron, zinc, and vitamin B_{12}.

► People with certain illnesses, with impaired immune systems, or taking medication may need supplements.

► People who spend their winters in Canada may need vitamin D (see the box *Cancer Society Recommends Vitamin D Supplementation*).

If your clients choose to use nutrient supplements, help them do some research. Overdosing on water-soluble vitamins (e.g., B and C) is not hazardous, but it is a waste of money. Overdosing on fat-soluble vitamins (A, D, E, and K) can be dangerous since they accumulate in the body. Realize, too, that generic vitamins are just as good as brand-name nationally advertised products. They are made in the same factories. Encourage your clients to compare labels for content and go with the lowest price.

Cancer Society Recommends Vitamin D Supplementation

Because of the growing body of evidence that vitamin D substantially lowers the risk of a number of cancers, the Canadian Cancer Society is now making the following recommendations:

• Adults living in Canada should consider taking vitamin D supplementation of 1,000 international units (IU) each day during the fall and winter.

• Adults at higher risk of having lower vitamin D levels should consider taking vitamin D supplementation of 1,000 IU each day all year round. This includes people who are older, who have dark skin, who don't go outside often, and who wear clothing that covers most of their skin.

• At this time, the Canadian Cancer Society does not have a recommendation for vitamin D supplementation for children. Although humans can absorb vitamin D when ultraviolet rays from the sun trigger vitamin D synthesis in the skin, the Cancer Society is not changing its SunSense guidelines, as skin cancer is the most frequently diagnosed cancer in Canada.

Can diet make a fitness program more effective?

What advice should a fitness professional give to a client who says, "Now that I'm doing a 60-minute aerobics class, I have no energy about 45 minutes into the session. What can I do about it?"

Advanced fitness enthusiasts going for longer runs and taking longer classes can take some hints from the world of marathon sports. These clients may want to eat extra carbohydrates in the 48 hours before a demanding workout, a strategy called "carbohydrate loading." There should be at least a 2-hour gap between their last small meal and the beginning of the exercise session to allow for food to pass into the intestines and avoid stomach upset. Eating a lot of carbohydrate-rich foods immediately after the exercise (within 30 minutes) will replenish glycogen storage (energy stored within the muscles) and speed recovery.

Your clients may want to try sports drinks if their activity lasts more than an hour. Sports drinks will replenish electrolytes lost through sweating. If the exercise session is less than an hour, remind clients to drink water before, during, and after the session.

When it comes to diet, the only precaution about fat and exercise is the timing. Fatty foods take longer to digest. Digestion may take up to 4 hours for a meal that has a lot of fat. This should be taken into account when planning meals around activity times.

What about protein supplements?

High-protein meals such as steak were once a longstanding tradition in many sports, probably as a result of the belief that "eating muscle" helps an athlete develop muscle. This idea is still often seen in the weight training community, where protein and amino acid supplements are far too common. The truth is that amino acids, the compounds from which proteins are made, cannot be stored in the body. In fact, when an excess of protein is ingested, the body just eliminates it, placing increased demands on the kidneys.

Regardless of popular media reports that consuming large quantities of certain amino acids may improve strength, there is no advantage to consuming large quantities of protein supplements. Athletes can make greater performance improvements by determining how much protein they need and working to meet this requirement through a healthy diet. Finding the truth in advertisements can be difficult, especially for those eager to do almost anything to build muscle, look stronger, or increase power. By knowing what the body does with proteins and amino acids, your clients can evaluate claims about high-protein programs and amino acid supplements and decide if the cost is worth it.

How Much Protein Is Enough?

The average adult should eat 0.8 g/kg of body weight (0.36 g/lb of body weight) of protein per day, or about 54 grams for a person weighing 68 kg (150 pounds). This allowance is more than adequate for persons of average activity. But athletes who train intensively (e.g., every day) do require more protein. According to one study, elite runners require 1.67 times this level because blood cells are crushed from the pounding of foot against ground and need to be replaced. Bodybuilders need 1.12 times this level. At these levels, a 68-kg runner would need to eat 90 grams of protein, while a 68-kg bodybuilder would need 60 grams of protein.

Even at these higher levels, most athletes who eat a balanced diet should have little difficulty getting enough protein. A 3-ounce portion of roasted white chicken meat (likely just half the amount consumed at a typical meal) contains 26 grams of protein, while a half-cup of low-fat cottage cheese weighs in at 14 grams. Beans average about 15 grams per cup, pasta contains 5 grams per cup, and bagels pack 5 to 10 grams of protein each depending on size and variety. Unless an athlete avoids all legume, meat, dairy, and egg products, his diet will already contain a solid protein foundation. Vegetarians and those following special dietary restrictions can meet their requirements by identifying the high-protein foods they can eat and planning meals around these foods.

Do ergogenic aids work? Are they safe?

Dietary supplements fall under a larger category called ergogenic aids. An **ergogenic aid** is any food, substance, chemical, or training method that helps the body work harder, perform better, and recover faster. Only a few are safe and useful. Others have not been proven to be safe or even useful but have caught on through "word of mouth" or aggressive advertising. Many are harmful to the pocketbook. Several are banned in amateur and professional sport as giving an unfair advantage. Some are even life-threatening.

Participants are always looking for a "magic bullet," a way to make their progress to fitness, weight loss or gain, or athletic success easier. As a fitness leader, you have a role to play in recommending safe methods and warning against useless, harmful, and illegal ones. Some of the more popular allowed and banned substances are described here.

Creatine

Creatine is a natural compound created from three amino acids. It is found in red meats, poultry, and fish and is also produced in the body by the liver and kidneys. It plays an important role in producing energy for explosive, powerful movements such as jumping, sprinting, and lifting heavy weights.

One of the most popular nutritional supplements on the market today, creatine is sold in its supplemental form (creatine monohydrate, or CrH_2O) and comes in powder, tablet, capsule, and liquid form. Marketers claim that it increases muscle mass in just two weeks; it is therefore attractive to those seeking to quickly build a muscular physique. Most of this mass is attributed to water retention, however, and creatine only marginally improves performance in high-intensity activities. In fact, muscle mass or bulk may be detrimental to proper technique. Creatine has no significant effect on aerobic endurance, although it will increase power during aerobic exercise. For reasons that are not known at this time, some people do not respond to creatine supplementation.

The most common side effect associated with creatine, even at very low doses, is diarrhea. High doses produce stomach cramps, nausea, weakness, and dizziness. A person encouraged by increased muscle mass may overtrain, and muscle cramping or strained ligaments and tendons can result. The strained tendons occur because the tissues have not had time to adjust to the increased intensity of the workouts. High doses, such as 20 grams per day, used regularly for a few weeks can potentially cause kidney damage and place stress on the liver. There are no studies on the effects of long-term use. It is not recommended for use by those under 16 years of age. Some authorities see creatine as a safe alternative to the use of steroids, however, and suggest that a minimal dose of 2 to 4 grams per day during one sports season could be acceptable for older teens.

Creatine supplementation is not considered doping and is not banned by any professional or amateur sports governing bodies, including the IOC. In the United States, the NCAA recently ruled that colleges could not provide creatine supplements to their players, although the players are still allowed to obtain and use creatine independently. In some countries, such as France, creatine is banned.

Ephedra

Ephedra, an extract of the Chinese plant Ma Huang, stimulates the cardiovascular and central nervous systems. It is found in numerous weight-loss, fat-burner, energy-boosting, and bodybuilding products. Known risks associated with ephedra are elevated blood pressure, abnormal cardiac rhythms, heart palpitations, heart attacks, psychosis, seizures, stroke, and death. Health Canada has approved ephedra only for

*A*lthough creatine supplementation has shown benefits for developing muscle mass, it has also been associated with a host of side effects, including diarrhea, stomach cramps, nausea, weakness, and dizziness.

*E*phedra is used by millions of people for weight loss and as an energy booster. This herbal supplement was implicated in the death of 23-year-old pitcher Steve Bechler – a pitching prospect for the Baltimore Orioles – in 2003.

short-term use in some nasal decongestants. Supplements that contain both ephedra and a stimulant or that are marketed for bodybuilding or weight loss are not authorized by Health Canada. However, these products are sold routinely over the Internet and in health food stores at concentrations far exceeding the recommended dose for the purposes noted here. Often it is found mixed with other ingredients. People working in the fitness field must educate their clients about the dangers of ephedra.

Steroids

Anabolic steroids are a group of powerful drugs or compounds that duplicate the function of the male sex hormone testosterone. They are used medically to treat certain kinds of anemia, severe burns, endocrine problems, and some types of breast cancer.

Bodybuilders and professional and amateur athletes use steroids to give them a competitive advantage. Research has shown that anabolic steroids increase lean muscle mass, strength, and the ability to train longer and harder. However, research also indicates that steroid use comes at a huge cost to health because it generates numerous harmful side effects, as shown in Figure 9.5. For adolescents using steroids, growth may be stunted through premature skeletal maturation and accelerated puberty changes. The consequences certainly outweigh any potential performance benefits.

Anabolic steroids are either taken orally or injected in cycles of weeks or months, rather than continuously. Multiple types of steroids are often combined to maximize their effectiveness while minimizing negative effects, a process known as stacking.

The use of anabolic steroids by athletes is contrary to the rules and ethical principles of athletic competition as set by the IOC and all international and national sports governing bodies.

Caffeine

Commonly found in coffee beans, tea leaves, cocoa beans, cola nuts, chocolate, and so-called energy drinks (e.g., Red Bull), **caffeine** is a stimulant of the central nervous system. It is the most commonly taken drug to increase alertness, but it has two applications to fitness training as well. It can aid a participant who wants to work out longer before becoming fatigued, and it increases fat burning during aerobic exercise. It does this by enhancing the release and use of free fatty acids, thus conserving glycogen stores in the muscle. Caffeine is also a diuretic and hence should not be used to replace water as a deterrent against dehydration. Because some individuals react negatively to caffeine, its use as an ergogenic aid should be controlled and introduced on a trial basis only.

Recreation and Fitness Leadership

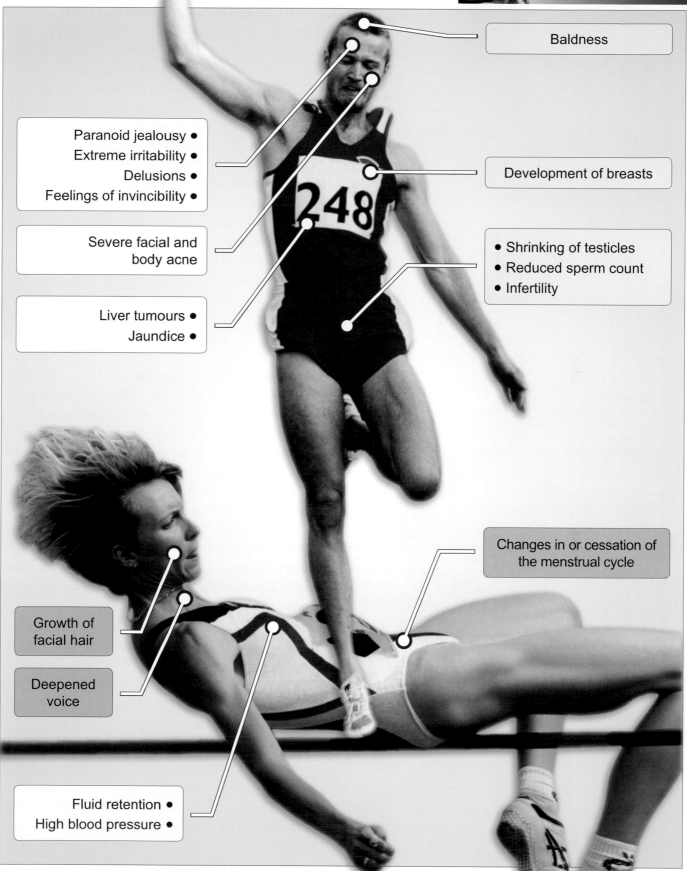

Baldness

Paranoid jealousy ●
Extreme irritability ●
Delusions ●
Feelings of invincibility ●

Development of breasts

Severe facial and
body acne

● Shrinking of testicles
● Reduced sperm count
● Infertility

Liver tumours ●
Jaundice ●

Changes in or cessation of
the menstrual cycle

Growth of
facial hair

Deepened
voice

Fluid retention ●
High blood pressure ●

Figure 9.5 The major health-related harmful side effects of anabolic steroid use to men (indicated in blue), women (indicated in purple), and users in general (indicated in yellow).

Is vegetarianism a healthy alternative?

Some people choose to eliminate or restrict meat and other animal-derived foods in their diets for various reasons (e.g., philosophical, health, environmental). A **vegetarian** diet can provide the necessary nutrients required by the body if a few rules are followed (children and pregnant women require special individual guidance). In fact, a well-planned vegetarian diet can offer immense benefits to adults and can lead to better health.

Vegetarians are often placed under one broad heading, but there are several types. Vegans restrict their diets to plant foods; lacto-vegetarians also eat plant foods but include dairy products; lacto-ovo-vegetarians choose to eat plant foods and dairy products as well as eggs; finally, semi-vegetarians eat plant foods, dairy products, eggs, and usually a small selection of poultry, fish, or other seafood. Those vegetarian diets that offer a wider variety make it easier to meet nutrition requirements. Although there is relatively little risk associated with the others, a vegan diet requires a higher degree of nutritional understanding to avoid malnourishment.

One potential concern is whether a vegan diet includes sources of all the essential amino acids because no single plant source contains all of them. However, a careful combination of high-quality nonmeat complementary proteins (proteins that supply the essential amino acids missing in each other) can prevent amino acid deficiencies. Examples include black beans and rice, peanut butter and wheat bread, and tofu and stir-fried vegetables with rice. Other potential difficulties include maintaining adequate intakes of vitamin B_{12}, calcium, iron, and zinc, as well as a concern about satiation (satisfaction of hunger). Early satiation as a result of large amounts of fibre in the diet may lead to a decrease in carbohydrate intake.

It takes planning and common sense to put together a vegetarian diet that works. If any of your clients are vegetarians or are considering adopting a vegetarian diet, stress the importance of eating a variety of foods and planning ahead to ensure that their nutrition needs are adequately met.

Although no single plant source contains all the essential amino acids, a carefully planned combination of complementary proteins can help strict vegetarians avoid amino acid deficiencies.

How bad is fast food, really?

The term "fast food" is synonymous with greasy, high-fat foods that have little or no nutritional value. But unlike junk foods, the nutritional value of fast foods prepared in walk-in or drive-through restaurants can vary immensely (Table 9.8). Still, the amount of trans and saturated fat found in most fast foods (especially those that are fried) – along with their high salt content – makes consumption of these foods something to enjoy in moderation.

Table 9.8 Selected fast food facts.

Food	Calories	Protein (g)	Carbohydrate (g)	Fat (g)	Calories from Fat (%)	Cholesterol (mg)	Sodium (mg)
Hamburgers							
McDonald's hamburger	250	12	32	8	28.8	25	510
McDonald's Big Mac	540	24	44	29	48.3	70	1020
Dairy Queen single hamburger with cheese	400	22	35	19	42.8	60	880
Wendy's junior bacon cheeseburger	400	21	26	24	54	65	900
Burger King Whopper	670	28	48	40	53.7	80	970
Chicken							
Arby's crispy chicken sandwich	530	23	54	25	42.5	50	1960
Burger King original chicken sandwich	680	23	50	43	56.9	70	1430
Dairy Queen crispy chicken sandwich	530	23	50	28	47.5	125	1250
KFC crispy strips (three)	330	27	21	15	40.9	60	1200
Others							
McDonald's Filet-O-Fish	410	16	38	20	43.9	45	580
Arby's classic roast beef sandwich	340	22	35	13	34.4	45	930
McDonald's French fries (small)	220	2	30	11	45	0	170
Wendy's French fries (small)	320	4	41	15	42.2	0	360
Drinks							
Dairy Queen vanilla shake (small)	530	12	80	18	30	50	210
McDonald's vanilla shake (small)	540	11	95	13	21.7	55	330
Coca-Cola (small)	150	—	39	—	—	—	5
Diet Coke (small)	1	—	0	—	—	—	20
Sprite (small)	140	—	35	—	—	—	30
Barq's root beer (small)	160	—	41	—	—	—	35

The picture is not all bad, however. In response to consumer demand, fast food restaurants have recently extended their menus to include salads, lower-fat meats, whole wheat breads, and lower-fat milk products. Nutrition information is also provided by the larger restaurants. Switching from frying with lard (animal fat) and low-grade hydrogenated fats to healthier fats has been a big improvement. Although an excess of fast food consumption as a primary source of nutrition is undoubtedly unwise (and expensive), it can offer variety and convenience.

What's the scoop on sugar? And sugar substitutes?

*Although sugar itself does not make us fat, sugary foods also tend to be high in fat and calories, which **can** make us fat.*

Many of us crave sugar but believe it is detrimental to good health. Sugar is often linked with fatness, despite research showing that fat people do not consume more sugar than do thin people. However, sugar can create a unique dilemma – while sugar itself does not make us fat, sugary foods in our diets also tend to be high in fat and calories, which *can* make us fat. And any calories consumed beyond body needs are inevitably stored as fat.

What about the effects of sugar on children's behaviour? Does sugar consumption increase hyperactivity, delinquency, or learning disorders in children? Although these are popular beliefs held by many, there is no evidence that clearly validates these claims.

The primary health problem linked to sugar is tooth decay (dental caries) – a problem that can be effectively combatted by regular brushing and flossing and dental checkups. It is worth noting that eating sweets with other foods is less damaging to the teeth, as a result of increased saliva and foods that buffer the acid effect in the mouth.

Alternatives to sugar are non-nutritive sweeteners (Table 9.9), which don't provide calories and don't influence blood sugar levels. All sweeteners available in Canada go through rigorous testing. Once they have been approved, it means they are suitable for use by all Canadians, including those with diabetes.

How do nutrition needs change as we age?

It should come as no surprise that nutrition needs change as we age. The main factors that account for this are the physiological changes that accompany the aging process, diseases that affect nutrition directly or indirectly, and psychosocial factors. We now look at these individually.

Aging leads to a drop in activity, a lower metabolic rate, and lower energy requirements. This in turn often leads to less food intake among

Table 9.9 Non-nutritive sweeteners, sugar substitutes, and artificial sweeteners.

Chemical Name	Brand Name(s)	Availability	Sweetness Compared with Sugar	Suitability for Baking and Cooking
Acesulfame Potassium (AceK)	Sunett	Beverages, fruit spreads, baked goods, dessert bases, tabletop sweetener, hard candy, chewing gum, breath fresheners	200x	Yes
Aspartame	Equal NutraSweet	Powdered tabletop sweetener, breakfast cereals, soft drinks, desserts, candy	200x	No
Cyclamate	Sucaryl Sugar Twin Weight Watchers	Tabletop sweetener Added to medications	30x	Yes
Saccharin	Hermesetas	Tabletop sweetener	300x	No
Steviol glycosides	N/A	Tabletop sweeteners, breakfast cereals, beverages, breath fresheners, chewing gum, dessert mixes, fruit spreads, baking mixes, confectioneries	200 – 300x	Yes
Sucralose	Splenda	Tabletop sweetener Found in many processed foods	600x	Yes

the elderly. Still, although the need for calories declines, the need for vitamins and minerals still remains vital. Not only do many elderly people have a decreased appetite, but changes in teeth, salivary glands, taste buds, and oral muscles make it harder to chew and make eating less pleasurable.

A variety of diseases and disorders can significantly affect the nutrition of older adults. Dental problems, swallowing disorders, mood disorders (e.g., depression), and gastrointestinal disorders are commonplace. But elderly individuals also suffer from chronic infections more regularly, and many must deal with musculoskeletal problems that indirectly affect nutrition (e.g., eating with arthritic hands can be a real challenge).

Perhaps psychological factors are the most overlooked influence on nutrition in the older adult. Social isolation, poverty, and transportation limitations are all factors that may change the enjoyment and ease with which foods are prepared and consumed.

Whom can you trust for nutrition information and counselling?

The professionals in the world of nutrition are the people with *R.D.*, registered dietitian, behind their names. The titles registered dietitian, professional dietitian, and dietitian are protected by law through provincial legislation and are awarded only to qualified practitioners who have met education qualifications. These professionals have completed a four-year university degree in nutrition; are members of their provincial regulatory bodies; and work in hospitals, health care institutions, government food agencies, food companies, and private practice.

People who have completed university degree programs in exercise science are also well versed in nutrition and can counsel their fitness clients about all aspects of the topic. The Canadian Fitness Professionals Association certifies nutrition and wellness specialists who have taken a 22-hour course and passed an exam. These people can provide nutrition advice, weight management counselling, stress management solutions, lifestyle consulting, a broad approach to well-being, and referrals to nutrition and wellness professionals, such as people with the much more extensive credentials outlined already. In Canada, dietitians are the only ones qualified to develop detailed daily menus for individuals and groups.

In some U.S. states, the term *nutritionist* is equivalent to the term *registered dietitian*, and a master's or PhD is required to be registered as a nutritionist. In Canada, many health food store owners call themselves nutritionists, and although they may be well informed, they also have an agenda – to sell their products.

Putting It All Together

Plenty of information about nutrition and healthy eating is available, and it is your job to help your clients sort through the facts and the fallacies. Registered dietitians, certified professionals, and exercise science graduates can provide information and develop programs. Fortunately, the Canadian government has produced excellent print resources as well.

Understanding nutrition is the key to understanding the rationale behind the guidelines presented by Canada's Food Guide. Following the

There are numerous reputable print and online nutrition resources. Look for ones that do not accept support or advertising from members of the food and drug industry.

- Agriculture in the Classrom Canada – an informal network of provincial AITC organizations working together to enhance the knowledge, understanding, and appreciation of agriculture in everyday life

- Canadian Diabetic Association – provides accurate and up-to-date health information and education for people with diabetes

- Dietitians of Canada – the national association for professional dietitians in Canada

- Eat Right Ontario – offers feature articles on food and nutrition, meal planning advice, healthy eating tips, and recipes

- Health Canada – responsible for establishing policies, setting standards, and providing advice and information on the safety and nutritional value of food

- Healthy Canadians – Health Canada initiative to provide access to specific healthy living social marketing campaigns

- National Eating Disorder Information Centre – promotes healthy lifestyles, including both healthy eating and appropriate, enjoyable exercise

- Teach Nutrition – a site created by registered dietitians for teachers in Ontario, Quebec, Nova Scotia, New Brunswick, and Prince Edward Island

Guide's recommendations about which foods to eat and how much will ensure a healthy diet.

There are many products that can be ingested in hopes of improving fitness, performance, or body image. The facts and cautions presented here will help you give your clients sound advice. The dietary needs of vegetarians and the older population provide interesting challenges.

Key Terms

amino acids	creatine
anabolic steroids	dehydration
antioxidants	ephedra
caffeine	ergogenic aid
Canada's Food Guide	fats
carbohydrates	fat-soluble vitamins
cholesterol	fibre
coenzymes	free radicals
complete proteins	functional foods

glycemic index
glycogen
high-density lipoprotein (HDL)
hydrogenation
incomplete proteins
insoluble fibre
low-density lipoprotein (LDL)
macronutrients
micronutrients
minerals
nutraceuticals
nutrition
probiotics
proteins

saturated fats
soluble fibre
starches
sugars
trace elements
trans fat
triglycerides
unsaturated fats
vegetarian
very low-density lipoprotein
   (VLDL)
vitamins
water-soluble vitamins

Review Questions

1. Create a graphic organizer to help you remember the macronutrients and micronutrients that make up a healthy diet.

2. List the calorie densities of the three classes of macronutrients.

3. Distinguish between the health impacts of five different kinds of fat.

4. Give four examples with serving sizes for each food group in Canada's Food Guide.

5. Explain the function of antioxidant foods.

6. When are vitamin and mineral supplements necessary for health?

7. Rate and discuss the relative safety of these popular ergogenic aids: protein, anabolic steroids, ephedra, creatine.

8. Describe the different vegetarian diets. Which type puts you at the most risk for nutrient deficiencies?

9. What are the healthiest food choices at your favourite three fast food restaurants?

10. What factors affect the nutrition of older adults?

Recreation and Fitness Leadership

CAREER PROFILE

NAME: Melissa Archer
OCCUPATION: Recreation Assistant, Victoria Manor Nursing Home
EDUCATION: Activation Coordinator (Gerontology), George Brown College

▶ What do you do?

As recreation assistant in the Life Enrichment Department, I plan and implement programs to meet the physical, emotional, social, intellectual, and spiritual needs of our elderly residents. Some of these programs are ongoing, such as Fun and Fitness, Tai Chi, Sit and Dance, therapy walking, Trivia and Tea, and men's groups; some are special events, such as Caribbean Days, Victorian teas, and so on. I not only work with groups but also give individual attention, visiting one-on-one to chat and help residents with their personal concerns. Another one of my tasks is coordinating the many community and high school volunteers who assist us.

▶ Why did you choose a career in gerontology?

My volunteer work at a seniors' facility during high school led to a part-time job as a receptionist, so I came to know a lot about nursing homes and knew that I enjoyed being around older people.

▶ What are the future job prospects in the field? Where is it heading?

Gerontology is not a profession the average student even thinks about, so there is a great need for people trained to work with the elderly in the many nursing homes that are being built as the population ages. Salaries and benefits are better in larger centres and government-operated facilities.

▶ What do you enjoy most about your profession?

I learn so much from the residents. They are so wise and experienced in life, and their stories amaze me. It is so interesting to hear about their experiences, such as bringing up a family in a different era, wartime, travel, and so on. The residents are really appreciative of the programs I lead and the interest I take in them. I know I am doing something worthwhile, whether helping someone write a letter or polish her nails or exercise his mind and body. I

feel I am a "life enricher," and my job is one of the most rewarding parts of my life.

▶ What other career options are available to students interested in working with the elderly?

The field is huge, with jobs in nursing, administration, food service/nutrition, recreation, occupational therapy, physiotherapy, and so on, in private and government-run nursing homes and adult day care programs. You could focus on assessing the elderly to establish what level of care or assistance they need, or you might specialize in the psychology of the elderly. To further your career you could pursue a university degree in gerontology, and you will get some exemptions if you completed the college program.

▶ What career advice would you give to students interested in entering this field?

Volunteer in a nursing home to see if you feel comfortable around older people. The college admissions boards look very favourably on a record of related volunteer work in your application.

In This Chapter:

CHAPTER 10
Vitality, Health, and Weight Management

In this chapter, you will learn about the following:

❶ Supporting others in shifting from an emphasis on weight control to an emphasis on a healthy lifestyle

❷ Supporting others in making appropriate revisions to their eating habits and activity levels

❸ Using body composition as a guide to goal setting

❹ Recognizing disordered eating patterns

❺ The concept of caloric balance for weight control

> **"Life is not merely to be alive, but to be well."**
> **Marcus Valerius Martialis**

Overheard in a high school locker room . . .

Sammy: My doctor is concerned about my blood sugar level. She says I have to eat healthier, cut out junk food, and get more exercise or I could develop type 2 diabetes. I have to lose 20 pounds.

Tommy: I know what you mean! My physician says my blood tests show I am at risk for heart disease, and my blood pressure is a bit elevated. I have to take gym class every day, join a fitness club next semester, and cut down on the fats in my diet.

Despite the efforts of many people, organizations, and government agencies, the state of health in Canada is clearly in crisis and in need of sound remedies. On the one hand, we live in an environment where physical activity has been engineered out of day-to-day life. We have become a nation of fans, as sports are considered the domain of the athletically gifted. Our sedentary lifestyles and poor eating habits have drastically increased the occurrence of obesity. Collectively, we have grown fatter over the years. Too many children and young adults are facing an epidemic of numerous obesity-related diseases, a situation that was unheard of just a generation ago.

On the other hand, disordered eating patterns and reliance on substances that claim to reduce appetite, "burn fat," or build muscle are on the rise, as the media bombard us with images of "ideal" male and female bodies as the norms that anyone can and should strive for. The pressure on girls and women to be model thin has led to the prevalence of dieting, disordered eating patterns, and even clinical eating disorders. For males, the pressure to achieve a muscular masculine physique drives the abuse of expensive supplements.

Why can't we get it right? What's keeping us from achieving and maintaining a healthy weight?

Vitality

Ask a person how he is feeling and you will get a response that relates to **vitality**. He feels "well" or "so-so" or "lousy." Delve further and you will find out that he is feeling "energized," "could be better," or "listless"; he slept well or poorly; he looked in the mirror that morning and liked what he did or didn't see. These self-reports lack scientific validity yet are the meat of what vitality is all about: having energy, feeling great, sleeping well, having a good appetite, and feeling confident about one's appearance and capabilities.

What feelings were aroused the last time you looked in the mirror?

The vitality concept grew out of Health Canada's strategy to promote healthy body weight. This strategy recommends focusing on health-enhancing behaviours to achieve and maintain a healthy weight, rather than focusing on weight alone. Vitality's educational materials provide health, nutrition, and fitness professionals and leaders in schools, workplaces, and communities with opportunities to take a more holistic approach by moving beyond weight control, calorie-restricted diets, and prescriptive exercise regimes.

The vitality approach encourages people to

► choose to meet the body's energy and nutrient requirements through a lifetime of healthy, enjoyable eating;

► discover and pursue physical activities they find useful, pleasurable, and satisfying;

► take charge of their lives and accept and respect themselves; and

► be critical of media messages that focus on unrealistic physiques as symbols of success and happiness.

Underlying the vitality message is the concept that one's weight on a scale should not be the sole criterion by which health is measured. The goal is to convince people to make a few changes in their diets and add more activity to their lifestyles.

Metabolic Health

Metabolic health is a relatively new term in the fitness lexicon. It refers to healthy blood levels of fat and glucose (see the box *From Your Doctor's Files*, page 193) and a healthy blood pressure. In a healthy person, blood sugar levels stay relatively steady throughout the day and within normal limits. People who are "insulin resistant," however, don't respond normally to insulin (the hormone that regulates blood sugar), resulting in abnormal amounts of glucose in the blood.

Although it is observed more often in overweight people than in thin people, a person does not have to be obese to be insulin resistant. Genes do play a factor, but the major causes of insulin resistance (also known as "metabolic syndrome") are lack of exercise and consuming a diet low in fibre and high in refined sugar and fat (especially fat from meat, dairy, and bakery products).

Insulin resistance is associated with a high risk for type 2 diabetes and cardiovascular disease. Cardiovascular disease is the number one killer of Canadians, and type 2 diabetes is one of the fastest growing

Insulin resistance can become a long-term issue for people who consume a diet low in fibre and high in refined sugar and fat.

chronic diseases in the country. Formerly called adult-onset diabetes, type 2 diabetes is a lifelong illness in which the body cannot effectively use the insulin it produces. The condition usually develops in middle age, but an alarming number of young people are now being diagnosed with the disease. Diabetes carries an increased risk of heart attack, stroke, blindness, kidney failure, nerve damage, and foot problems (often leading to amputation).

*Formerly called adult-onset diabetes, **type 2 diabetes** is a lifelong illness in which the body cannot effectively use the insulin it produces. It is also associated with a host of cardiovascular and other conditions.*

From Your Doctor's Files

High blood sugar (hyperglycemia) refers to greater than normal levels of glucose in the blood. Symptoms include thirst, frequent urination, hunger, sudden unexplained weight loss, and fatigue. These symptoms are what prompt a person to visit a doctor for a diagnosis, which is usually diabetes.

Low blood sugar (hypoglycemia) is a condition in which blood glucose levels drop too low. Symptoms may include sweating, trembling, hunger, dizziness, moodiness, confusion, blurred vision, and nausea. Pulse is increased. People with diabetes experience these symptoms when they skip a meal or exercise too long. The remedy is a readily digestible snack such as orange juice.

How Are Vitality and Health Linked?

As just mentioned, the major causes of insulin resistance are lack of exercise and consuming a high-fat, high-calorie, and low-fibre diet. This is where the vitality approach comes in. Convincing your clients to make a few significant changes in their diets and to add more activity to their lifestyles can have a rapid and significant effect on their blood pressure and blood test results. Lifestyle changes can bring about substantial improvements in a matter of weeks, with or without weight loss. Over time, these changes can significantly reduce the risk of developing insulin resistance and its associated conditions. The achievement of "metabolic fitness" does not require having a lean body, nor does it depend on having the cardiovascular system of an endurance athlete. Eating well and exercising regularly are the keys to metabolic fitness.

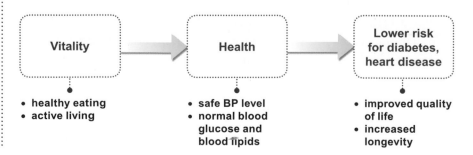

Vitality	→	Health	→	Lower risk for diabetes, heart disease
• healthy eating • active living		• safe BP level • normal blood glucose and blood lipids		• improved quality of life • increased longevity

Recreation and Fitness Leadership

A Teenager's Story: Living with Diabetes

Nothing has changed my life as much as my diagnosis of diabetes. Apart from having to prick my finger four times a day to check my blood sugar level and inject myself with insulin, there have been so many other changes I wouldn't even have thought of. I can't sleep in on the weekends because I have to eat my meals on time. I'm always the designated driver because I'm not allowed to drink alcohol. I need to carry extra food with me at all times in case something happens that keeps me from being at home for a meal, or in case I get too much exercise and my blood sugar level drops. My sister is annoyed with me because we never have her favourite sugar-coated cereal or home baking in the house any more. And then I worry about the consequences if I can't keep my blood sugar level normal and constant. It scares me that I might go blind or need to have my feet amputated.

Assessing Vitality

You can make judgments about a client's need for lifestyle changes through personal record keeping and questionnaires (Table 10.1 and 10.2). In addition, focused discussions and your own observations of your client's behaviour will give you a starting point. Once you have gathered this information, the next step is to evaluate your findings.

Healthy eating can be evaluated using the food group method outlined in Canada's Food Guide (see Chapter 9). Activity levels can be assessed by comparing them with the recommendations of Canada's Physical Activity Guide and public health programs such as ParticipACTION. Since people are generally open and honest about how they rate their bodies, and it is a subjective opinion, it is easy to determine their level of body image satisfaction by simply asking them.

Measurements of body mass, body composition, and body proportions help determine if a person's body image dissatisfaction is justified or not. These results may even indicate that the person has no need to make any lifestyle changes. In any case, the information gleaned from these assessment strategies is essential for helping your client set goals.

*P*ublic health programs such as ParticipACTION can help you and your clients assess activity levels.

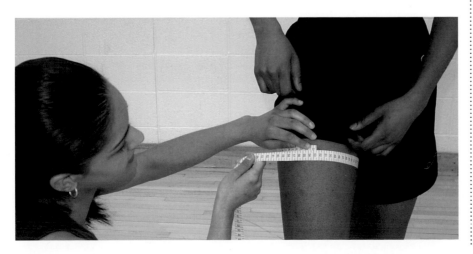

Measurements of body mass, body composition, and body proportions can help identify and focus your client's goals and needs for lifestyle changes.

Table 10.1 Nutrition self-analysis: Reflecting on your nutrition.

Issue	How About You?	Usually Sometimes Never	Why It's Important
Limiting fat intake	Do you limit your intake of high-fat foods (chocolate bars, doughnuts, muffins, granola bars)? Do you use fat-free or low-fat salad dressings?		Each gram of fat produces twice as much energy as a gram of carbohydrate or protein – it is twice as hard to burn off! **Note:** You need some fat because it carries vitamins A, D, E, and K; keeps your skin from drying out; and aids the immune system.
Limiting salt intake	Do you limit your intake of high-fat, salty snacks (potato chips, cheese sticks, corn chips)?		Salt can increase blood pressure.
Limiting saturated fat intake	Do you use margarine instead of butter? Do you trim the fat from beef, pork, and chicken? Do you drink skim or 1 percent milk? Do you limit your intake of bacon, sausage, bologna, cold cuts, hotdogs?		Fats from animal sources contain saturated fats, which can build up plaques inside blood vessels, causing heart attacks, strokes, and high blood pressure.
Limiting trans fat intake	Do you limit the number of manufactured cookies, cakes, and crackers you eat?		Trans fat is even worse than saturated fat! Many companies are changing to healthier fats – look on the labels.
Using healthy fats	Do you cook with olive or canola oil? Do you eat salmon, tuna, or mackerel regularly?		Monounsaturated fats counteract the build-up of fatty plaques in arteries. So do the omega-3 fats in coldwater fish (along with offering many other benefits).
Getting the vitamins, minerals, and fibre you need	Do you eat 5 to 10 servings of fruits and vegetables each day? Do you eat whole grain breads and pastas?		Your body functions better when all the micronutrients are present – they act as catalysts. Fruits, veggies, and whole grains also aid in digestion, preventing constipation.
Preventing osteoporosis	Do you eat calcium-rich foods each day (dairy products, fortified orange juice, broccoli)? Do you do weight-bearing exercise every day (walking, dancing, playing sports)?		You build your bones until you are 30. After that you only maintain them. Aging and menopause result in bone loss.
Hydrating your body	Do you drink 5 to 8 glasses of fluid each day (count water, juice, milk, tea, lemonade, soup, popsicles, coffee)?		Water is perhaps the most essential nutrient for life. Keep yourself hydrated!
Drinking nutritiously	Do you drink more milk and pure juice than pop, coffee, and tea?		Limit empty-calorie drinks, caffeine, and alcohol.
Eating regularly	Do you eat breakfast? Do you eat five or six times a day? Are your eating habits better or worse on weekends?		"A starved brain don't think too good!" Keep blood sugar levels steady to avoid that "afternoon slump."
Avoiding choking	Do you sit down to eat?		Eating on the run sets you up for choking.
Maintaining body image satisfaction	Do you weigh yourself no more than once a week? Do you have the energy and strength you need for your everyday activities? Do you discard clothes that don't fit?		Modify your eating and exercise based on how you feel, how your clothes fit, and how much of you jiggles, rather than on what the scales or BMI charts tell you. Don't obsess about your body size – it's not the most important thing about you!

Recreation and Fitness Leadership

Table 10.2 Vitality journal.

	Friday	Saturday	Sunday	Monday	Tuesday
Five-Day Vitality Record				**Name:**	
Breakfast					
Lunch					
Snack					
Dinner					
Snack					
Weight					
Activity (min)	20 40 60 >60	20 40 60 >60	20 40 60 >60	20 40 60 >60	20 40 60 >60
Mood	−− − 0 + ++	−− − 0 + ++	−− − 0 + ++	−− − 0 + ++	−− − 0 + ++
Energy	hi med low	hi med low	hi med low	hi med low	hi med low

Instructions: Enter your food at each meal, including the size of the serving. Assess your activity level, mood, and energy each day.

Assessing Eating Habits

To assess nutrition based on Canada's Food Guide, refer to the client's five-day food intake record and evaluate his daily servings from each food group. Keep in mind the serving sizes in the Food Guide. Calculate a daily average number of servings for each food group. Use this information to guide your client in following the recommendations of Canada's Food Guide more closely. Encourage the client to eat five or six small meals a day, including breakfast, to maintain steady blood sugar levels throughout the day. Suggest that he consider any food group in which he is lacking when selecting an evening snack.

Teach your client how to use the information on food labels to select foods that are lower in saturated fats, trans fats, and sodium, while higher in fibre (refer to Chapter 9). Review your client's nutrition self-analysis, and make suggestions regarding areas for improvement.

Dial a Dietitian

Ontarians can now learn how to make healthy eating choices just by picking up the phone. The toll-free EatRight Ontario telephone service, launched in 2007 by the Ministry of Health Promotion, connects people with registered dietitians who can answer any and all diet and nutrition questions. Ontarians can contact a dietitian on weekdays at 1-877-510-5102 or visit the EatRight Ontario website to submit an electronic question that will be answered within three days.

In British Columbia, HealthLink BC offers trusted health and nutrition information via telephone. Residents can call 8-1-1 on weekdays to speak with a dietitian about nutrition and healthy eating. Manitoba residents can reach a registered dietitian at 1-877-830-2892 through the province's Dial-a-Dietitian program. These services are especially valuable to people in rural communities that have few dietitians.

Assessing Active Living

Canada's Physical Activity Guide recommends that nonactive people start by accumulating 60 minutes of mild physical activity every day to maintain or improve their metabolic health. Work with your client to find ways to add enjoyable activities to her daily schedule. As the individual becomes more active, she can participate in moderate to vigorous physical exercise for 20 to 40 minutes per day on most days of the week, and real improvements in aerobic and muscular endurance will be achieved.

The intensity and duration of the activity can be modified to suit individual needs. If time is not a constraint, the duration can be emphasized while exercising at the lower end of the intensity range. Just as effective, however, is high-intensity exercise of only 20 to 30 minutes' duration. This activity can be accumulated in bursts of effort that are

Recreation and Fitness Leadership

only 10 minutes long.

Teach your client how to judge the intensity of his effort using one of two simple subjective methods (see the box *The Talk Test* and the box *Rating of Perceived Exertion Scale*). More objective measures, such as using a heart rate monitor to keep the heart rate in a target zone, are discussed in the next chapter.

The Talk Test

If you can't talk as you exercise or are completely breathless, you are exercising too hard.

If you can't say more than a few words without pausing for breath, you are exercising vigorously.

If you can carry on a conversation with little trouble, you are exercising at a moderate level.

If you can sing your favourite song, you should pick up the pace.

Rating of Perceived Exertion Scale

On a scale of 1 (no effort) to 10 (maximum effort), rate your level of exertion. This is totally dependent on your feelings, ranging from ease to breathlessness, not on the speed of the activity. Walking on level ground at a pace you feel is brisk but comfortable might be ranked a 3 or 4, while hill climbing may change your ranking to 5 or 6. A fit person will need to work harder to achieve a higher level on the RPE scale.

No exertion	1
Very light exertion	2
Light exertion	3
Moderate exertion	4
Somewhat difficult	5
Difficult	6
Hard	7
Very hard	8
Extremely hard	9
Maximum exertion	10

> "Lack of activity destroys the good condition of every human being, while movement and methodical exercise save it and preserve it."
> *Plato*

Walking for Health

Walking is one of the best exercises for general health. You can do this activity just about anywhere; it requires no special equipment other than a pair of comfortable, sturdy shoes; and it can be done with companions or alone. You can set your own pace, from a stroll to a brisk walk. As a low-impact activity, it is easier on your joints than jogging, running, or playing sports.

A recent innovation called Nordic walking makes walking an even better fitness activity. Using specially designed walking sticks similar to cross-country ski poles raises your heart rate without raising your level of perceived exertion. Nordic walking provides a total body workout that burns approximately 400 calories per hour (compared with 280 calories per hour for normal walking). It has several other advantages:

▶ Releases pain and muscle tension in the neck and shoulder region, increasing the lateral mobility of the neck and spine

▶ Compared with ordinary walking, reduces the load on knees and other joints and reduces heel strike force, making it an excellent low-impact activity

▶ Reduces balance problems for people with impaired ability

Nordic walking is a recent innovation that improves upon the fitness benefits of walking without raising your level of perceived exertion. These specially designed walking sticks offer a versatile total body workout for people of all ages and abilities.

Assessing Body Image Satisfaction

Unless you know the signs, it is easy to overlook a developing problem with body image and eating. The term **disordered eating** describes irregular and unhealthy eating patterns. Be aware of weight fluctuations, skipping meals, cutting out certain foods or food groups, or simply unusual eating habits. Listen for expressions of guilt or shame about eating, concern about body weight and shape, comparisons to others, unrealistic goals, and excessive self-criticism. Phrases such as "I feel fat and useless," "I'm such a string bean," "I hate my body," and "I shouldn't eat that" are signposts.

There is a continuum ranging from disordered eating to the clinical **eating disorders** known as anorexia nervosa and bulimia. If you think a client is developing an eating disorder, discuss it openly with her. Then refer your client to a specialist who is trained to deal with this issue. On the other hand, if your client has concerns about body shape and image without the alarming symptoms described below, you can provide facts and support.

> *Don't go out of your weigh to please anyone but yourself.*
> *Anonymous*

Anorexia Nervosa

Individuals with **anorexia nervosa** fail to eat an adequate amount of food to maintain a reasonable body weight – to the point of starvation. Anorexics have an intense fear of gaining weight or becoming fat, so they often avoid eating and may exercise compulsively to reduce body weight. They begin by restricting their intake of high-calorie foods, which eventually leads to a restriction of virtually all foods from their diet. Typically, anorexics weigh less than 85 percent of normal weight for their age and height.

The psychological problems associated with anorexia, such as depression and other clinical disorders, can be even more serious than the physical ones. Anorexia has the highest suicide rate of all the mental illnesses. But mortality usually results from damage to internal organs as the body's protein is metabolized for energy.

Anorexia nervosa is a serious condition that warrants immediate attention. The psychological impact can be even more serious than the physical one.

Bulimia Nervosa

Bulimia nervosa is characterized by continual episodes of binge eating (consuming large amounts of food over a short period of time) followed by purging (vomiting or using laxatives or diuretics to rid the body of the food). Avoiding eating in public and making trips to the bathroom immediately after eating are signs of bulimia.

Bulimia is generally considered to be less serious than anorexia, since treatment with antidepressants is effective in the majority of cases, and most individuals experience a full and lasting recovery.

Athletes and Eating Disorders

Female Athlete Triad Female athletes are not immune to the societal pressures to be thin. In addition, athletes who participate in judged sports such as gymnastics, dance, figure skating, ballet, diving, and synchronized swimming face additional pressure because their bodies are constantly being evaluated. The medical syndrome known as **female athlete triad (FAT)** has long been recognized. It is a combination of three health conditions: disordered eating, amenorrhea, and osteoporosis.

FAT begins with **disordered eating** and possibly overexercising. When body fat percentage drops, menstrual periods cease (**amenorrhea**). Simultaneously, estrogen production decreases, leaving the bones susceptible to **osteoporosis** (a bone disease characterized by low bone mass). Bones become weak and brittle, which in turn increases the risk of fracture. A woman who suffers a stress fracture may also be struggling with FAT. Indeed, a stress fracture or a fracture occurring when a sprain may have been expected should be considered by coaches and athletes as a possible indicator of an unhealthy approach to eating.

Males and Eating Disorders Eating disorders are not solely a female issue. Males involved in occupations (such as modeling) or sports (bodybuilding) where body image is important are also prone to developing an eating disorder. Many athletes competing in sports with weight divisions strive to "make weight" in lower weight classes (e.g., wrestling, boxing, weightlifting) or maintain the low weight required (e.g., jockey in horse racing, coxswain in rowing) to gain a competitive advantage. They use food restrictions, purging, and intentional dehydration, sometimes with fatal results. For these athletes, the issue of body weight is secondary to the objective of performing well.

Body Composition

Body composition refers to the amounts of body constituents, such as fat, muscle, bone, and other organs, and is regarded as one of the major components of physical fitness. Educating your client about body composition leads to a better understanding of weight gain and loss and more appropriate goal setting.

Lean body mass (LBM) refers to the "nonfat" or "fat-free" component of the human body and generally consists of skeletal muscle, bone, and water. By subtracting **total body fat (TBF)** from **total body mass (TBM)**

we arrive at lean body mass. TBF is calculated by multiplying TBM or weight by **percent body fat**. For example, if a client weighs 70 kg and has 10 percent body fat, he has 7 kg (70 kg x 10/100 = 7 kg) of TBF. If TBF is known, LBM can be calculated. In our example, this works out to an LBM of 63 kg (70 kg – 7 kg).

Table 10.3 presents body composition classification according to percent body fat.

Table 10.3 Classification of percent body fat for men and women.

Age	Gender	Underweight	Excellent	Good	Moderate	Overweight	Significantly Overweight
≤19	males	<3.0	3.0 – 12.0	12.1 – 17	17.1 – 22.0	22.1 – 27	≥27.1
	females	<12.0	12.0 – 17.0	17.1 – 22.0	22.1 – 27.0	27.1 – 32.0	≥32.1
20 – 29	males	<3.0	3.0 – 13.0	13.1 – 18.0	18.1 – 23.0	23.1 – 28.0	≥28.1
	females	<12.0	12.0 – 18.0	18.1 – 23.0	23.1 – 28.0	28.1 – 33.0	≥33.1
30 – 39	males	<3.0	3.0 – 14.0	14.1 – 19.0	19.1 – 24.0	24.1 – 29.0	≥29.1
	females	<12.0	12.0 – 19.0	19.1 – 24.0	24.1 – 29.0	29.1 – 34.0	≥34.1
40 – 49	males	<3.0	3.0 – 15.0	15.1 – 20.0	20.1 – 25.0	25.1 – 30.0	≥30.1
	females	<12.0	12.0 – 20.0	20.1 – 25.0	25.1 – 30.0	30.1 – 35.0	≥35.1
≥50	males	<3.0	3.0 – 16.0	16.1 – 21.0	21.1 – 26.0	26.1 – 31.0	≥31.1
	females	<12.0	12.0 – 21.0	21.1 – 26.0	26.1 – 31.0	31.1 – 36.0	≥36.1

Total body fat can be divided into two types of fat: essential fat and storage fat. A certain amount of fat is required for normal physiological functioning. This **essential fat** makes up about 3 percent of body weight for the average man and 12 percent for the average woman. The additional sex-specific essential fat found in females is located in the mammary glands and pelvic region and is required for hormone-related functions and pregnancy.

Storage fat serves as an energy reserve (should the body be subjected to starvation) and also protects internal organs by cushioning them. It also plays a role in regulating body temperature. The average man carries about 12 percent storage fat, while the average woman has about 15 percent. Fat is stored in the body in two ways. **Subcutaneous fat** accumulates beneath the skin surface, and **visceral fat** accumulates in and around the organs (heart, lungs, liver, spleen, kidneys, and so on).

You can't flex flab! Educating your clients about body composition leads to a better understanding of weight gain and loss and allows them to make more informed decisions when setting goals.

Measuring Body Fat Percentage

The two most accurate methods of assessing body fat (cadaver measurement and underwater weighing) are also the two least practical. Cadaver measurement is obviously not an option for assessing your clients' body composition, and underwater weighing requires expensive equipment. As such, we restrict our discussion here to one method that

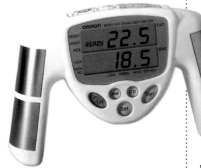

can be carried out by a trained fitness appraiser (skinfold testing) and several readily accessible methods for the general public.

Skinfold Assessment

This accurate but time-consuming method is based on the assumption that subcutaneous fat is directly related to total body fat. A fitness professional who is proficient in this type of testing takes five **skinfold measurements** at specific sites on the body and uses a formula to estimate total body fat (for details, see Chapter 12). To perform this technique, the skin is pulled away from muscle and pinched between the two flattened prongs of special skinfold calipers, which exert a constant tension.

Although underwater (or hydrostatic) weighing is one of the most accurate methods of measuring body fat, it is also one of the least practical.

Bioelectrical Impedance Analysis

Bioelectrical impedance analysis (BIA) is based on differences in electrical conductivity between fat-free mass and fat mass. By passing an extremely mild electric current through the body, voltage changes can be detected, which allows body density, and hence percent body fat, to be calculated. This reading can be taken at home on a reasonably priced combined weight and body fat scale or at the gym using a hand-held device.

One disadvantage of BIA is the extent to which readings are influenced by hydration level. Another is that this method does not distinguish between subcutaneous fat and visceral fat, which have very different implications for health status. BIA is valuable however for tracking trends over the course of weeks or months and is more accurate and valid than the tests that follow.

Waist-to-Hip Ratio

An alternative method of assessing body composition is to measure the hips around the widest part and the waist around the narrowest part (make sure your client isn't sucking in his stomach!). Divide the waist circumference by the hip circumference. A ratio of more than 1.0 in men and more than 0.8 in women is an indicator of health risk.

Body Mass Index

The **body mass index (BMI)** is used by CPAFLA (Canadian Physical Activity, Fitness and Lifestyle Appraisal) to assess if a person's body weight is matched to her height. BMI is generally intended for men and women aged 20 to 65 and is not suitable for babies, children, teenagers, pregnant women, the frail elderly, or very muscular people, such as athletes. BMI is calculated by dividing total body weight (kg) by body height (metres) squared.

$$\text{BMI} = \text{weight (kg)} / \text{height (m)}^2$$

Recreation and Fitness Leadership

Once the client's BMI has been obtained, its relationship to desirable body mass indexes can be determined using Table 10.4 A and B.

Table 10.4 A. BMI values in relation to sex. **B.** Desirable BMIs in relation to age.

A

Weight Status	Men	Women
Underweight	<20.7	<19.1
Acceptable weight	20.7 – 27.8	19.1 – 27.3
Overweight	27.8	27.3
Severely overweight	31.1	32.3
Morbid obesity	45.4	44.8

B

Age Group (years)	BMI (kg/m²)
19 – 24	19 – 24
25 – 34	20 – 25
35 – 44	21 – 26
45 – 54	22 – 27
55 – 65	23 – 28
>65	24 – 29

Waist Circumference

Another way to measure abdominal fat is to check waist measurement. Wrap a tape measure around the torso at or near the belly button. Keep the tape snug but not too tight. For women, health risk begins to rise with a waist measurement of more than 88 cm (35 inches). For men, risk increases with a measurement over 102 cm (40 inches). Measurements should be taken every two weeks.

Research suggests that the location of body fat affects the risk for disease. Some individuals tend to store fat in the abdominal area. This produces the "apple" shape. Others store fat mainly around the hips and thighs, which creates the "pear" shape. According to research, apple-shaped individuals are at higher risk for heart disease, hypertension, type 2 diabetes, and stroke than are pear-shaped individuals.

Using Body Composition to Guide Goal Setting

Let's say your client (Linda) is a 130-pound female with 23 percent body fat, and her goal is to "lose 20 pounds." Linda's initial TBF is 30 pounds (130 lb x 0.23 = 30 lb), and her LBM is 100 pounds (130 lb – 30 lb of fat = 100 lb). Her goal is to achieve a weight of 110 pounds (130 lb – 20 lb = 110 lb).

As you can see, the goal of losing 20 pounds is not realistic or healthy. If Linda lost only fat, she would still have 100 pounds of LBM but would be carrying only 10 pounds of fat, or only 9 percent body fat. This is a dangerously low percentage. A more likely scenario would see Linda lose both fat and LBM (usually metabolically active muscle tissue), which is clearly not desirable.

A better goal for this client might be to "reduce body fat from 23 percent to 18 percent," or 23 pounds (130 lb x 0.18 = 23 lb). This way Linda will achieve a TBM of 123 pounds (100 lb + 23 lb = 123 lb). To achieve a lean but healthy 18 percent body fat requires the loss of only 7 pounds of fat to reduce weight from the current 130 pounds to 123 pounds.

Somatotyping: Healthy Bodies Come in All Shapes and Sizes

Each of us is born with a body type we live with for the rest of our lives, whether we like it or not. Somatotyping is a way of classifying people based on these body types (Figure 10.1). People with soft, round bodies (**endomorphs**) and large, muscular bodies (**mesomorphs**) and combinations of the two can have a tendency to accumulate body fat. Trying to change one body type to another (think of those tall, sleek **ectomorphs**) is not only frustrating but also impossible. Instead, we must learn to make the most of our natural body types. Here is an example: Skeletal bone structure is largely a matter of genetics. If your parents are short, you will probably be short. In any case, you cannot change your height. However, whether you stand up straight or slouch is your choice and affects how others perceive you.

Another example: One of your clients may feel she has inherited a tendency to be overweight from her parents, and indeed she may have inherited a pear-shaped body, but in reality, living in an environment where overeating and underexercising are the norm likely has had a greater effect. Our friends also have an influence on us. Recent research suggests that your risk of developing obesity increases by 57 percent if someone you consider a friend gains weight.

Exercise and diet can modify genetic destiny only so much. The human body is not an infinitely malleable mass of calories that can be burned down to any desired shape or size. In terms of health and longevity, the scientific evidence is abundantly clear: It is far more important to be fit than it is to be thin. Encourage your clients, regardless of body shape, to choose to live more actively and to be more selective about what they eat.

Figure 10.1 Can you identify the predominant body type exhibited by these athletes?

Current Issues in Weight Management

> Take care of your body – it's the only place you have to live.
> *Jim Rohn*

Obesity

Obesity, defined as having an excess of body fat, has become prevalent in the developed world. In Western countries, 30 percent of all adults can be considered obese. In Canada, approximately 15 percent of adults are considered obese. Unfortunately, these numbers seem to be getting worse.

Recreation and Fitness Leadership

Obesity is a complex condition that may involve environmental, social, psychological, and genetic factors, although only a small percentage of people are genetically predisposed to being obese. Research has shown that obesity poses serious health problems (see the box *Health Risks of Obesity*). On the bright side, obesity can be prevented, and increasing physical activity decreases the health risks associated with excess body fat.

Psychological Impact of Obesity

The psychological difficulties caused by social stigmatization are just as serious as the physical conditions associated with obesity. Obese people face discrimination in the workforce because of the stereotyped belief that they lack self-control. Modern society portrays these individuals as unhealthy, comical, awkward, and unattractive. They are victims of bullying and teasing. Perfect strangers feel they have the right to make disrespectful comments about them. No doubt it is a challenge for obese people to maintain positive self-esteem under these circumstances.

Obesity is a complex condition that may involve environmental, social, psychological, and genetic factors.

Health Risks of Obesity

Obesity is associated with several increased health risks:

- Type 2 diabetes

- Osteoarthritis (degeneration of cartilage and bone in joints), often requiring joint replacement surgery

- Elevated blood pressure

- Cardiovascular disease

- Sleep apnea (breathing stoppage, heavy snoring)

- Asthma

- Cancer (uterine, colon, kidney, gallbladder, and postmenopausal breast cancer)

- Complications during pregnancy for mother and child

- Menstrual irregularities

- Stress incontinence (urine leakage caused by weak pelvic floor muscles)

- Complications during surgery

- Falls

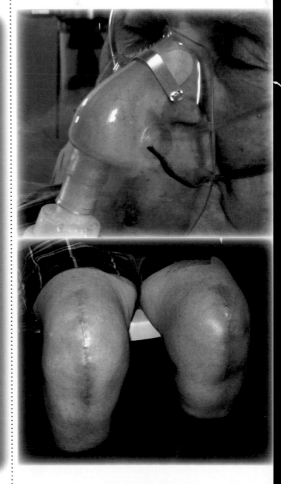

Creeping Weight Gain

Although obese individuals are often viewed as gluttonous, they generally do not consume large amounts of calories. In fact, physically active individuals have been shown to consume more calories than do obese individuals. Thus, obesity is often the result of too little activity rather than overeating.

As people age, their metabolic rates and physical activity patterns decline. If their caloric intake is not reduced to balance their energy expenditure, body mass will increase because excess calories are stored as fat. For instance, consuming just 100 calories more each day than you need results in a 10-pound weight gain over the course of a year.

Although obesity is often the result of too little activity rather than overeating, consuming foods in excess of caloric expenditure can slowly result in creeping weight gain.

This **creeping weight gain** is often experienced by individuals who were active in their teens and twenties but for various reasons (e.g., work, family) reduced their physical activity levels later in life, only to realize years later that they have an excess amount of body fat.

Dieting

Weight loss has become a billion-dollar industry as more and more people in all weight ranges seek quick solutions from food-industry experts and nutritionists. Chronic dieting, especially among teenagers, is a serious concern because it can stunt physical growth, cause menstrual irregularities, lower the metabolic rate, and lead to eating disorders. Commercial diet programs can be expensive, ineffective (weight loss is usually not permanent), and physically harmful. In addition, failure to lose weight can result in a drop in self-esteem. Weight management needs to be done in an atmosphere that is both positive and realistic – not under conditions in which eating itself seems like a crime.

Are You In Control?

Q I'm a woman in my early 20s, a college graduate, and in a caring, supportive relationship. However, while I pride myself on being a thin person, it's in my head that I need to follow a rigorous eating regimen to stay thin. I consume extremely small portions of veggies, fruits, grains and dairy (less than 1,200 calories a day), and that keeps me in control over my weight. I'm currently 5-foot-9 and 128 pounds. If I ever accidentally give in to my cravings, say for an ice cream cone, I feel unbelievably guilty. I examine myself in the mirror and am convinced I've instantly grown chubby.

I've become food-obsessed. It's all I think about all day: I calorie-count, keep a food journal, and silently torment myself over a cookie. I fear this will turn into an eating disorder; especially when I nearly stuck my finger down my throat after "giving in" on a piece of cake. I had a panic attack afterwards. Are these the first signs of anorexia/bulimia?

A You're mistaken in thinking you have control. Right now your obsession is controlling your behaviour, and you need to deal with it before it distracts you from functioning normally and/or negatively affects your health. Panic attacks are already an alarm signal.

Your BMI (based on your height and weight) is 18.9, which is considered on the very low end of normal. A low BMI (underweight) is associated with health problems such as osteoporosis, poor nourishment, and eating disorders. I recommend counselling, because something has you focusing on "staying thin" as if to avoid facing any other, deep-rooted problems.

Energy Balance Equation

The **energy balance equation** (Figure 10.2) describes the relationship between energy input and expenditure. On one side of the equation are the calories we burn through exercise and other bodily processes; on the other side are the calories we consume in food. Weight will remain constant if caloric input and output are the same – the body is said to be in **caloric balance** (Figure 10.2 A). Excess calories are stored as fat at the rate of 3,500 calories equalling one pound. A person gains weight when energy input exceeds energy output (Figure 10.2 B) and loses weight when the opposite occurs (Figure 10.2 C).

Although it is more common to hear about people who want to lose weight, there are those who have the desire to put on a few pounds to look better, or to "bulk up" for athletic events. Just as weight loss is based on your balance of calories, so is weight gain. This can be achieved by

Figure 10.2 The energy balance equation.

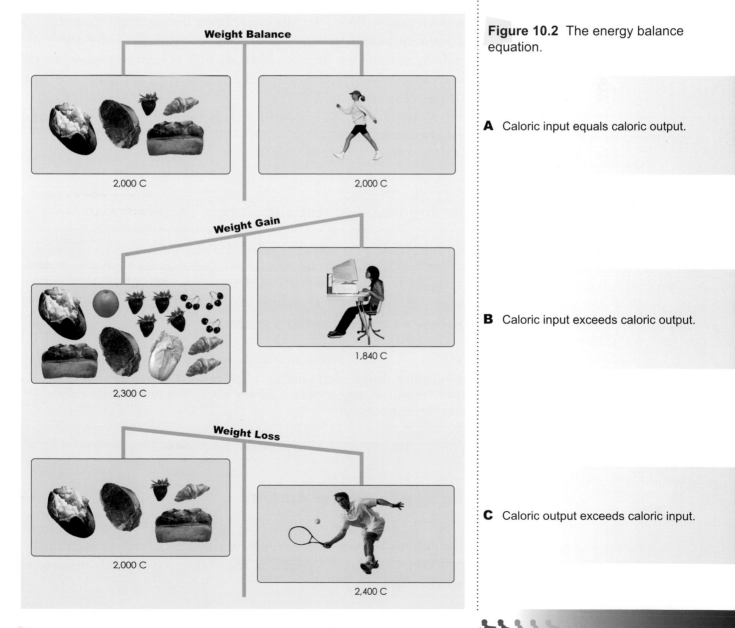

A Caloric input equals caloric output.

B Caloric input exceeds caloric output.

C Caloric output exceeds caloric input.

Weight Balance

2,000 C   2,000 C

Weight Gain

2,300 C   1,840 C

Weight Loss

2,000 C   2,400 C

increasing your food intake while participating in an activity program aimed at developing muscular strength. This increase in mass is due to an increase in functional muscle tissue, not fat.

Energy Needs of the Body

Of the total calories that we require on a daily basis, the highest proportion is used for our basal metabolisms. Basal metabolism, or **basal metabolic rate (BMR)**, is defined as the minimum amount of energy the body requires to carry out all vital functions (including blood circulation, respiration, and brain activity). Our basal metabolisms vary throughout our lives. As a general rule, BMR is relatively high at birth and continues to increase until the age of two, after which it gradually declines as we age (except for a rise at puberty).

Other variables besides age also affect BMR, such as body composition (muscular bodies have higher BMRs), physical fitness (fit people have higher BMRs), sex (the BMRs of men are 5 percent higher than those of women), sleep (BMRs are 10 percent lower during sleep), pregnancy (a 20 percent increase in BMR), and body temperature (a one degree rise in body temperature increases BMR about 7 percent). People often fail to recognize their changing metabolic needs and do not adjust their food intake accordingly.

To calculate BMR, use the formula presented in the box *Calculating Basal Metabolic Rate.*

As a general rule, BMR is relatively high at birth and continues to increase until the age of two, after which it gradually declines as we age. Other variables that affect BMR include body composition, physical fitness, sex, pregnancy, and body temperature.

Calculating Basal Metabolic Rate

Basal metabolic rate (BMR) reflects the amount of energy in calories (C) needed to maintain basic body functions such as breathing and blood circulation. Use the simple equation below to help you determine the approximate BMR. NOTE: a woman's BMR is approximately 5 percent lower than that of a man the same age.

> **BMR per day = 1 C x body weight (kg) x 24**

Example: 70-kg man

BMR per day = 1 C x 70 x 24
= 1,680 C

This individual needs approximately 1,680 calories to maintain his body at rest. Of course, any additional activity above this level raises calorie requirements accordingly.

Energy Needs for Activity

Once the body starts moving, the body's needs for energy increase significantly beyond basal metabolic needs. The amount of extra energy, or calories, required depends on the volume, type, and intensity of activity (Table 10.5).

Recreation and Fitness Leadership

Table 10.5 Approximate calories expended for male (70 kg) and female (55 kg) participants in sporting and recreational activities lasting an hour.

Activity	Male (70 kg)	Female (55 kg)	Calories/hour/kg
Sporting Activity			
Basketball	581.0	456.5	8.3
Cycling (racing)	714.0	561.0	10.2
Ice hockey	875.0	687.5	12.5
Running 8 min/mile	868.0	682.0	12.4
7 min/mile	959.0	753.5	13.7
6 min/mile	1050.0	825.0	15.0
Cross-country skiing	679.0	533.5	9.7
Soccer	546.0	429.0	7.8
Squash	889.0	698.5	12.7
Swimming breaststroke	686.0	539.0	9.8
Tennis (singles)	462.0	363.0	6.6
Weight training	294.0	231.0	4.2
Leisure Activity			
Cycling 10 km/hour	266.0	209.0	3.8
15 km/hour	413.0	324.5	5.9
Canoeing	182.0	143.0	2.6
Dancing	350.0	275.0	5.0
Golfing	357.0	280.5	5.1
Hiking	385.0	302.5	5.5
Jogging (11 min/mile)	553.0	434.5	7.9
Rowing ergometer	735.0	577.5	10.5
Walking	329.0	258.5	4.7

Using Food Energy

Exercise on its own can be a slow way to lose weight. For example, a woman weighing 55 kg would need to walk for more than two hours or cross-country ski for more than one hour to burn off the calories consumed in a large vanilla milkshake (Figure 10.3). But exercise combined with controlled eating patterns involving calorie reduction greatly enhances the chances for success.

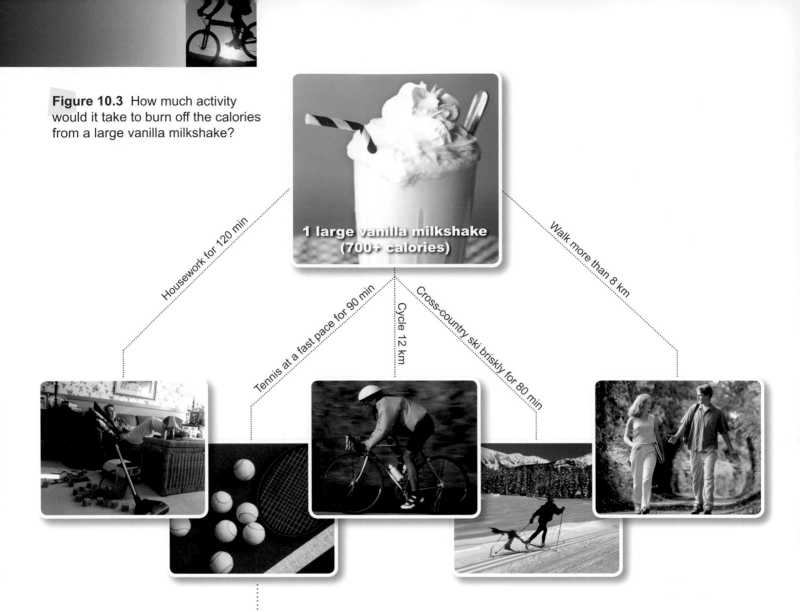

Figure 10.3 How much activity would it take to burn off the calories from a large vanilla milkshake?

1 large vanilla milkshake (700+ calories)

Housework for 120 min

Tennis at a fast pace for 90 min

Cycle 12 km

Cross-country ski briskly for 80 min

Walk more than 8 km

Calorie Counting

To calculate the calories consumed by your client, check the labels of packaged foods (look for *Energy* or *Calories*). Tables of the calorie content of common unpackaged foods are readily available on the newsstands and the Internet (e.g., MyFoodDiary.com). Go back to your client's five-day nutrition record and total the calories in each food item eaten. Then calculate the average daily caloric intake. Look at the client's activity record to determine the level of activity, from sedentary to very hard, on a daily basis. Then refer to Table 10.6 to compare this real caloric intake with the predicted total daily caloric requirement based on weight, gender, and activity level.

Calorie counting may be the best way to match food consumption to the body's energy needs, but it neglects an important consideration: the nutrient value of the food we eat. Food does more than provide calories for living and moving. We can take in that "magic number" of calories

Table 10.6 Quick estimate of total daily caloric requirements based on activity level.

Wt in kg (lb)	Gender	Males: kg x 24.2; Females: kg x 22 = BMR* in cal/day	Sedentary (little or no exercise) x 1.2	Light activity 1 – 3 days/week x 1.375	Moderate activity 3 – 5 days/week x 1.55	Hard activity 6 – 7 days/week x 1.725	Very hard activity daily x 1.9
40 (88)	males	968	1161	1331	1500	1670	1839
	females	880	1056	1210	1364	1518	1672
45 (99)	males	1089	1306	1497	1689	1878	2069
	females	990	1188	1361	1534	1707	1881
50 (110)	males	1210	1452	1664	1875	2087	2299
	females	1100	1320	1512	1705	1897	2090
55 (121)	males	1331	1597	1830	2063	2296	2529
	females	1210	1452	1664	1875	2087	2299
60 (132)	males	1452	1742	1996	2251	2505	2759
	females	1320	1584	1815	2046	2277	2508
65 (143)	males	1573	1888	2163	2438	2713	2989
	females	1430	1716	1966	2216	2466	2717
70 (154)	males	1694	2032	2329	2626	2922	3219
	females	1540	1848	2117	2387	2656	2926
75 (165)	males	1815	2178	2496	2813	3131	3448
	females	1650	1980	2269	2557	2846	3135
80 (176)	males	1936	2323	2662	3001	3340	3678
	females	1760	2112	2420	2728	3036	3344
85 (187)	males	2057	2468	2828	3188	3548	3908
	females	1870	2244	2571	2898	3225	3553
90 (198)	males	2178	2614	2995	3376	3757	4138
	females	1980	2376	2722	3069	3415	3762
95 (209)	males	2299	2759	3161	3563	3966	4368
	females	2090	2508	2873	3239	3605	3971
100 (220)	males	2420	2904	3327	3751	4174	4598
	females	2200	2640	3025	3410	3795	4180
105 (231)	males	2541	3049	3494	3939	4383	4828
	females	2310	2772	3176	3580	3984	3489
110 (242)	males	2662	3194	3660	4126	4592	5057
	females	2420	2904	3327	3751	4174	4598
115 (253)	males	2783	3340	3827	4314	4801	5287
	females	2530	3036	3478	3821	4364	4807

* BMR refers to the calories required to maintain body functions at rest

*F*or the record . . .
The sugar content of a typical
20-ounce bottle of pop is about 16
teaspoons. Each level teaspoon of sugar
provides 16 calories. Thus a typical bottle
of pop contains around 250 calories.

in many ways. For instance, the need for 2,400 calories would be met by three cups of table sugar! However, these are known as **empty calories** because the sugar provides no vitamins, minerals, or fibre. Those 2,400 calories could also be provided by a diet of snacks and pop, or a diet limited to a few favourite foods, or even alcohol. But this person would be *malnourished.* That is why Canada's Food Guide is such a valuable tool for assessing food intake. Tracking the number of servings consumed from each food group ensures that your client is consuming the correct amounts of nutrients. And it's almost impossible to eat too many calories if the focus is on eating lots of fruits and vegetables. These foods are low in calories and have virtually no fat content.

Goal Setting for a Healthy Lifestyle

*B*etween the ages of 9 and 16 years, it is normal and healthy for females to gain, on average, between 2 and 5 kg (5 to 10 pounds) every year and to grow as many as 28 cm (10 inches) during those growing years. Males will gain even greater amounts as their testosterone levels allow for increased muscle mass to develop.

Wouldn't it be wonderful if you could get your clients to reword their goals from "I want to lose/gain weight" to "I want to be in better shape," "I want to have more energy," or "I want to get rid of my spare tire"? Then you could help them describe what that means exactly – usually a leaner physical appearance and improved fitness. When clients clarify their goals in this way, you can suggest lifestyle and dietary changes and design exercise programs to build muscle and lose fat. In time your clients will feel better about their bodies because they actually look more toned. They will gain strength and muscular endurance and lower their risk of cardiovascular disease and diabetes, too.

For many adolescent boys, the common question is "How do I gain weight?" when they actually want to gain muscle. If they have not yet reached puberty, they need to realize that they won't gain significant muscle mass until their testosterone levels increase. They may be tempted to use protein supplements and other chemicals to assist the process.

So if your client expresses a goal about weight, try to find out the specific reason. Are clothes no longer fitting? Is the number on the bathroom scale not to her liking? Has a friend made a remark about his size? Does she want to look like a particular media or sports figure? Are his friends maturing faster than he is? Then provide specific information (e.g., normal weight and height gains to be expected during adolescence; the tendency to inherit body shape). Educate the client about recognizing body fat percentage as an important factor to monitor. Finally, ask the client to restate the goal without using the word *weight.*

Practical Tips for Lifestyle Changes

What advice would you as a lifestyle counsellor give to a client who has been told to lose some weight? An understanding of metabolism and the mechanism of energy input and output will help you give advice about possible strategies. There are six variables to consider (Table 10.7):

Recreation and Fitness Leadership

Table 10.7 Components of the energy balance equation.

Energy Intake		Energy Output		
All foods and beverages with a caloric content	Change total number of calories eaten	BMR (basal metabolic rate)	65 – 75% of TDEE*	• Can be raised slightly by increasing muscle mass • Do resistance training
	Exchange high-fat, calorie-dense foods for healthier choices	TEF (thermal effect of food) – calories burned in digestion, absorption, transport	5 – 10%	• Varies directly with amount of food eaten • Eating breakfast increases TEF by 5% • Eating fibre raises TEF • Skipping meals slows down TEF
	Read food labels to maintain a balance of nutrients	NEAT (non-exercise activity thermogenesis)	15 – 30%	• Daily spontaneous activity • Less sitting • More standing and walking • Fidget!
	Drink water and calorie-free beverages	TEPA (thermal effect of physical activity)		Planned, structured physical exercise: • join a class or a gym • play sports • use home exercise equipment regularly
	Meal replacement drinks can provide extra calories if weight gain is the goal	EPOC (excess postexercise oxygen consumption)		Intense exercise (>70% of maximum effort) for at least 20 minutes keeps metabolism elevated slightly for several hours

*TDEE refers to Total Daily Energy Expenditure

❶ Energy intake – the number of calories ingested from all sources

❷ Basal metabolic rate (BMR) – energy expended due to ongoing processes within the body (liver, kidneys, heart, brain)

❸ Thermic effect of food (TEF) – energy expended in the digestion of food

❹ Non-exercise activity thermogenesis (NEAT) – energy expended due to daily activities

❺ Thermic effect of physical activity (TEPA) – energy expended due to planned physical exercise

❻ Excess postexercise oxygen consumption (EPOC) – energy expended after exercise has ceased due to increased metabolic rate

Thus, there are several ways to swing the balance towards increased energy consumption:

❶ Eat five or six healthy meals a day including breakfast, with a reduced caloric content and more fibre.

❷ Add resistance training to build more muscle and raise your BMR.

❸ Be more active in your daily living: stand instead of sitting, walk instead of standing, fidget more.

❹ Add a planned exercise component to your life: attend a fitness class, go jogging, use a treadmill, join a team.

❺ Add an intense workout component to boost EPOC.

Get Moving

According to ACSM (2006), approximately 50 percent of people drop out of exercise programs within one year. Yo-yo fitness is becoming as common as yo-yo dieting. If someone quits an exercise program out of failure to reach a particular weight-loss (or reduced body fat) goal, then additional benefits of the exercise program – such as increased strength, endurance, and flexibility – are lost as well. Therefore, an important approach to helping others achieve their weight-loss and health goals is to find ways for them to be more mobile in their daily lives. Educating your clients to make small changes may very well contribute to some desirable profound changes in their overall weight management goals.

Approximately 50 percent of people drop out of exercise programs within one year. Can you think of any strategies that might improve a client's exercise adherence?

Suggestions to Help Your Client Add Activity to His or Her Lifestyle and Burn Calories

- Take the dog for a walk.
- Limit time in front of a TV or computer.
- Stand up and walk around when taking a phone call.
- Fidget.
- Put on your make-up standing up.
- Do sit-ups during commercials.
- Walk during lunch hour.
- Walk instead of driving whenever you can.
- Avoid labour-saving devices (e.g., ride-on lawn mowers, snow blowers).
- Get off the bus a stop early and walk.
- Work around the house.
- Bicycle to the store instead of driving.
- Go for a half-hour walk instead of watching TV.

- Sit up straight at your desk.
- Wash the car by hand.
- Run when running errands.
- Play actively with the kids you baby-sit or care for.
- Dance to music.
- Stretch before bed to give you more energy when you wake.
- Take the stairs instead of the escalator.
- Walk the beach instead of sunbathing.
- Carry your groceries instead of pushing a cart.
- Buy a set of hand weights and pump them while you watch TV.
- Walk briskly through the mall, and shop 'til you drop . . . pounds.

Putting It All Together

Vitality and health are clearly linked. Healthy eating and an active lifestyle help ensure metabolic health, consisting of healthy blood pressure and healthy blood levels of fat and glucose.

Gathering and assessing information about your clients' lifestyles allows you to analyze their eating habits, offer advice on nutrition and exercise, and recognize disordered eating and exercise patterns. Encourage your clients to base their goals on achieving a healthy body fat percentage – along with greater muscle mass for strength and higher metabolic rates – rather than focusing on their weight. The weight-loss industry would have us believe that we should all strive for a certain body type, when, in reality, healthy bodies come in all shapes and sizes.

Choosing to follow the main ideas of the vitality message – developing healthy eating habits, being active, and achieving body image satisfaction – will put your clients on the road to good health and longevity.

Regular physical activity and healthy eating should not be viewed merely as means to an end, but rather as having their own intrinsic value. Teach your clients that having more energy, feeling good about their bodies, and spending more time doing things they enjoy are the results of a commitment to the principles of vitality.

A man's health can be judged by which he takes two at a time: pills or stairs.
Joan Welsh

Key Terms

amenorrhea

anorexia nervosa

basal metabolic rate (BMR)

bioelectrical impedance analysis (BIA)

body composition

body mass index (BMI)

bulimia nervosa

caloric balance

creeping weight gain

disordered eating

eating disorders

ectomorphs

empty calories

endomorphs

energy balance equation

essential fat

female athlete triad (FAT)

high blood sugar (hyperglycemia)

lean body mass (LBM)

low blood sugar (hypoglycemia)

mesomorphs

metabolic health

obesity

osteoporosis

percent body fat

skinfold measurements

somatotyping

storage fat

subcutaneous fat

total body fat (TBF)

total body mass (TBM)

visceral fat

vitality

Review Questions

1. Outline the vitality message and why it is so important in today's culture.

2. What is metabolic health, and how is it measured?

3. How would you assess a new client's vitality?

4. What are the signs and symptoms of disordered eating?

5. Distinguish between the two types of body fat.

6. Evaluate the pros and cons of the different methods of determining body fat percentage.

7. What are the hazards of obesity?

8. What are the pitfalls of dieting?

9. Briefly describe the energy balance equation. What situation would need to exist for someone to lose weight? To gain weight?

10. What are the six aspects of the energy balance formula that can be modified to manage weight?

NAME: Michelle Federer
OCCUPATION: Recreation Coordinator, Facility Booking, Town of Collingwood
EDUCATION: Recreation Facilities Management, Seneca College, King Campus
General Business, Seneca College, King Campus

▶ What do you do?

I am responsible for the coordination and administration of all recreation facility permits/contracts and functions. Our facilities in Collingwood include arenas, pools, community halls, meeting rooms, sports fields, harbour launches, and docks. I help groups book the facilities they need in order to organize and run recreation programs. I also assist with the many special events that occur in Collingwood, such as the annual Elvis Festival, the Ontario Winter Games, and municipal conferences.

▶ What is unique about your job?

Every day is different from the last. You never know what will happen when you arrive at work each day! I meet new people all the time and help them meet their recreation needs. Collingwood is a four-season recreation area with many activities to offer, and I am able to use my skills to assist in their delivery.

▶ What was your motivation for pursuing this field?

I have always been an active participant in recreation and sports activities, and now I have the opportunity to help community groups with their recreation activities. I am an enthusiastic and energetic person, and I can use my personality to work with others and promote recreation here in Collingwood.

▶ How competitive is the field?

Recreation and leisure services is a growing field. With the government recognizing the need for programs that promote healthy, active living, the pressure is on in the recreation field to create and operate programs that encourage this lifestyle but at the same time can be done as a family unit and on a flexible schedule. This focus on healthy Canadians has increased the need for recreation facilities and programs, which in turn has created new jobs and opportunities in the recreation field.

▶ What career advice would you give to students interested in this area?

If you are interested in a career in recreation and leisure services, start volunteering and looking for part-time employment in the field. This gives you a foot in the door and introductory experience in recreation programming. There are many recreation career options these days – municipal, private, and nonprofit. Investigate the pros and cons of each of these, and choose the career option that suits your own interests and needs. Be prepared for long hours and working on weekends. The rewards are not always visible, but to see smiles on participants' faces makes it all worthwhile.

In This Chapter:

Fitness Training Principles
    FITT Principle
    Overload Principle
    Progression Principle
    Reversibility Principle
    Specificity Principle

Components of Physical Fitness
    Muscular Strength
    Muscular Endurance
    Cardiorespiratory Endurance
    Flexibility
    Body Composition

Components of Motor Ability
    Power
    Agility
    Coordination
    Reaction Time
    Balance
    Speed

Fitness Training Activities
    Resistance Activities
    Cardiorespiratory Activities
    Functional Fitness Activities
    Group Fitness Classes

Putting It All Together

CHAPTER 11
Developing Physical Fitness

In this chapter, you will learn about the following:

❶ The characteristics of fitness training principles

❷ The components of physical fitness and motor ability

❸ The benefits of different types of fitness training activities

❹ Designing a training program to meet specific fitness goals

> "You may never know what results come of your actions, but if you do nothing there will be no result."
> Mahatma Gandhi

> "
> Those who think they have no time for bodily exercise will sooner or later have to find time for illness.
> *Edward Stanley*
> "

The health, joie de vivre, and creativity of a well-developed personality depend to a large degree on total fitness levels. **Total fitness** is the functional readiness and level of effectiveness required for everything a person does. It involves the ability to adapt to the demands and stresses of daily life and is directly related to the amount and intensity of **physical activity**. The term *total fitness* is used in many ways and has many dimensions, including physical, emotional, social, spiritual, and intellectual. The focus of this chapter is physical fitness.

Physical fitness is more than just a concept – it is a way of life. It incorporates many components important for health, such as muscular strength, muscular endurance, cardiorespiratory endurance, flexibility, and body composition. Each of these components offers unique benefits and advantages that affect your client's health in a positive way. Engaging in **physical exercise** provides numerous benefits that help control weight, manage stress, and boost the immune system, as well as protect against disease. Exercise not only helps a person look and feel good but also provides enjoyment while developing a state of health and vitality.

To best advise someone whose goal is to improve physical fitness, you must understand how to exercise properly and most effectively. In this chapter you will learn about the principles involved in planning training programs, the importance of the various components of physical fitness and how to develop them, and activities that can be used in fitness training. Attaining physical fitness need not be boring and monotonous or restricted to running and cycling; there are many options available, and all you need to do is discover what activities interest your client most.

In the previous two chapters we have focused our discussion on people who want to improve their health status. Many of your clients will want to take the next step. They will want to set goals for specific improvements in aspects of physical fitness such as strength, flexibility, and endurance. They may want to improve their ability to handle the physical requirements of their jobs. They may want to achieve a certain muscle mass (18-inch biceps) or a "six-pack" abdomen. They may want to improve their sports performance by improving their speed, agility, and balance. These are valid and relevant goals for many people and are dealt with in this chapter.

Recreation and Fitness Leadership

Fitness Training Principles

Before we discuss the components of fitness and the types of training activities, it is important to know something about the principles that govern training. Programs that adhere to these well-established principles are more likely to generate the greatest improvements in your client's fitness levels.

Does the training program FITT?

FITT Principle

The **FITT principle** is a simple method of recalling the four important design elements of any training program: Frequency, Intensity, training Time, and Type of activity. Each of these components is described in more detail here.

Training Frequency

Training frequency refers to the number of times a person exercises each week. This can depend on an individual's goals, abilities, fitness level, and sport. If the goal is to maintain an achieved level of fitness, two or three sessions per week are sufficient; however, if the goal is to improve physical fitness, four to six sessions are recommended.

Training Intensity

Training intensity describes how hard a person needs to work in order to achieve a fitness benefit or see an improvement. It is measured differently for each physical fitness component. For instance, intensity in cardiorespiratory endurance training is monitored by measuring the pulse, or heart rate, with the goal of keeping the heart rate between 50 and 85 percent of the client's predicted maximum. Other measures of intensity include resistance to be overcome, number of repetitions, speed of movement, and percentage of maximum performance effort.

Another intensity consideration is the **work-to-rest ratio** (e.g., 1:2 – the rest phase is two times the length of the work phase). The rest phase allows for recovery from muscle fatigue. Generally, the lower the intensity of exercise, the shorter the rest periods required.

*The **work-to-rest ratio** indicates how long the rest phase should be relative to the length of the work phase. Generally, the lower the intensity of exercise, the shorter the rest periods have to be.*

Training Time

Training time refers to the total time devoted to developing fitness. It is based on the duration of each training session. **Training volume**, another element of exercise time, is measured in various units depending on the type of activity. For instance, in cyclic movements (e.g., walking, running, swimming, kayaking, rowing), the total distance in one workout or several workouts over the course of one week represents the volume of training. For strength training, the volume may refer to (a) the total number of all repetitions of each exercise, (b) the total of all repetitions during a workout, (c) the total resistance moved, or (d) the number of times a circuit was completed.

Type of Activity

Choosing a type of exercise is also important. Physical activity can include **formal fitness activities**, where the development of fitness is the participant's main goal (e.g., circuit training, group fitness classes, jogging, weight training), or **informal fitness activities**, which emphasize the social aspect of exercising – such as camaraderie, cooperation, and fun – as the main goal, with fitness being a by-product (e.g., pick-up street hockey, social dancing, three-on-three basketball, mall walking).

Often the participant will determine whether an activity falls into the formal or informal category. One person may engage in pick-up shinny hockey or mall walking to improve fitness, while another may participate in these activities to meet people and make new friends.

*Do you understand the difference between **formal** and **informal** fitness activities? As a fitness leader, you must be aware of the client's specific goals in order to maximize his or her training experience.*

FITT Principle

The mnemonic FITT can be used as a simple method of recalling the four important design elements of any training program:

Frequency – How often should I train this component?

Intensity – How hard do I need to work to achieve a benefit?

Time – How long should I train for?

Type – What activities should I do?

Overload Principle

The **overload principle** states that for improvement to occur, training demands must be higher than normal performance requirements in order to stress the capacity of the targeted muscle or body system. The additional overload can be achieved by increasing the frequency, intensity, or time of the exercise program.

Progression Principle

After a period of training, the load that previously created a level of stress will no longer provide an adequate overload stimulus. This stimulus is now a

Recreation and Fitness Leadership

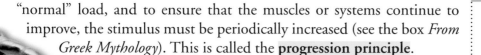

"normal" load, and to ensure that the muscles or systems continue to improve, the stimulus must be periodically increased (see the box *From Greek Mythology*). This is called the **progression principle**.

From Greek Mythology

In his youth, Milon of Croton (disciple of Pythagoras, scholar, and multiple Olympic wrestling champion in ancient Greece) decided to become the strongest man on earth. To achieve this he lifted and carried a calf every day. As the calf grew and became heavier Milon's body adapted to the growing weight of the animal and became increasingly stronger. When the calf had grown into a bull and Milon a man, he had become the strongest man of his time.

There are various ways to increase load, depending on one's fitness level and the particular method of training used. Gradually increasing the training load, in small steps from one training cycle to another, is recommended for beginners and recreational trainees. An example is shown in the box *How to Overload*.

How to Overload

One way to determine whether to increase the load is by judging the number of times a given weight can be lifted before causing fatigue. For example, if you start lifting 25 kg 10 times and, after training for a length of time (two to five sessions), you can lift the same weight 15 times, then to increase muscle strength, the load should be increased to what can be lifted maximally (until exhaustion) 10 times. This new weight will most likely be 30 kg. This ensures that the muscles are working in the overload zone and the "signals" that stimulate adaptation are being sent to the muscles.

Reversibility Principle

Illness, injury, or even a vacation can cause an unavoidable break in your training routine. According to the **reversibility principle**, training interruptions have a negative effect on personal fitness, resulting in stagnation or a temporary decline in performance. Fitness instructors or mentors need to be ready to encourage clients who have lost ground during the interruption and are discouraged as a result.

Generally, cardiorespiratory and muscular endurance performance declines faster than maximal strength and power performance. Motor ability performance factors such as coordination and muscle integration

Use it or lose it!
Endurance athletes can lose up to 10 percent of their performance $\dot{V}O_2$max following a one-week layoff from cardiorespiratory training.

also decline with training interruptions because these factors are all interrelated. Remember the saying "Use it or lose it!"

Specificity Principle

The **specificity principle** states that exercises cause specific physiological responses or changes. This means that if you wish to improve a particular fitness or skill component, you must select a training modality that is as close in action as it can be to the end result.

When You Exercise for Performance, Be Specific!

- If you train arm strength by pushing with bent arms against immovable walls, you will become strong at pushing walls but not at doing push-ups, which require dynamic contractions.

- It makes little sense for basketball players to practice shooting at an 8-foot basket if they shoot at a 10-foot one in a game or for hockey players to practice shooting drills without a goalie in the net.

- If a person has to lift 30-kg boxes at work, it makes little sense to use a 10-kg resistance while training to improve work efficiency.

- Performing bench presses will not help you improve the endurance of your leg muscles.

- Sprinters will do themselves little good if they train by running long distances.

Components of Physical Fitness

Physical fitness incorporates components important for general health (Figure 11.1), such as muscular strength, muscular endurance, cardiorespiratory endurance, and flexibility. Each of these components is essential for people of all ages and abilities. Body composition, which was discussed in the previous chapter, is another component of health-related fitness.

Muscular Strength

Muscular strength is defined as the ability of a muscle or muscle group to exert force against a resistance. The greater the muscle diameter, the greater the force it should be able to generate. Before puberty, girls and boys have equivalent strength. Because of the influence of testosterone during and after puberty, however, males have the capacity to develop larger muscles and thus can generally develop greater strength.

In sports, the force generated by a muscular contraction may be applied against a movable object, as in weightlifting, or against a fixed object, such as the starting blocks in sprinting. If you think of sports that require great strength, the athletes that participate in these sports have large muscles. However in daily life, the average person needs only enough strength to manipulate his own body weight; lift and carry items such as a backpack, groceries, or children; or carry work-related items such as tools.

We can differentiate between absolute and relative strength. **Absolute strength** is the total force a person can apply in a single effort against a resistance: how much weight or mass she can move regardless of her weight or mass. **Relative strength** takes the mass of the body into account and is calculated by taking the person's maximum (absolute) strength and dividing it by the mass of her body. For example, a fourteen-year-old girl who can do a chin-up can lift her own body weight. A year later, after gaining 6 kg, her upper body may be just as strong, but she may no longer be able to do a chin-up. She has maintained her absolute strength, but her relative strength has decreased.

PHYSICAL FITNESS

- Muscular Strength
- Muscular Endurance
- Cardiorespiratory Endurance
- Flexibility
- Body Composition
- Motor Abilities

Figure 11.1
The components of physical fitness.

The amount of strength required in our daily lives depends to a large extent on our age, occupation, and specific life circumstances.

Age-Related Muscle Loss

Muscle loss in the elderly is a very real medical condition known as *sarcopenia* (Greek for "vanishing flesh"). Research has shown that by age 70, sedentary individuals have lost 30 percent or more of the muscle they had at age 30, when muscle mass peaks. Muscle loss inevitably means diminished strength and balance, which may lead to falls and fractures, a major cause of age-related disabilities.

The elderly benefit greatly from strength-training programs. Resistance weight training can halt or even reverse sarcopenia, enabling older people to continue functioning independently in their golden years.

Training Muscular Strength

It is important to give muscles time to adapt to training – normally at least 48 hours is required between strength-training sessions. It is during this time between sessions that optimal muscle adaptation occurs (i.e., increased size or capacity to produce force) in response to the training challenge. If your client prefers to work out every day, focus on training different body areas in each session. For example, the client could train upper-body muscles on one day and leg muscles on the next day before returning to the muscles of the upper body. In general, for building maximum strength, the resistance should be high and the repetitions low.

Resistance or strength training can incorporate free weights, strength-training machines, body weight, medicine balls, and so on. It is important to overload the muscles by working at an intensity that makes it difficult to perform more than 8 to 12 repetitions per set. Generally, strength exercises must be repeated to muscular failure. For example, your client can use a leg press machine, selecting a resistance that is about 75 to 80 percent of her 1RM and performing sets of 8 to 12 repetitions. However, if she can perform more than 12 repetitions, she is starting to work on muscular endurance rather than strength, and it is time to increase the weight resistance.

One repetition maximum (1RM): The amount of weight (resistance) that can be moved in a single maximum effort of a particular exercise, such as a bench press.

Resistance Training Terminology

What is a set? What is a rep? What is resistance?

Resistance is the amount of mass a client moves. It can be his own body weight or the specific weight of a dumbbell, barbell, or weight machine (often based on a percentage of one repetition maximum, or 1RM).

Number of reps (repetitions) is the number of times a client does a movement without stopping.

A *set* is one group of reps.

> **Example:**
> A student bench presses 45 kg 12 times, rests 3 minutes, and repeats. This is recorded as 2 x 12 x 45.

The variety of exercises and the respective order of exercises within a training session must also be considered. The variety depends on the overall goal. Recreational athletes seeking to develop all-around strength of as many muscle groups as possible may train using more than 40 different strength exercises. Competitive athletes striving to develop strength capacities that are sport- or event-specific may find it necessary to perform only 3 to 5 exercises. Weightlifters customarily include 8 to 12 different exercises in their regular training programs. In comparison, bodybuilders use the greatest number of exercises by far in their training regimens, as they wish to target almost all the muscles of the body.

FITT Principle for Strength Training

Frequency – To allow muscle adaptation, working out every other day is usually best unless the daily routines focus on different muscle areas.

Intensity – Generally, strength training requires high resistance (i.e., 75 to 80 percent of 1RM) and low repetitions (8 to 12).

Time – The length of the training session is dependent on the number of sets and repetitions that are planned as well as the number of different exercises involved in the workout session.

Type – Examples include using free weights, body weight, strength-training machines, and medicine balls.

Testing Muscular Strength

One way to evaluate the strength of a muscle group is to determine how much weight can be moved in a single maximum effort of a particular exercise. This is called **one repetition maximum**, or 1RM. It is used to determine the starting resistance in a training program, to compare strength against norms, and to track improvement. Assessing strength is discussed in greater detail in Chapter 12.

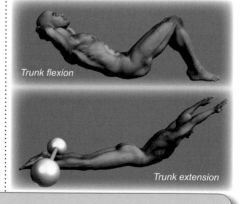

Trunk flexion

Trunk extension

Agonist–Antagonist Training

When planning training activities or programs, always include exercises that stimulate both the agonists (working muscles) and the antagonists (muscles that work in opposition, or counter-acting muscles). This approach to strength training is referred to as **agonist–antagonist training**.

A program that focuses on increasing only biceps strength, for example, tends to shorten this muscle and weaken the triceps, possibly resulting in a muscle-pair imbalance. A shift in strength equilibrium of the biceps and triceps (or other muscle pairings such as trunk extensors and trunk flexors, or quadriceps and hamstrings) can lead to injuries. More on agonist–antagonist training is presented in Chapter 15.

Muscular Endurance

Muscular endurance is defined as the ability of a muscle or muscle group to sustain a given level of force repeatedly at a given resistance. **Static exercises**, such as the flexed arm hang, involve sustained contractions to keep the body in position. During this type of contraction, lactic acid (a by-product of energy production) accumulates, generating a strong burning sensation and rapidly fatiguing the muscle.

In contrast to static exercises, **dynamic exercises** involve continual rhythmical contractions and relaxations that allow for continuous delivery of oxygen to the muscles, thus delaying fatigue and the burning sensation. The body's ability to deliver blood to the muscles plays a large role in endurance, reducing fatigue depending on the exercise intensity. Activities such as cycling require muscular endurance in the legs, but cardiorespiratory endurance is equally important to deliver blood to these muscles. Thus, exercises that depend on the contraction of large muscle groups for prolonged periods of time, such as distance running, cross-country skiing, cycling, and swimming, also involve cardiorespiratory endurance, another important component of physical fitness.

Training Muscular Endurance

Circuit training is a common method of training for muscular endurance and will be discussed in more detail later in the chapter. Other common

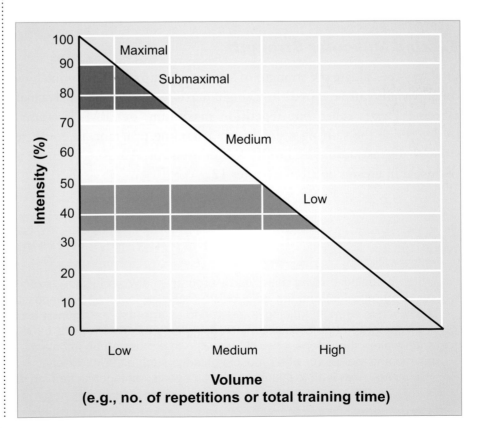

Figure 11.2 Diagram showing the relationship between intensity and volume of exercise.

Recreation and Fitness Leadership

methods of endurance training include resistance training using free weights or exercise machines as well as moving the weight of the body during activities such as chin-ups, pull-ups, and push-ups. When training for muscular endurance, resistance needs to be relatively low to allow for 15 to 30 repetitions per set. When the weight of the body offers too much resistance, muscular strength is worked instead of muscular endurance.

Figure 11.2 shows the relationship between the number of repetitions required to train for strength (low volume) as compared with the number of repetitions needed to train for endurance (high volume), along with the inverse relationship of resistance variables.

FITT Principle for Muscular Endurance

Frequency – No limitations on the frequency.

Intensity – Choose a resistance (e.g., free weight, body weight) that allows the client to complete 15 to 30 repetitions of the exercise before fatiguing (i.e., 30 to 60 percent of 1RM).

Time – Whatever time it takes to complete the repetitions.

Type – Use free weights, body weight, strength-training machines, medicine balls, circuits, and calisthenics.

Testing Muscular Endurance

Common tests of muscular endurance include push-ups and chin-ups (for measuring upper-body endurance) and partial curl-ups (for measuring abdominal endurance). These exercises are done as many times as possible before muscle fatigue sets in or before a set time limit is reached. See Chapter 12 for details on testing protocols.

Weight-Training for Kids?

How many times have you seen signs in fitness facilities requiring a minimum age of 16? How many times have you heard someone say that children should not lift weights? That their growth will be stunted or their growth plates will be damaged?

How true is this common belief? According to Wayne Westcott, co-author of *Youth Strength Training*, published by ACE (American Council on Exercise), there is no evidence that a supervised, well-designed strength-training program will negatively affect a child's growth. In fact, along with its expected benefits, regular weight training can protect against osteoporosis in later life. Individuals between the ages of 8 and 18 can increase their bone density faster than at any other time of their lives.

Weight training is especially recommended for overweight children, who are less likely to join in team sports since these individuals often lack endurance or feel awkward.

So don't be surprised when you see weight-training gyms equipped with scaled-down machines opening up in your neighbourhood!

Cardiorespiratory Endurance

As its name implies, **cardiorespiratory (or cardiovascular) endurance**, also known as cardiorespiratory fitness, involves the heart (cardio), the lungs (respiratory), and the blood vessels (vascular). The main function of the cardiorespiratory system is to provide oxygen to the muscle cells. The body's ability to sustain aerobic activities is a measure of this system's endurance.

Most of the time we operate in the aerobic zone – that is, our circulatory systems supply the required oxygen without our experiencing oxygen debt (getting breathless). A well-trained individual can put forth more effort without reaching this threshold than an untrained person. For example, a person with good cardiorespiratory endurance can jog at a relatively high pace without gasping for air. What eventually stops this person is muscular fatigue or lack of time. An unfit person, on the other hand, may need to stop halfway up the staircase to catch his breath.

Training Cardiorespiratory Endurance

The training principles for cardiorespiratory endurance are simple. To improve cardiorespiratory endurance, your client should train at least three times a week. As long as there is no evidence of fatigue or injury, more training is better. The client should train in her **target heart-rate zone**, a level that is 50 to 85 percent of her maximum heart rate (see the box *Finding the Target Heart-Rate Zone*). Heart rate below this level is ineffective at creating an overload; a higher intensity is too difficult to maintain long enough and does not produce any greater results.

The client should keep her heart rate in the target heart-rate zone for 15 to 20 minutes. There are several options here. She can try to maintain a steady heart rate within the zone, or she can vary her heart rate within the zone by working harder for a short time and then easing off. The client can even take short breaks (under two minutes) and then resume training. The best way to monitor heart rate is to wear a heart-rate monitor watch. Stopping for brief periods to do 10-second pulse checks is another alternative (see the box *Pulse Checks*).

Heart-rate monitor watches are one of the best and easiest ways to monitor heart rate during a bout of physical activity.

> ## FITT Principle for Cardiorespiratory Endurance
>
> *Frequency* – Training at least three times per week is recommended.
>
> *Intensity* – Choose an intensity that allows the client to work at 50 to 85 percent of maximum heart rate.
>
> *Time* – Sessions of 15 to 30 minutes; may be broken into intervals if the time between intervals is short (less than 2 minutes).
>
> *Type* – Any total body activity using large muscle groups.

Recreation and Fitness Leadership

Finding the Target Heart-Rate Zone

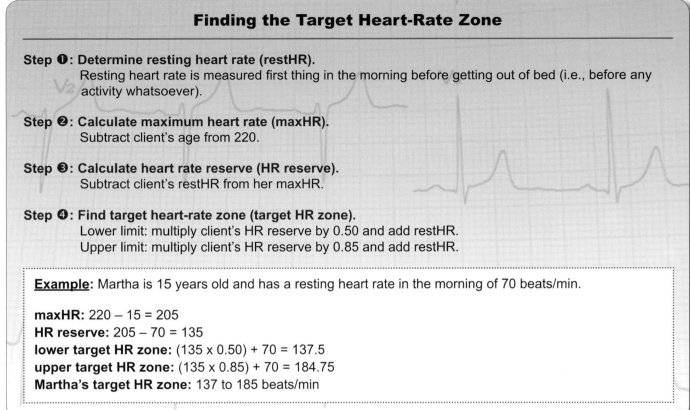

Step ❶: Determine resting heart rate (restHR).
Resting heart rate is measured first thing in the morning before getting out of bed (i.e., before any activity whatsoever).

Step ❷: Calculate maximum heart rate (maxHR).
Subtract client's age from 220.

Step ❸: Calculate heart rate reserve (HR reserve).
Subtract client's restHR from her maxHR.

Step ❹: Find target heart-rate zone (target HR zone).
Lower limit: multiply client's HR reserve by 0.50 and add restHR.
Upper limit: multiply client's HR reserve by 0.85 and add restHR.

> **Example:** Martha is 15 years old and has a resting heart rate in the morning of 70 beats/min.
>
> **maxHR:** 220 − 15 = 205
> **HR reserve:** 205 − 70 = 135
> **lower target HR zone:** (135 x 0.50) + 70 = 137.5
> **upper target HR zone:** (135 x 0.85) + 70 = 184.75
> **Martha's target HR zone:** 137 to 185 beats/min

There are many ways to train cardiorespiratory fitness, and they all involve exercising the whole body: step aerobics, tae box, spinning classes, swimming lengths, dancing, cycling, running, cross-country skiing, and so on. Clients can also do strength and endurance circuits and reduce or eliminate the rest between sets to ensure that they stay within their target heart-rate zones.

Pulse Checks

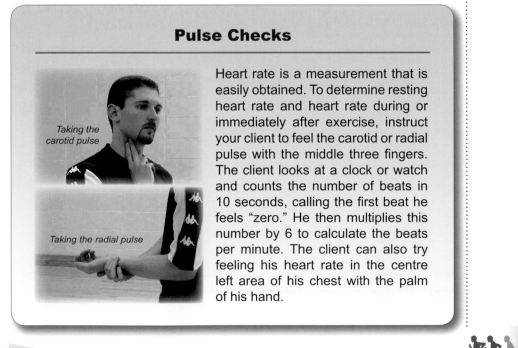

Taking the carotid pulse

Taking the radial pulse

Heart rate is a measurement that is easily obtained. To determine resting heart rate and heart rate during or immediately after exercise, instruct your client to feel the carotid or radial pulse with the middle three fingers. The client looks at a clock or watch and counts the number of beats in 10 seconds, calling the first beat he feels "zero." He then multiplies this number by 6 to calculate the beats per minute. The client can also try feeling his heart rate in the centre left area of his chest with the palm of his hand.

Testing Cardiorespiratory Endurance

Cardiorespiratory fitness testing is easily accomplished using the 12-minute run–walk test, the beep test, or the mCAFT test. The protocols and norms involved in performing these tests can be found in Chapter 12.

Flexibility

Have you ever wondered how gymnasts or ballet dancers perform the splits or arch their spines so far? This type of performance illustrates their ability to execute movements that require a great deal of flexibility. **Flexibility** is the ability of a joint to move through its full range of motion. It is determined primarily by joint structure and to a lesser extent by muscle elasticity and length.

Flexibility promotes joint health, slows the process of joint deterioration, and generally improves quality of life for most individuals. It may also help prevent lower back pain and injuries as well as reduce the frequency and severity of musculoskeletal injuries. A number of factors such as age, sex, and inactivity can affect flexibility. Just compare the level of flexibility of a young and active rhythmic gymnast with that of an elderly person with arthritis. When applying the FITT principle to flexibility, there is no limit on the frequency of training. A minimum of three times per week is recommended.

Active and Passive Flexibility

Flexibility can be active or passive. **Active flexibility** is the range of movement generated by individual effort; it is dependent on the strength of the muscles on the opposite side of the joint. As a result, strength training goes hand in hand with flexibility training. For example, strong hamstrings are required to hold the leg high in a skating spiral (flexibility at the hip joint). **Passive flexibility** is the range of movement achieved with the help of external forces (e.g., using the arms to pull the leg closer to the torso; a partner, weight, or rubber band assisting range of motion).

Passive flexibility exercises help achieve a wider range of movement than do active flexibility exercises (Figure 11.3). For most sports activities, the goal is to increase the active range so that it approaches the passive range. Another goal of flexibility training is to be equally flexible on both sides of the body.

Older adults with arthritis must adapt their everyday habits and lifestyles to deal with the lack of flexibility in their joints.

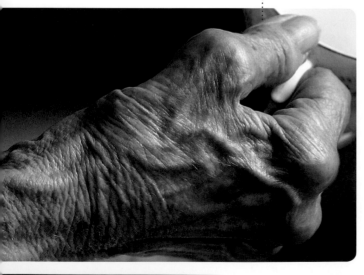

Recreation and Fitness Leadership

Figure 11.3 Stretching the muscles of the lower back and hamstrings. **A.** Active range of movement. **B.** Passive range of movement.

Training Flexibility

There is no limit to the frequency of training sessions for flexibility. The more a person trains, the faster the rate of improvement. However, the intensity of flexibility training must be carefully monitored. Make sure your client does not stretch to the point of pain; it is enough to feel tension, or stretch, in the muscle group. Pain is a warning sign of stretching too far.

The three stretching methods are dyamic, static, and proprioceptive neuromuscular facilitation. The length of a stretching session varies depending on the type of training method used. Dynamic warm-up stretching may last from 5 to 15 minutes depending on the person and the sport, but it may take 15 to 60 minutes to complete slow, static stretching or a PNF stretching program for the whole body.

Dynamic Stretching Dynamic stretching refers to moving a joint through its full range of motion, such as the arm of a baseball pitcher. Dynamic stretching is typically seen in warm-ups. When a competitive swimmer swings his arms around in circles while standing on the starting block, he is doing dynamic stretching. Runners warming up by leaping and bounding are also doing dynamic warm-up stretching. Golfers are learning the importance of warming up, and it is becoming more common to see players using the club to limber up the torso and shoulders.

Dynamic stretching is not the same as ballistic stretching. Ballistic stretching, or bouncing, is not a recommended method of stretching and should be avoided. It has been shown to cause micro-damage to the muscle fibres, resulting in soreness after the exercise.

CAUTION

Never stretch a cold muscle! A short session of total body exercise that raises the pulse rate, breathing rate, and muscle temperature must precede stretching! Breaking a sweat is a good sign that the warm-up has been sufficient and it is okay to begin dynamic stretching.

Static Stretching Holding a fully stretched position, such as the splits, is known as **static stretching**. Using this method, a person slowly relaxes the muscles to be stretched and holds herself in a stretched position for 10 to 30 seconds. The process may be enhanced by an assisting partner and repeated four to six times for maximum efficiency. This method of developing flexibility is time consuming and best performed at the end of a practice when the muscles are tired (Figure 11.4).

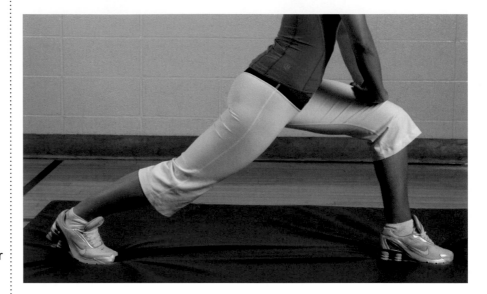

Figure 11.4 Loosening-up exercises are most beneficial after an exhausting exercise session.

PNF Stretching The **proprioceptive neuromuscular facilitation (PNF)** method bypasses the natural reflexes of the muscle and its tendon sensors that protect against overstretching. Regarded as the most efficient stretching method, PNF is carried out in three phases.

❶ During the first phase (passive stretching), the muscles to be stretched are pulled or pushed to the very limit of the movement range. This initial stretching movement should be performed slowly and continuously. This prevents the muscle spindles from initiating the stretch reflex, which contracts the muscles and is counterproductive.

❷ In the second phase (pre-tension), the person being stretched contracts the targeted muscle group by pushing against resistance for approximately seven seconds. The force of this contraction can be minimal.

❸ In the third phase (passive stretching), the limb is pulled or pushed into a stretched position again, but not to the point of pain. This final position is then held, with all muscles relaxed, for approximately six seconds. The sequence is repeated three or four times.

PNF stretching can be executed independently or with the assistance of a partner, who slowly and constantly applies pressure and must be alert to the stretcher's sensation of full stretch in the passive phases.

The proprioceptive neuromuscular facilitation (PNF) method is the most efficient stretching method and involves three phases: passive stretching, pre-tension, and passive stretching.

Recreation and Fitness Leadership

> ### FITT Principle for Flexibility
>
> *Frequency* – As much as can be fit into the client's schedule.
>
> *Intensity* – Instruct your client to stretch until she perceives muscle tension. Stretching to the point of pain can be harmful.
>
> *Time* – Sessions of 5 to 60 minutes.
>
> *Type* – Dynamic, static, or PNF, with or without a partner.

Testing Flexibility

Flexibility is joint specific, but a test for forward flexion (i.e., the sit-and-reach test) is often used as an indicator of overall body flexibility. See Chapter 12 for other testing methods.

Body Composition

Body composition refers to the various tissues that make up the body, in particular fat/adipose tissue and muscle tissue as well as organs, bones, and fluids. It is regarded as one of the major components of physical fitness. Of particular interest are percentages of lean body mass and fat body mass. An active, physically fit person typically has a lower percentage of body fat than an inactive, unfit person.

For a detailed discussion about body composition, weight management, the effects of obesity, and vitality, see Chapter 10.

Components of Motor Ability

A subset of physical fitness is **motor ability**, or skill-related fitness. Motor ability refers to the integration of the central nervous system and the muscular system. In short, it is what determines how well the body moves. The brain constantly monitors both its internal and external environments, collecting information and making decisions about what is relevant information and what is irrelevant information. It then applies this information to physical movement.

Although skill-related components of fitness are often overlooked, they are necessary for effective functioning in all environments. Motor abilities are of varying importance for the general population, but they are especially important for athletes. The most significant motor abilities are power, agility, coordination, reaction time, balance, and speed.

Power

A combination of strength and speed, **power** involves the ability to overcome external resistance at a high rate of muscular contraction. It is a function of how fast a force can be generated to overcome gravity and thus accelerate the body or an implement. Power is important for performance in many recreation activities and sports. Throwing or kicking a ball, blocking a spike in volleyball, punching in boxing, sprinting out of the blocks in running, leaping in a dance routine, driving a golf ball, or doing a layup or dunk in basketball are all examples of power (Figure 11.5).

Training Power

When training power, it is important not to train more than three or four times per week. The total volume of the training should be monitored to reduce the chance of overuse injuries. The intensity needs to be at or close to maximum, involving quick and intense movements that are repeated 8 to 10 times in each of 2 to 4 sets. To prevent injury and increase the effectiveness of your client's workouts, it is usually best to develop strength before adding power training.

Any type of resistance training can be used to develop power if the exertion phase is done as quickly as possible while recovering slowly to the start position. Most strength exercises can be modified to develop power (e.g., clapping push-ups). Throwing a medicine ball is an example of training for power. An effective way to improve the explosive power of the legs is through **plyometric training**. It involves moving a muscle to a "prestretched" position and then explosively contracting the stretched muscle. This method places high amounts of stress on tendons, however, so great care should be taken in order to avoid injury.

Plyometric training is one of the best ways to improve the explosive power of the legs.

Testing Power

The vertical jump and the standing long jump are examples of commonly used tests to assess power in the legs. Measuring the distance a client can throw a baseball or a weighted medicine ball can provide an assessment of upper-body and arm power. Some of these tests are presented in Chapter 12.

Figure 11.5 Activities requiring explosive power.

Recreation and Fitness Leadership

Agility

Agility is the ability to execute movements at high speed with rapid changes in direction, level, or plane. It is important in sports such as basketball, volleyball, football, and hockey. A football player who dodges several players on the opposing team on his way to scoring a touchdown demonstrates a high level of agility.

Training agility is as easy as practicing any sport at high intensity while performing quick changes in movement. Agility evaluation is similar to practice drills used in various sports. These tests include shuttle runs, zigzag runs, and the hexagon jump. See Chapter 12 for protocols and norms.

Coordination

The ability to perform movements in the correct order and with the proper timing is known as **coordination**. Coordinated movements are smooth and efficient. Compare the wild splashing of an inexperienced swimmer with the apparently effortless action of a skilled swimmer.

Coordination involves the integration of eye, hand, and foot movements. This component is necessary for success in team sports such as baseball, soccer, and basketball, where good coordination is essential for shooting, catching, throwing, trapping, dribbling, and kicking a ball.

Coordination can be developed by using simple drills and games, such as bouncing two basketballs at the same time and then starting to walk or move. Tests of coordination are similar to the agility tests (e.g., shuttle run) and practice drills used in various sports.

Integrating eye, hand, and foot movements is critical in team sports such as baseball, where coordination can mean the difference between a hit and a strikeout.

Reaction Time

Reaction time is one of the most cherished motor abilities in sports and everyday life. Stated simply, **reaction time** is the ability to react quickly. It is the time it takes to initiate a response to a stimulus. It is not possible to react or to move the instant you observe, hear, or feel the stimulus.

Various physiological processes are involved from the time a stimulus is observed (e.g., traffic light turning green) or heard (e.g., reacting to a telephone ring) to the time it takes to initiate the movement. The sensory organs (eyes and/or ears) must be aroused, the nerves must conduct an impulse to the brain (where decisions are made) and from the brain to the muscles, and the muscles must contract before an overt movement can be initiated. These processes require time – reaction time.

To improve reaction time in sports, coaches can devise speed and reaction drills that are general and/or specific to their sport. A simple test for reaction time involves catching a metre stick as shown in Figure 11.6.

Figure 11.6 A simple hand reaction test that involves catching a metre stick can be used by coaches as a way to test and improve reaction time.

Figure 11.7 Balance can be developed by holding a static "stork stand" and focusing on body awareness and positioning.

Balance

The ability to achieve and maintain body stability is called **balance**. This component of functional fitness is important in everything we do, from walking down the street to standing on our tiptoes with our eyes closed.

We distinguish between static and dynamic balance. **Static balance** is the ability to balance on a stable surface when no locomotion is required. Sporting examples of static balance include holding the body position while standing on a balance beam or over a golf ball. **Dynamic balance** encompasses a wider range of activities. It refers to the ability to balance on a moving surface (e.g., rowing on water, white-water kayaking, surfing) or to balance while involved in locomotion (e.g., in-line skating, dribbling a soccer ball, avoiding defensive players, skiing).

Balance can be developed with practice during functional training (described in the following section of the chapter) and by focusing on body awareness and body positioning. To track improvements, time how long a client can hold a static position in a "stork stand" while keeping the eyes closed (Figure 11.7).

Speed

Speed is the highest rate at which a movement or series of movements can be executed, or the ability to cover a given distance in the shortest possible time during an all-out effort of short duration (e.g., less than 10 seconds). Speed is important in many sport situations, but it is useful for everyone in emergency situations.

Speed can be developed through interval training at very high intensity. Short runs are used to evaluate speed. Examples of such tests are the 50-metre and the 100-metre dash.

Fitness Training Activities

An overview of fitness training activities is presented in Table 11.1. These activities are designed to develop various aspects of physical fitness. Strength and muscular endurance are developed using resistance

Recreation and Fitness Leadership

activities, whereas aerobic and anaerobic capacity are developed through cardiorespiratory activities. Motor abilities are best developed by using functional fitness activities. If combined, these activities can improve your client's overall physical fitness.

Table 11.1 An overview of fitness training activities and their effects.

Training Method	Training Effect
Resistance Activities	
• Station training	Strength
• Circuit training	Strength, muscular endurance
• Fitness classes	Strength, muscular endurance
Cardiorespiratory Activities	
• Walking, jogging	Aerobic fitness
• Speed play training	Aerobic fitness
• Interval training	Aerobic and anaerobic fitness
• Cross-training	Aerobic fitness, muscular endurance
• Aerobic fitness classes	Aerobic and anaerobic fitness
• Circuit training	Aerobic fitness, muscular endurance
Functional Fitness Activities	
• Personal training	Motor abilities
• Fitness classes	Motor abilities, strength, muscular endurance
• Pilates	Core stability, balance, muscular endurance
• Ashtanga yoga	Flexibility, muscular endurance

*A*erobic capacity, or aerobic power, is synonymous with cardiorespiratory fitness (i.e., the efficiency of the heart, lungs, and circulatory system). Anaerobic capacity is the amount of work per second performed in muscular activity between 30 and 90 seconds' duration. Anaerobic means "without oxygen" – the energy expended is supplied by chemical reactions within the muscle fibres.

Resistance Activities

Station Training

Station training refers to the completion of all the sets of one exercise before moving to the next exercise. When performing a series of sets within a station, the same muscle groups are stressed over and over again. This dynamic resistance training promotes the development of strength by using free weights (popular with elite athletes) and strength-training exercise machines with constant or variable resistance (popular with recreational athletes).

Station training can incorporate free-weight exercises (popular with elite athletes) and strength-training exercise machines (popular with recreational athletes).

Circuit Training

A **circuit training** exercise program allows an individual to combine specific exercises to achieve specific fitness goals. Exercises can be selected to work all major muscle groups – legs, abdominals, arms, shoulders, back, chest, and torso – in one session. This aspect of circuit training is illustrated in the circuit training layout in Figure 11.8.

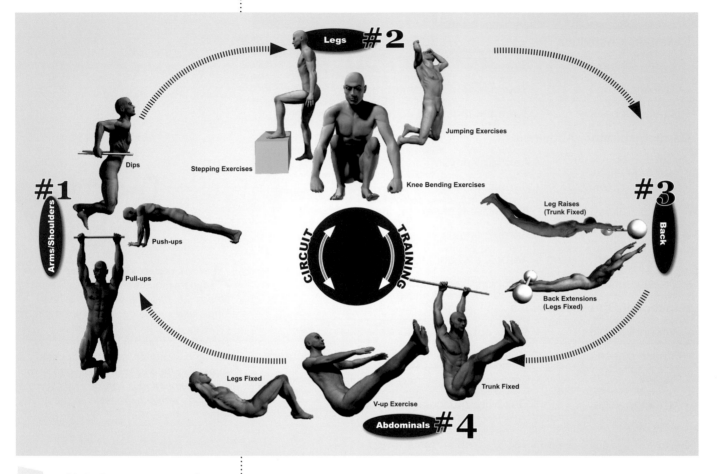

Figure 11.8 General layout of a circuit training program.

Circuit training differs from station training because only one set is completed (or the exercise is performed for a specified period of time) before moving to the next exercise. It is possible to design a circuit that has no rest between stations, thus maintaining heart rate in the target zone and resulting in cardiorespiratory fitness improvement. With a little creativity, you can design a circuit exercise program that challenges clients at all levels of fitness. Examples of popular circuit training programs are shown in Tables 11.2 and 11.3.

Circuit Training Variables The major variables of circuit training programs include the number of exercises, time spent at each station, sequence of exercises, number of trips around the circuit, number of repetitions, resistance levels, rest period between sets and circuits, and types of exercises.

Table 11.2 General structure of three popular circuits designed for general or specific fitness development.

Variation 1
- 10 – 12 exercise stations
- 30 seconds on, 30 – 60 seconds off (perform as many repetitions as possible in 30 seconds, followed by 30-second recovery)
- Instructor uses whistle to indicate start and end of exercising; commands can be prerecorded
- Trainee records number of repetitions achieved/station (example: 15/7)

Variation 2
- 10 – 12 exercise stations
- 10 – 15 repetitions at each station
- Set exercise time to 10 minutes
- No recovery between stations
- Trainee records number of laps and number of exercises achieved in the last lap (example: 2/7)

Variation 3
- 10 – 12 exercise stations
- 10 – 15 repetitions at each station
- No recovery between stations
- Trainee records total time achieved per circuit (example: 8 min 27 sec)

▶ *Number of stations:* Circuits with 8 to 12 stations are the most popular.

▶ *Time at station:* Varies between 30 seconds and 60 seconds.

▶ *Exercise sequence:* Exercises should be arranged so that no two consecutive exercises involve the same muscle group. Thus, a set to develop the arm extensor muscles could be followed by a set to exercise the leg extensors, followed by exercises to develop the abdominal muscles, and so on.

▶ *Number of laps:* A circuit is normally repeated one to three times.

▶ *Number of repetitions and level of resistance:* The number of repetitions per exercise and the resistance level depend on the objective of training, whether it is strength, endurance, or power.

▶ *Recovery between exercises:* The recovery between exercises and laps depends on the training objectives: for muscular endurance development, relatively short or no recovery is planned (the trainee moves from one exercise station to another with no interruption in exercising); for strength development, the rest intervals are longer, or every other station is a stretching station.

▶ *Types of exercises:* Circuit training can be carried out by using a wide variety of means: own body weight, partner-assisted exercises, medicine balls, dumbbells, barbells, and exercise machines.

Depending on your specific training goals, the number of stations, time at each station, number of laps, number of repetitions, and recovery time can be adjusted to meet your needs for strength and endurance.

 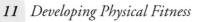

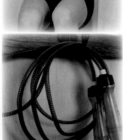

Table 11.3 A 30-minute circuit training program that alternates cardiorespiratory activities with muscular endurance activities.

Station Number	Activity
Station 1	Rope skipping – two-foot bounce
Station 2	Bench press
Station 3	Stepping: up, up, down, down
Station 4	Trunk extension
Station 5	Jogging on the spot
Station 6	Curl-ups
Station 7	Seated row
Station 8	Heel raise
Station 9	Stationary bicycle
Station 10	Lat pull-downs
Station 11	Rope skipping – hop 8 x right leg, 8 x left leg
Station 12	Leg adductor machine
Station 13	Stepping: up, knee lift, down, down
Station 14	Trunk rotation machine
Station 15	Heel jacks

*Participants spend 50 seconds at each station and are given 10 seconds to change stations. The circuit is repeated twice for a total of 30 minutes.

Cardiorespiratory Activities

Brisk Walking and Jogging

Brisk walking and jogging are believed to be the best overall exercises for developing and maintaining cardiorespiratory fitness. These activities can be done almost anywhere at almost any time. The intensity of exercise is typically "conversational," whereby the walkers/joggers are able to talk without undue respiratory distress. Walking has the advantage of being low impact (i.e., less damaging to the joints). You can add novelty to the jogging session by varying the speed and adding some short sprints.

Walking is one of the best overall activities for developing and maintaining cardiorespiratory fitness, and it can be done just about anywhere at almost any time.

Interval Training

Interval training involves a timed, systematic alternation of exertion and recovery (i.e., a series of exercises interspersed with rest periods). Interval training is very popular with athletes, but it can be used by anybody. It benefits both the aerobic and anaerobic energy systems as well as muscular endurance. You don't need to be an elite athlete to require at least a minimum level of training for both these systems. The aerobic system is called on in everyday life when a person climbs multiple flights of stairs or goes for a walk in the park. Running for the bus, racing up the

Recreation and Fitness Leadership

stairs to get to an appointment on time, and sprinting to catch a Frisbee are examples of when the anaerobic energy system is used.

Four variables that must be considered in interval training are (1) distance or length of time, (2) speed or rate, (3) rest period, and (4) number of repetitions. Manipulation of these variables, one or all, can provide your client's desired workout intensity. Table 11.4 applies the concept of interval training to a variety of activities.

Interval Training Variables

❶ Distance or length of time

❷ Speed or rate

❸ Rest period

❹ Number of repetitions

Table 11.4 Examples of interval training applied to various activities.

Activity	Freq./Wk	Distance (m)	Time (sec)	Rest (sec)	Reps
Jogging	3	50	8	40	10
Swimming	3	50	120	180	8
Bicycling	2	1,000	150	180	8
Kayaking	2	100	30	90	12

Another type of interval training is often seen in group fitness classes. The exercise leader pushes the group by working at maximum intensity until the participants are breathless for a specific period of time, then the leader reverts to less energetic movements. This allows the participants' heart rates to return to the lower end of their target heart-rate zones. If this strategy is repeated several times during the class, interval training is being employed.

Cross-Training

Performing various kinds of exercise or doing activities that differ from your usual routine is known as **cross-training**. Athletes often use this method when recovering from injuries. Cross-training is also popular among competitive athletes in the off-season. To provide variety and prevent boredom and burnout, recreational athletes use cross-training throughout the year. An additional benefit of this approach is that it may help prevent overuse injuries.

Aerobic cross-training may involve cycling, cross-country skiing, swimming, water running, and skating. Muscular endurance cross-training may involve working on a rowing machine, stair climber, cycle ergometer, and NordicTrack (Figure 11.9). Activity cross-training may involve participating in several different activities, such as soccer, beach volleyball, mountain biking, and hockey (Figure 11.10).

Figure 11.9 Working on a rowing machine requires little skill, but it provides great fitness benefits.

Figure 11.10 Cross-training involving many different activities is a good way to achieve total body fitness.

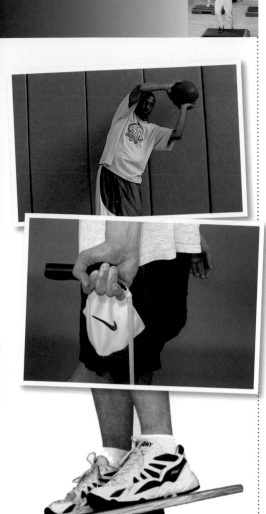

Functional Fitness Activities

A relatively new area of focus in the fitness industry is **functional fitness**. This training type helps individuals function better in their homes and workplaces and is extremely valuable in rehabilitation. A personal trainer designs exercises that give an elderly person the flexibility to tie his shoelaces, that give a parent with a back injury the strength and stability to move wet clothes to a laundry hamper and carry it safely, that give a grocery store cashier the muscular endurance and core strength to bag an endless conveyor belt of purchases. The fitness training principle of specificity is key in designing the most effective exercises.

Similarly, sport performance training programs are very specific. They emphasize the development of the neuromuscular system and motor abilities (such as balance, power, and agility) rather than pure strength or endurance. Countless new exercises have been designed to train athletes using the specific stances and movement patterns required in their sports.

In general, since it is important that skills and actions be performed with perfect technique for motor learning to occur, exercises are continued only as long as correct form and technique can be maintained. They are never performed to the point of fatigue.

Functional fitness training often incorporates simple equipment such as stability balls, resistance bands, medicine balls, and balance boards (Figure 11.11). Other ways to train functional fitness include Pilates and yoga.

Figure 11.11 Functional fitness training incorporates the use of simple equipment such as stability balls, resistance bands, medicine balls, and balance boards.

Group Fitness Classes

Group fitness classes are designed to develop all the physical fitness components. Various types of group aerobic fitness classes are offered including step, low- and high-impact aerobics, aquacise (aerobics in shallow or deep water), spinning classes on stationary bicycles, rope jumping, gliding, combative aerobics such as boxercise and tae bo, and many others. These classes usually last from 45 to 60 minutes and include basic elements such as a warm-up, cardio work for at least 20 minutes, muscular endurance work, and cool-down stretching.

Pilates, yoga, and various format combinations (e.g., Pilates on the ball, Step and Stretch) offer an endless selection of choices. Group fitness classes are a fun way to get fit and meet new people, and participants often enjoy the motivation of working out with others (Figure 11.12).

Figure 11.12 Group fitness classes, such as aquacise, can be a fun way to get fit and meet new people at the same time.

Recreation and Fitness Leadership

Group Fitness Activities

Hi/lo classes utilize both high- and low-impact moves for an aerobic workout. Participants have the choice between high- and low-impact exercises, with the option of modifying impact intensity throughout the class.

Low-impact classes include movements whereby one foot is always on the floor. Options are provided to incorporate power movements. This type of workout is as challenging as hi/lo for the cardiorespiratory system, with less stress on the joints.

Step classes include cardio and muscle conditioning exercises using a raised platform. Lateral low-impact moves off the step may be incorporated for muscle balance and exercise safety. Participants have the option of modifying steps or adding power for intensity.

> **Note:** *Hi/lo, low-impact, and step classes may have different choreography levels. For example,* **basic** *choreography puts the focus on technique and learning the moves. These basic moves are linked together into simple routines.* **Intermediate** *choreography is taught with an emphasis on creating and repeating combinations.* **Advanced** *choreography incorporates complex moves and patterns. In addition to the various choreography levels, different cardiorespiratory intensity levels may be marked. For example, an asterisk (*) could be used to designate a 20-minute cardio section, while two asterisks (**) could designate a 30-minute cardio section, and three asterisks (***) could mark a 40-minute cardio section.*

Total muscle conditioning focuses on strengthening all the muscles of the body including the lower body, the upper body, and the midsection (trunk). There is no cardiorespiratory component in this workout. Weights, Dyna-Bands, or other types of resistance equipment may be incorporated. Compound muscle groups are generally worked before isolating specific muscles. The abdominal and back muscles are worked near the end of the workout, or core stabilization is integrated throughout the entire class.

Core stability is a muscle conditioning class with no cardio component. It focuses on strengthening the trunk muscles. Standing balance exercises and core mat work are incorporated for stability. The trunk exercises are generally slow and controlled, with attention to breath, body alignment, and movement awareness.

Yoga, which in Sanskrit means "union," integrates the body, mind, and spirit to create a state of internal peacefulness. This exercise form utilizes stretching postures, breathing, and meditation techniques to enhance flexibility, increase lubrication of the joints, massage all organs of the body, balance the nervous system, increase circulation, improve immune functioning, and calm the emotional state. There is a diversity of yoga styles such as ashtanga, hatha, iyengar, kundalini, and restorative.

Ashtanga is a challenging series of sequential poses that focus on strength, flexibility, and building of heat by synchronizing movement with the breath.

Hatha is an ancient system combining the body, mind, and breath to achieve self-improvement through postures, breathing, and meditation that help purify the body, mind, and spirit.

Iyengar is a style that holds poses for a longer amount of time while incorporating props such as straps, blankets, and wooden blocks, with a focus on body alignment.

Kundalini focuses on raising energy up the spine and, in the process, awakening potential. This style focuses on postures, chanting, meditation, and breathing exercises.

Continued on next page . . .

Restorative is geared to restore energy through gentle, supportive poses. The exercises are suitable for the less able or those recovering from illness.

Pilates, pronounced pi-laa-teez, is a mind–body exercise approach that builds strength in the abdomen, back, and chest. This core stability exercise helps improve posture. The priority is thinking, sensing, and feeling what the body is doing in order to develop movement awareness. For many decades, Pilates was popular with dancers and athletes, while now the general public enjoys this challenging yet gentle workout. Pilates teaches participants to value the body's interrelated parts and focus on quality rather than quantity.

Pilates offers a wide selection of choices with various format combinations.

Capoeira is a multicultural art form blending acrobatic sport, dance, culture, and philosophy. It promotes constructive, nonviolent assertiveness and healthy interaction with others. With emphasis on community harmony, this integrative movement class reinforces cooperative energy. The physical benefits include strength, flexibility, coordination, speed, rhythm, and grace. Capoeira is of Brazilian origin, but it traces its roots to Africa, Brazil (through Aboriginal peoples), and Europe.

NIA is a barefoot workout that combines dance, martial arts, and healing arts. It blends the spirit and energy of Eastern and Western disciplines, including nine movement forms. From dance it integrates jazz, modern, and Duncan styles. From martial arts it draws upon tai chi, tae kwon do, and aikido. From the healing arts it incorporates yoga, the Feldenkrais method, and the Alexander technique. The word NIA was originally an initialism for neuromuscular integrative action. Today NIA is known as the "Now I Am" fully alive workout. It is an expressive cardio experience integrating choreographed routines, free dance, sounding, toning, and vocal release. The music used in NIA classes is eclectic and culturally diverse. NIA is a unique, inspirational, and soulful whole-body workout.

ExerBall uses 55- to 65-cm stability balls to develop trunk strength in the abdominal, back, and chest muscles. This type of exercise also improves posture, flexibility, mobility, and circulation. By simply bouncing on the ball, the abdominal and back muscles co-contract and work isometrically to stabilize the body. Pilates exercises may also be adapted for use with the ball, providing more challenging core training.

Capoeira is a multicultural art form blending acrobatic sport, dance, culture, and philosophy.

Recreation and Fitness Leadership

Putting It All Together

Physical fitness encompasses many components that are important for health, including, muscular strength, muscular endurance, cardiorespiratory fitness, flexibility, and body composition, as well as components that help you move more effectively – the motor abilities – such as power, agility, coordination, reaction time, balance, and speed.

Functional fitness activities and resistance training activities can be used to develop and maintain muscular strength and endurance. Cardiorespiratory endurance can be enhanced through any type of total body activity during which the target heart rate is achieved. Flexibility can be improved by three methods: static stretching, dynamic stretching, and proprioceptive neuromuscular facilitation (PNF). PNF is considered the most effective technique.

Understanding the four design components of any fitness program (frequency, intensity, time, and type of activity) and the training principles that produce the most effective results (overload, progression, reversibility, and specificity) allows you to mentor others in discovering purposeful and rewarding physical exercise. In addition, choosing enjoyable activities can have a significant impact on how rewarding physical activity is for a client. The secret lies in putting together a fitness plan that is personalized for each individual.

> "Commit to be fit."
> *Anonymous*

Key Terms

absolute strength
active flexibility
agility
agonist–antagonist training
balance
body composition
cardiorespiratory (cardiovascular)
  endurance
circuit training
coordination
cross-training
dynamic balance
dynamic exercises
dynamic stretching
FITT principle
flexibility
formal fitness activities
functional fitness
informal fitness activities
interval training

motor ability
muscular endurance
muscular strength
one repetition maximum
overload principle
passive flexibility
physical activity
physical exercise
physical fitness
plyometric training
power
progression principle
proprioceptive neuromuscular
  facilitation (PNF)
reaction time
relative strength
reversibility principle
specificity principle
speed
static balance

static exercises

static stretching

station training

target heart rate zone

total fitness

training frequency

training intensity

training volume

work-to-rest ratio

Review Questions

1. Describe the FITT principle of exercise training.

2. Explain the importance of the progressive overload and reversibility principles in any training program.

3. List the four components of physical fitness described in this chapter. Explain how each dimension relates to physical fitness.

4. Describe how you can promote improvement in each of the following: muscular strength, muscular endurance, cardiorespiratory endurance, and flexibility.

5. What is agonist–antagonist training? Why is it important that this approach to training be incorporated into a strength training schedule?

6. What is the difference between static and dynamic exercises?

7. Differentiate between the three flexibility methods discussed in this chapter. In what phase of a training session is each of these methods most effective?

8. Discuss how motor abilities relate to other components of fitness.

9. Describe the elements of a circuit training program. How can you incorporate circuit training into your overall fitness regimen?

10. Discuss some important features of functional fitness. How does functional fitness differ from traditional training techniques?

NAME: Karen Gray

OCCUPATION: Manager, Spectrum Centre for Creative Fitness
Fitness Consultant (Canadian Society for Exercise Physiology)
Personal Trainer (Canadian Association of Fitness Professionals)

EDUCATION: Fitness Instructor (YMCA)
Program Director Specialist (Can-Fit-Pro)
Shotokan Karate Brown Belt (3rd Kyu) (Hiryu Bushido Kai)

▶ *Why did you choose to pursue a career in personal fitness training?*

Fitness has always been an important part of my life, and I have spent a lot of time in gyms for many years. Working in the fitness field was simply a natural option when I started back to work after raising my family.

I started instructing fitness classes (combining knowledge from years of participating in classes, my karate training, and taking an instructors' course). I progressed to acquiring my personal trainer and fitness consultant certifications. Circumstances led me to buying and operating my own small fitness centre and several years later selling it to my competition and becoming the manager, where I'm presently employed.

▶ *What do you do as a manager?*

My workdays are mostly spent in the gym office and reception area handling daily business, such as greeting the members and handling inquiries. I oversee the staff and facility (rentals, maintenance, reports, and so on). It's a pleasure to be able to spend my working time in an atmosphere I truly enjoy.

▶ *What do you do as a personal trainer/fitness consultant?*

The most satisfying part of my job is dealing with the members, especially when I can utilize my personal training skills. When I'm able to help individuals achieve their specific goals, whether it's weight loss, muscle building, sport or job requirements, or simply improved health and fitness, I enjoy watching their progress, and it's gratifying to know I've made a difference.

▶ *What do you see in the future for personal trainers/fitness consultants?*

The fitness field is fairly competitive, but I think there is always going to be room for people who are truly passionate about fitness, about sharing their knowledge with others, and who have good social skills. We are constantly learning more about the benefits of being fit and about new ways to develop and present fitness programs. As the public becomes more aware of the importance of physical activity for maintaining or regaining health, the need for fitness leaders who can teach, inspire, and guide others will likely only increase. The fitness industry is working hard to persuade the government to provide a tax break for fitness memberships, which would surely encourage even more people to participate and more businesses to promote and support an active, healthy lifestyle.

Fitness and personal training is not limited to the gym setting. Trainers can work from their own homes or clients' homes, and outdoors as well. Depending on how far an individual who is serious about fitness wishes to take his or her career, it might be wise to pursue a kinesiology or exercise science degree, which would open a whole other avenue of options. Although education is a must, believing in fitness as a lifestyle, maintaining your own fitness level, and having a keen desire to help others are the keys to having a successful and rewarding career as a personal trainer.

In This Chapter:

CHAPTER 12
Fitness Evaluation

In this chapter, you will learn about the following:

❶ The value of fitness testing, measurement, and evaluation

❷ The importance of reliability and validity in fitness testing

❸ Using appropriate appraisal tools to assess others' physical fitness

❹ Analyzing the results of physical fitness appraisals

> ## "Your biggest task is not to get ahead of others, but to surpass yourself."
> Anonymous

Fitness testing, measurement, and evaluation all serve an important purpose. We all make decisions on a daily basis, and the best decisions are made with accurate and relevant information. Such information allows us to make the most effective fitness choices.

What would it be like to go through life without knowing what effect poor nutritional habits have on our quality of life, or how smoking adversely affects our health? Today, society is preoccupied with issues of weight management, health, and exercise, so obtaining a precise evaluation of your client's fitness levels is an increasingly important tool in decision making. Decisions can be enhanced with the aid of testing, measurement, and evaluation.

People want to know how they can improve their health through exercise, which aspects of their fitness need improvement, and possibly how they compare to other similar populations. The information you receive through simple **field tests** is often enough to determine whether your client's physical condition is consistent with good health and can help you plan an appropriate program to maintain or improve your client's current fitness levels.

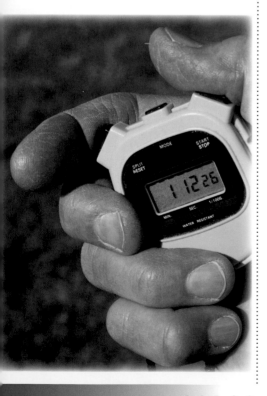

The Importance of Fitness Testing

Diagnosis – Testing can be used to identify and evaluate deficiencies or weaknesses in a person's fitness.

Goal setting – Results from testing can be used to develop reasonable and attainable fitness goals.

Placement – Tests may be used to group individuals on the basis of their common characteristics or goals.

Motivation – Tests can be used to help individuals put forth their full effort and to provide challenge and stimulation to more accurately measure personal fitness.

Achievement – Testing can promote achievement by measuring movement towards the accomplishment of a set of objectives.

Prediction – Testing has long been used to predict future events or outcomes based on past or present data.

Recreation and Fitness Leadership

Norms – Your Client's Reference Perspective

Humans are social beings, and we often like to know how we compare to those around us. It sometimes isn't enough to know how we placed – we want to know how many people finished ahead of us and how many people finished behind us. Standardized tests can provide such information. For example, to evaluate a client's explosive power, you can administer a vertical jump test. The client's results can be compared to norm-referenced standards (**norms**) to determine his level of achievement relative to a clearly defined subgroup (e.g., people of the same age or sex).

Norms also indicate where improvements need to be made and where training efforts are best directed. They provide a starting reference point against which your client's performances can later be compared.

However, norms can sometimes be demoralizing or even dangerous if they make your client try to attain unrealistic goals. The most important reference point is the personal improvement of your client's fitness over time.

Standardized tests, such as push-ups, can provide us with information about how our level of achievement compares with others in the same group, as well as where improvements might need to be made.

Reliability and Validity

Both reliability and validity are essential for testing, measurement, and evaluation. Testing involves careful planning, and you must look for accuracy and consistency when making measurements. A test that fails to demonstrate precision and reproducibility runs the risk of yielding faulty results. Choosing the correct test is the first major consideration, but you must also know how to properly administer the test.

Reliability refers to the consistency or repeatability of scores, data, or observations. A test is reliable if it produces measurements that are the same (or approximately the same) each time the test is administered to the same individual. This ensures that the test results are dependable and consistent.

Whereas reliability refers to the consistency of scores or data, validity is a characteristic of the instrument or test being used. **Validity** is the extent to which a test measures what it proposes to measure. Most people would agree that curl-ups are a valid measure of abdominal muscular endurance. But do they measure upper-body strength? Obviously they do not. In order to be deemed valid, a test must measure what it claims to measure.

When administering any test, accuracy and consistency are required to produce reliable results.

Assessing Physical Fitness

The benefits of living an active lifestyle and maintaining a high level of physical fitness have been emphasized throughout this text. Having said that, how can fitness levels be accurately measured? You may have seen, or experienced firsthand, fitness appraisals being conducted at health clubs or at school. But what do these tests actually measure? Do they provide an accurate indication of physical fitness levels? When mentoring others about fitness, it is important to set attainable and relevant goals that make sense for your client – diagnostic fitness appraisals can help in this respect. These test scores also help you produce specific and measurable goals.

Becoming a Certified Fitness Appraiser

Health Canada endorses the Canadian Society for Exercise Physiology (CSEP), which includes an educational branch for certification of fitness appraisers. The CSEP currently has two levels of certification, certified personal trainer (CPT) and certified exercise physiologist (CEP). There are certain prerequisites for starting the certification process:

Level 1: CSEP Certified Personal Trainer (CSEP-CPT)
Candidates must have completed at least two years of a college diploma or university degree program that addresses the CSEP-CPT core competencies.

Level 2: CSEP Certified Exercise Physiologist (CSEP-CEP)
Candidates must have completed a four-year university degree in kinesiology or a related field. This professional certification is for students who wish to specialize in the health, fitness, and rehabilitation industry.

When courses are successfully completed, the individual registers and pays annual membership fees to become a CSEP-CPT or CSEP-CEP. Membership fees include professional liability insurance.

Understanding the components of physical fitness and how they can be measured will assist you in your own pursuit of physical fitness and health as well as help you mentor others. This section will help you become more familiar with the various ways fitness is evaluated so you can choose valid tests and administer them in a reliable way.

Measuring Cardiorespiratory Endurance

Simple practical field tests have been devised to measure **cardiorespiratory endurance**, or the ability to sustain aerobic exercise. Popular field tests include running and step tests. **Running tests** require subjects to run a prescribed distance or run for a predetermined length of time; the time required to cover the distance and the distance covered in the allotted time, respectively, are the measurements used to assess aerobic capacity. **Step tests** involve stepping up and down steps of a certain height at a particular rate for an established period of time. Cardiorespiratory endurance is then estimated from the heart rate response or recovery heart rate following the activity.

Step tests were originally designed to test the aerobic capacity of adults, and as such, they are submaximal tests, stopping before the heart rate reaches 85 percent of the estimated maximum level. Other tests such as the 12-minute run–walk test and the beep test are maximal tests, which are more commonly used for younger individuals or populations with higher fitness levels.

12-Minute Run–Walk Test

This test is designed for males and females of all ages. Little equipment is required – a stopwatch, whistle, and distance markers are really all you need to complete the test. However, a course of a specified distance will make counting the number of laps completed an easier task; the number of laps can then be easily multiplied by the course distance. Distance markers can also be used effectively to divide the course into 100-metre increments so that the tester can quickly and accurately determine the distance covered after 12 minutes have elapsed.

The goal of the test is to simply run or walk (or both) around the course as many times as possible in 12 minutes, following the starting signal, from behind a designated start line. It is also helpful if the tester announces the participants' lap times as they are completed as well as indicates the 10-minute and 11-minute marks. A spotter/partner, assigned to each runner, should maintain an accurate count of each lap and any portion of a lap completed by the subject when the stop signal is given after 12 minutes. The runner should keep track of laps as well. The distance covered is calculated by multiplying the number of laps completed by the distance of each lap (including the incomplete lap), and the result should be recorded. The spotters and the runners can then reverse roles and complete the testing process again.

If 12 minutes seems too long for a particular age level, 9-minute

*W*here do certified fitness consultants (CFCs) and certified personal trainers (CPTs) work?

- Hospital settings
- Fitness gyms
- Rehabilitation centres
- Homes for the elderly
- Individual home settings

Running tests are relatively easy to administer and require minimal equipment, making them one of the more popular field tests for measuring cardiorespiratory fitness.

run–walk tests may also be appropriate. Evaluative norms for the 12-minute run–walk are presented in Table 12.1, but clients may want to focus on improving their performance on future trials rather than on tracking their normative position on the table.

Table 12.1 Fitness rating based on distance covered (km) in the 12-minute run–walk test.

Rating		Distance Covered by Age (years)		
		13 – 19	20 – 29	30 – 39
Excellent	males	≥3.01	≥2.85	≥2.74
	females	≥2.45	≥2.35	≥2.25
Above Average	males	2.78 – 3.00	2.66 – 2.84	2.53 – 2.73
	females	2.32 – 2.44	2.17 – 2.34	2.09 – 2.24
Average	males	2.53 – 2.77	2.41 – 2.65	2.35 – 2.52
	females	2.09 – 2.31	1.98 – 2.16	1.92 – 2.08
Below Average	males	2.22 – 2.52	2.12 – 2.40	2.11 – 2.34
	females	1.92 – 2.08	1.80 – 1.97	1.71 – 1.91
Needs Improvement	males	≤2.09	≤1.96	≤1.91
	females	≤1.61	≤1.54	≤1.53

Beep Test

The beep test, aka the Leger test, is a multistage fitness test consisting of a continual shuttle run over 20 metres. It is called the beep test because the client runs to the 20-metre line, turns around, and then waits until the beep before running to the other 20-metre line. The time between the recorded beeps decreases during each minute (level).

There are several versions of the test, but a commonly used version has an initial fast walking or slow running velocity of 8.5 km/hr, which increases by 0.5 km/hr after every minute (or for each level). The test comes to an end when the runner is unable to complete two consecutive intervals or shuttles before hearing the beep. If a runner misses one beep and catches up before hearing the next beep, then she can continue. It is only when two beeps in a row are missed that the runner is eliminated. The level the client achieves and the number of shuttle runs she completes can be used to compare her fitness against norms and to estimate her maximum oxygen capacity, or $\dot{V}O_2max$. Simple beep test calculators are available online; they use the level and number of shuttles completed by the runner to calculate a predicted $\dot{V}O_2max$.

This test needs minimal equipment: a tape measure to accurately measure 20 metres, some cones or a rope to mark the 20-metre lines, a

nonslip running surface for safety, a prerecorded tape or CD, and a tape or CD player. The beep test is a maximal exertion test and is therefore not recommended for anyone with health issues. Like most tests, practice and motivation can influence the results. Evaluative norms for the beep test are presented in Table 12.2.

Table 12.2 Beep test norms for males and females.

Rating	Males		Females	
	Grade 9 – 10	Grade 11 – 12	Grade 9 – 10	Grade 11 – 12
Excellent	≥8/10	≥8/15	≥7/4	≥7/14
Above Average	7/9 – 8/9	7/14 – 8/14	6/2 – 7/3	6/7 – 7/13
Average	6/7 – 7/8	7/4 – 7/13	4/10 – 6/1	5/9 – 6/6
Below Average	5/9 – 6/6	6/2 – 7/3	4/5 – 4/9	4/11 – 5/8
Needs improvement	≤5/8	≤6/1	≤4/4	≤4/10

*The number preceding the "/" indicates the number of levels completed, while the number following the "/" indicates the number of shuttles completed within a level.

The beep test is typically structured into 23 levels. Things start getting quite difficult at about level 9, and by level 11 to 13, even fairly fit people begin dropping out. English soccer star David Beckham and American cycling legend Lance Armstrong are two of the very few people who can complete the beep test.

Modified Canadian Aerobic Fitness Test

Another commonly used cardiorespiratory fitness test is the Modified Canadian Aerobic Fitness Test (mCAFT). This test requires the following equipment: an accurate heart rate monitor, a double 20.3-cm step or a single 40.6-cm step, a prerecorded tape or CD of the stepping cadence, and a tape or CD player. The test is submaximal, unlike the beep test and the 12-minute run–walk test.

The mCAFT is especially good for beginners or people who are new to fitness testing. It involves one or more sessions of three minutes of stepping at a predetermined speed (based on age and gender). Everyone

If at any time during the mCAFT test a client attains or exceeds the ceiling level (Table 12.5), stop the test immediately. As in any fitness activity, if a client is dizzy, experiences excessive leg pain or chest pain, or feels nauseated, stop the test and monitor the client. Medical attention is advised.

begins the test on the double 20.3-cm step, but individuals with a high level of fitness can switch to the single 40.6-cm step to complete the test if they wish. In the initial three minutes of stepping, the cadence is set so that clients work well below 85 percent of their predicted maximum heart rate. The heart rate needs to be monitored closely for safety, making a heart rate monitor essential.

The client continues to perform three-minute stepping intervals, and with each stage the stepping cadence or intensity increases. The client stops stepping when her heart rate reaches the suggested ceiling for her age category. The number of the last stage completed is recorded, and this number is used to determine the O_2 cost using Table 12.3. Once the O_2 cost is determined, this figure can be plugged into the aerobic fitness score (AFS) formula to calculate the client's health benefits zone.

Table 12.3 Stepping cadence (in foot-plants per min) and O_2 cost (in ml/kg/min) for different stages of the mCAFT.

Stage	Males		Females	
	Cadence	O_2 Cost	Cadence	O_2 Cost
1	66	15.9	66	15.9
2	84	18.0	84	18.0
3	102	22.0	102	22.0
4	114	24.5	114	24.5
5	132	29.5	120	26.5
6	144	33.6	132	29.5
7	118*(single)	36.2	144	33.6
8	132*(single)	40.1	118*(single)	36.2

Table 12.3 gives the stepping cadence for different stages of the mCAFT. The starting stages for all ages are listed in Table 12.4. If the predetermined ceiling postexercise heart rate is not attained or exceeded after the starting stage, the client performs a second three minutes of stepping (Table 12.5 indicates ceiling levels, or 85 percent of predicted maximum heart rate for each age).

Table 12.4 Starting stages by age and gender.

Age	Males	Females
15 – 19	4	3
20 – 29	4	3
30 – 39	3	3
40 – 49	3	2

Recreation and Fitness Leadership

Table 12.5 Ceiling postexercise heart rate for the mCAFT.

Age	10-sec Count	Heart Rate Monitor	Age	10-sec Count	Heart Rate Monitor	Age	10-sec Count	Heart Rate Monitor
15	29	174	25	27	166	35	26	157
16	28	173	26	27	165	36	26	156
17	28	173	27	27	164	37	26	156
18	28	172	28	27	163	38	26	155
19	28	171	29	27	162	39	25	154
20	28	170	30	27	162	40	25	153
21	28	169	31	27	161	41	25	152
22	28	168	32	26	160	42	25	151
23	28	167	33	26	159	43	25	150
24	28	167	34	26	158	44	25	150

Here is an example of how to calculate the aerobic fitness score (AFS) based on an mCAFT. Jamal is 15 years old and weighs 70 kg. He successfully completed stage 6 of the mCAFT. According to Table 12.3, the O_2 cost of the final stage completed is 33.6. The calculation follows:

AFS = 10 x [17.2 + (1.29 x O_2 cost) – (0.09 x weight in kg) – (0.18 x age)]

AFS = 10 x [17.2 + (1.29 x 33.6) – (0.09 x 70) – (0.18 x 15)]

AFS = 10 x (17.2 + 43.34 – 6.3 – 2.7)

AFS = 515.40

According to norms presented in Table 12.6, Jamal's aerobic fitness is rated as "average."

Table 12.6 Health benefits rating from the aerobic fitness score (AFS).

Rating	Males				Females			
	Age 15 – 19	Age 20 – 29	Age 30 – 39	Age 40 – 49	Age 15 – 19	Age 20 – 29	Age 30 – 39	Age 40 – 49
Excellent	574+	556+	488+	470+	490+	472+	454+	400+
Above Average	524 – 573	506 – 555	454 – 487	426 – 469	437 – 489	420 – 471	401 – 453	351 – 399
Average	488 – 523	472 – 505	401 – 453	355 – 425	395 – 436	378 – 419	360 – 400	319 – 350
Below Average	436 – 487	416 – 471	337 – 400	319 – 354	368 – 394	350 – 377	330 – 359	271 – 318
Needs Improvement	<436	<416	<337	<319	<368	<350	<330	<271

Measuring Muscular Strength

Measures of muscular strength involve tests that require one maximal effort for a given movement, often lifting an external weight or contracting against external resistance. Two field tests, the one repetition maximum and the hand grip test, are presented here.

One Repetition Maximum (1RM)

One repetition maximum (1RM) refers to the maximum amount of weight an individual can lift just one time (**absolute strength**), often using values from the bench press or leg press. Dividing the 1RM value by the client's body weight allows you to make the strength measures equitable across weight classes, or to calculate the individual's **relative strength**. When testing for maximum strength, you must adhere to the following guidelines:

- ► Have the subject warm up with stretching and light lifting.

- ► Have two spotters present to assist the subject and prevent injury.

- ► Have the subject perform a lift below the maximum (a pretest session may be useful).

- ► Have the subject rest at least two minutes between lifts to prevent fatigue.

Relationship between Maximal Strength and Muscular Endurance

It is neither necessary nor safe for an athlete or student to work against maximal resistance to calculate maximal strength capacity for a given exercise. Due to the close relationship between maximal strength and muscular endurance, determining an athlete's maximum number of repetitions against submaximal resistance will produce an accurate conclusion about maximal strength.

The relationship can be illustrated best with the following example. Student A is able to lift a 100-kg barbell, but partner B masters only 90 kg. If both students are challenged to clean and press a barbell of 85 kg as often as possible, student A will perform 7 or 8 repetitions and B only 2 or 3 repetitions. Using an 80-kg barbell, student A can do 10 to 12 repetitions and athlete B only 5 or 6 repetitions. This comparison shows that the number of repetitions against high resistance is dependent on the maximal strength of the athlete. The table below shows the maximal number of repetitions possible for load levels of different resistance.

The maximal feasible number of repetitions of a particular load is referred to as the repetition maximum (RM). If the RM of an exercise is 2 or 3, it can be deduced that an athlete can resist a force corresponding to approximately 95 percent of maximal strength capacity. If the athlete is able to perform maximally 7 or 8 repetitions with a particular weight, then this weight approximates 85 percent of his or her maximal strength capacity.

Maximum number of repetitions as a function of resistance.

Resistance Level	100%	95%	90%	85%	80%	75%
Repetition Maximum	1	2 – 3	5 – 6	7 – 8	approx. 10 – 12	approx. 12 – 16

▶ Increase weight on subsequent lifts by small increments (2.5 or 5 kg).

▶ Continue procedure until the subject fails to lift a particular weight.

▶ Record the last weight successfully lifted as the 1RM.

▶ Divide the subject's 1RM by body weight.

Hand Grip Test

A test that measures grip strength with a special **hand-grip dynamometer** is sometimes used as a measure of overall body strength – research has shown high relationships between the two for the general adult population The dynamometer is adjustable to fit the size of any hand. A needle indicates scoring on the dial, which is marked off in kilograms (0 to 100). The subject simply takes a breath and, while exhaling, squeezes the device maximally to obtain a reading. This procedure is completed three times with each hand. Average scores are calculated and the results compared to the evaluative norms presented in Table 12.7.

Since grip strength correlates positively with overall body strength, the hand-grip dynamometer is used as a quick and easy way to measure muscular strength.

Table 12.7 Norms (kg) for grip strength based on age.

Rating	Grip Strength (Dominant and nondominant hands combined)	
	Males (15 – 19)	Females (15 – 19)
Excellent	113+	71+
Above Average	103 – 112	64 – 70
Average	95 – 102	59 – 63
Below Average	84 – 94	54 – 58
Needs Improvement	≤83	≤53

Measuring Muscular Endurance

Muscular endurance is characterized by the ability of muscle to maintain tension or to execute repeated movements against a submaximal resistance. Whether measures of endurance are static (e.g., flexed arm hang) or dynamic (e.g., chin-ups), most tests of muscular endurance are quite practical. The scoring for such tests usually involves recording the number of repetitions of a particular exercise completed in a set time (usually 60 seconds) or the length of time tension is maintained.

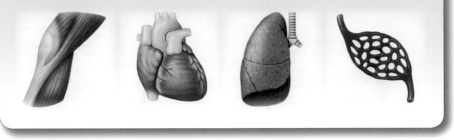
Chin-Up Test

Chin-up tests are popular for assessing upper-body muscular endurance. All that is required is a horizontal bar placed high enough so that the tallest subject cannot reach the ground with his feet. An overhand grip (palms facing away) must be used. The test begins with the subject maintaining a straight arm hang (Figure 12.1 A). The subject's task is simply to pull himself upwards until the chin is above the bar (Figure 12.1 B). After each chin-up, the subject returns to the starting position. This sequence is repeated as many times as possible to test muscular endurance of the arms and shoulder girdle. Evaluative norms are presented in Table 12.8.

Figure 12.1 The chin-up test. **A.** Starting position. **B.** Chin-up position. **C.** Flexed arm hang modification.

Table 12.8 Raw score norms (no. of repetitions) for the chin-up test for boys.

Rating	Age				
	13	14	15	16	17+
Excellent	10	12	15	14	15
Above Average	5	7	9	10	10
Average	3	4	6	7	7
Below Average	1	2	3	4	4
Needs Improvement	0	0	0	1	0

Flexed Arm Hang

The flexed arm hang is another effective test of muscular endurance, especially for participants who cannot pull up their own body weight. In this test, two spotters assist the subject in attaining a flexed arm position (palms facing in) so the eyes are level with the bar (Figure 12.1 C). The subject must hold this position as long as possible. The number of seconds (to the nearest second) the subject maintains this position is recorded. Evaluative norms are presented in Table 12.9.

Table 12.9 Norms (sec) for the flexed arm hang, boys and girls age 14–17.

Rating	Boys				Girls			
	14	15	16	17	14	15	16	17
Excellent	80.8	84.0	92.0	80.8	58.0	53.0	52.0	55.0
Above Average	61.1	62.4	65.8	65.2	31.9	31.3	35.8	37.1
Average	48.7	51.6	57.0	56.0	20.3	20.0	21.4	25.4
Below Average	33.8	38.3	42.0	41.5	10.2	10.6	10.6	14.8
Needs Improvement	12.5	15.5	18.3	24.5	3.5	3.3	3.9	4.5

Push-Up Test

It doesn't get any easier to assess upper-body endurance – all you need is a mat. The goal of the test is to perform push-ups to exhaustion. The basic push-up position with hands under the shoulders and toes on the ground must be maintained throughout the test, with no sagging or piking of the body (Figure 12.2 A). The upper arms should move into a parallel position with the mat, with the elbows at ninety degrees. The chest must not touch the mat in order for the repetition to count in the score. Less fit individuals may perform modified push-ups with the knees bent and the lower legs or toes on the mat (Figure 12.2 B). The score is simply the number of push-ups completed in succession. Evaluative norms are presented in Table 12.10.

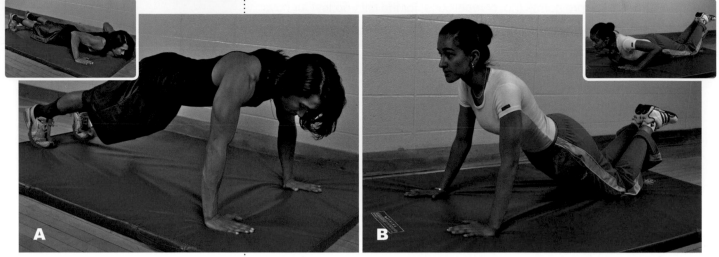

Figure 12.2 The push-up test. **A.** Standard push-up. **B.** Modified push-up.

Table 12.10 Norms (number of repetitions) for the push-up test.

Rating	No. of Push-ups	
	Males (15 – 19)	Females (15 – 19)
Excellent	39+	33+
Above Average	29 – 38	25 – 32
Average	23 – 28	18 – 24
Below Average	18 – 22	12 – 17
Needs Improvement	≤17	≤11

Partial Curl-Up Test

Participants begin in a supine position, with the head resting on the mat and arms outstretched at the sides, palms facing down. Knees are bent to 90 degrees, with the feet in contact with the mat. A 10-, 12-, or 8-cm wide measuring strip (made of cardboard, posterboard, rubber, smooth wood, or any similar thin, flat material) is secured to the mat under the knees, with the tips of the outstretched middle fingers at the nearest edge of the measuring strip (0-cm mark). The width of the measuring strip used is determined by the age of the participant (see Table 12.11).

Using the cadence provided by a metronome (50 beats per minute), participants slowly curl up far enough so that the tips of the middle fingers reach the other side of the 10-cm measuring strip. On return, the shoulder blades and head must contact the mat, and the fingertips of both hands must touch the 0-cm mark of the measuring strip. The hands and feet must remain in contact with the mat at all times, and no anchoring of the feet is permitted (Figure 12.3).

The movement is performed in a slow and controlled manner so that the time to perform the lifting and lowering stages of the curl-up stays the

Figure 12.3 Partial curl-up test demonstration.

same (25 curl-ups per minute). The curl-ups should be performed at a steady rate (without pausing) to a maximum of 75 curl-ups.

The test is terminated if the client is unable to maintain the required cadence or is unable to maintain the proper curl-up technique (e.g., palms or heels come off the floor) over two consecutive repetitions. A maximum of three corrections are allowed by the appraiser before termination of the test.

Table 12.11 gives the evaluation norms for muscular endurance of the core muscle groups.

Table 12.11 Partial curl-up scores for males and females.

	Males				Females			
Distance	10 cm	12 cm	12 cm	8 cm	10 cm	12 cm	12 cm	8 cm
Rating	Age 15 – 19	Age 20 – 29	Age 30 – 39	Age 40 – 49	Age 15 – 19	Age 20 – 29	Age 30 – 39	Age 40 – 49
Excellent	≥25	≥45	≥52	≥70	≥25	≥40	≥37	≥36
Above Average	23 – 24	31 – 44	35 – 51	48 – 69	22 – 24	31 – 39	27 – 36	28 – 35
Average	21 – 22	25 – 30	27 – 34	32 – 47	17 – 21	22 – 30	17 – 26	21 – 27
Below Average	16 – 20	14 – 24	14 – 26	22 – 31	12 – 16	13 – 21	4 – 16	6 – 20
Needs Improvement	≤15	≤13	≤13	≤21	≤11	≤12	≤3	≤5

Measuring Flexibility

Flexibility, or the range of motion around a joint, is an important measurement of overall fitness. Flexibility tends to be joint specific; therefore, a general test of flexibility really doesn't exist. Having flexible shoulders does not necessarily mean you will have flexible hamstrings. This creates a problem in measuring flexibility, unless the flexibility of a specific joint is being tested. Simple field tests that effectively measure specific flexibility can be used to predict overall body flexibility. These include the sit-and-reach test, the hamstring looseness test, and the total body rotation test.

Sit-and-Reach Test

This test assessing trunk and hamstring flexibility is designed for both males and females age five and above. Participants should warm up thoroughly before testing. The test involves reaching as far forward as possible with the legs held straight. Some tests use a specially constructed box of specific dimensions with a built-in measurement scale (Figure 12.4). Zero is placed at the soles of the feet, and the score is plus if the client reaches farther and minus if she can't reach to the soles of her feet.

Figure 12.4 The sit-and-reach test.

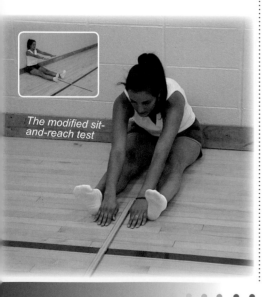

The modified sit-and-reach test

The sit-and-reach test may also be completed with a metre stick or measuring tape. For this modified test, the subject removes her shoes and sits with one leg on either side of the metre stick or tape measure, with the feet and arms outstretched and the hips, back, and head against the wall (see inset image to the left). The tape measure on the floor should be lined up with the edge of the subject's outstretched fingers. The subject can then move her head and back away from the wall and gradually reach forward along the metre stick for three trials. On the third trial, she stretches forward as far as possible, holding the final position for at least two seconds. The back of the person's knees must remain flat on the floor.

Each trial is scored to the nearest centimetre by recording the distance from the soles of the client's feet to the tips of the outstretched fingers. Two sets of trials are allowed, and the final test score is calculated as the average of the two scores. Evaluative norms are presented in Table 12.12.

Recreation and Fitness Leadership

Table 12.12 Norms (cm) for the modified sit-and-reach test.

Males			Females		
Rating	Age Category		Rating	Age Category	
	Under 18	19 – 35		Under 18	19 – 35
Excellent	≥46	≥44	Excellent	≥46	≥43
Above Average	41 – 45	39 – 43	Above Average	42 – 45	41 – 42
Average	37 – 40	36 – 38	Average	38 – 41	38 – 40
Below Average	34 – 36	33 – 35	Below Average	35 – 37	35 – 37
Needs Improvement	≤33	≤32	Needs Improvement	≤34	≤34

Hamstring Looseness Test

This test is designed to assess hamstring looseness. Before testing, subjects should be thoroughly warmed up. The client stands with the feet approximately hip-width apart. Keeping the knees straight, she bends over at the waist and lets the arms drop towards the ground, pushing the hands as far towards the floor as the hamstrings will allow. Refer to Figure 12.5 A–D and Table 12.13 to determine the client's performance level.

Figure 12.5 The hamstring looseness test. **A.** Palms touch the floor. **B.** Knuckles touch the floor. **C.** Fingertips touch the floor. **D.** Fingertips touch the ankles or higher.

Table 12.13 Performance level ratings for the hamstring looseness test.

Rating	Position Reached
Excellent	Palms touch the floor (Figure 12.5 A)
Above Average	Knuckles touch the floor (Figure 12.5 B)
Average	Fingertips touch the floor (Figure 12.5 C)
Below Average	Fingertips touch the feet
Needs Improvement	Fingertips touch the ankles or higher (Figure 12.5 D)

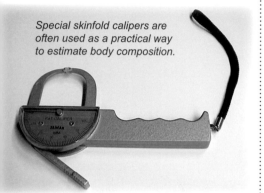

Special skinfold calipers are often used as a practical way to estimate body composition.

Measuring Body Composition

Skinfold measurements are one of the most practical, reliable, valid, and popular methods of estimating body composition. These tests involve using special calipers to measure skinfolds (actually "fat folds") at particular sites on the body. These measurements are based on the relationship that exists between subcutaneous fat (fat located directly beneath the skin), internal fat, and body density. The sum of a set of skinfolds can be used as an indication of the relative degree of fatness among individuals.

YMCA Skinfold Test

This test requires skinfold calipers. The process involves taking skinfolds at the abdomen, suprailium (crest of the hip bone), triceps (Figure 12.6), and thigh. The following steps should be followed when taking skinfold measurements:

❶ Lift skinfolds two or three times before placing the calipers for a measurement. Note: Gently pinch and pull the skinfold with the index finger and the thumb.

❷ Place the calipers below the thumb and fingers and perpendicular to the fold to allow easy reading of the measurement; completely release the caliper grip before reading the dial 1 to 2 seconds later.

❸ Repeat this procedure three times, allowing at least 15 seconds between each measurement; the measurements should not vary by more than 1 mm. Use the median value.

Plenty of practice is required to obtain reliable and consistent results. You can convert the skinfold measurements to percent body fat by using the equations in the box *Calculating Percent Body Fat*.

Figure 12.6 Caliper placement for measuring the triceps skinfold.

Recreation and Fitness Leadership

Body fat percentage can be compared to norms for percent body fat (Table 12.14). However, in calculating the percent body fat of a client, be aware that an estimated standard error of up to 3.98 percent exists. Thus, a calculated percentage of 16 may actually range from 15.4 to 16.6.

Table 12.14 Norms for percent body fat in males and females.

Rating	Males		Females	
	18 – 25	26 – 35	18 – 25	26 – 35
Very lean	4 – 7	8 – 12	13 – 17	13 – 18
Lean	8 – 10	13 – 15	18 – 20	19 – 21
Leaner than Average	11 – 13	16 – 18	21 – 23	22 – 23
Average	14 – 16	19 – 21	24 – 25	24 – 26
Fatter than Average	17 – 20	22 – 24	26 – 28	27 – 30
Fat	21 – 26	25 – 28	29 – 31	31 – 35
Overfat	27 – 37	29 – 37	32 – 43	36 – 48

Calculating Percent Body Fat

Skinfold measurements can be converted to percent body fat by using the equations below.

Four sites: abdomen, suprailium, triceps, and thigh:

Males
% fat = .29288 x (sum of 4) – .0005 x (sum of 4)^2 + .15845 x (age) – 5.76377

Females
% fat = .29669 x (sum of 4) – .00043 x (sum of 4)^2 + .02963 x (age) + 1.4172

Assessing Skill-Related Fitness

Skill-related components of fitness (motor abilities) can contribute to your client's ability to successfully complete everyday activities as well as possibly improve participation in sports. Individuals who have a high level of skill-related fitness are more likely to be physically active than those who have a lower level of skill.

Measuring Muscular Power

Activities that involve rapid muscular contractions such as the vertical jump and standing broad jump require power to execute movements explosively. Tests of **power** (strength x speed) are easy to administer and are very practical in terms of time, effort, and equipment.

Standing Long Jump

This simple test can be used for both males and females age six and up to measure explosive power in the legs. All that is needed for the test is a floor or mat, a tape measure, and a marking material (chalk or tape) to indicate the distance jumped. The development of standing long jump test mats (Figure 12.7) has made the test even simpler to administer. The mat eliminates taping measuring tapes to the gym floor and eyeballing the distance jumped; the measuring tape (in cm and in.) is printed directly on a thick, durable rubber material.

The goal of a two-foot long jump is to jump horizontally as far as possible from a standing start. After practising a few times to attain a feel for the jump, the client extends the hips, knees, and ankles from a crouch position as a unit while simultaneously swinging the arms forward for the jump. For best results, the trunk should be leaning slightly forward at the instant of take-off and then upward as the arms swing in the direction of the jump. There should be no extra hop or step prior to the jump; it must be performed cleanly, with both feet entirely behind the take-off line. The key to a successful jump is coordinating all parts of the body during the jump – ankles, knees, hips, arms, and trunk.

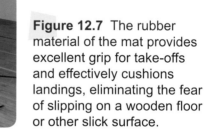

The measurement of the jump is the distance between the take-off line and the heel touchdown (or other body part) closest to the take-off line. Accurate readings are quick and easy with the specialized test mat. Allow at least three trials to obtain an average score. Evaluative norms are presented in Table 12.15.

Figure 12.7 The rubber material of the mat provides excellent grip for take-offs and effectively cushions landings, eliminating the fear of slipping on a wooden floor or other slick surface.

Table 12.15 Norms (cm) for the standing long jump test.

Rating	Males			Females		
	Age (years)			Age (years)		
	15	**16**	**17+**	**15**	**16**	**17+**
Excellent	217 – 235	228 – 244	235 – 255	185 – 204	190 – 208	193 – 208
Above Average	206 – 216	217 – 227	223 – 234	173 – 184	177 – 189	178 – 192
Average	195 – 205	207 – 216	214 – 222	163 – 172	166 – 176	170 – 177
Below Average	176 – 194	196 – 206	200 – 213	150 – 162	153 – 165	157 – 169
Needs Improvement	131 – 175	169 – 195	168 – 199	124 – 149	121 – 152	128 – 156

Vertical Jump

Another simple test for measuring power in the legs is the vertical jump, designed for males and females age nine and up. A measuring tape or metre stick, chalk, and a smooth wall is all that is required to complete the test. The client simply stands sideways beside the wall about an elbow's distance away (determined by placing the hand closest to the wall on the hip). Holding a small piece of chalk in the hand closest to the wall, the client reaches up as high as possible with the heels on the floor and makes an initial mark on the wall (Figure 12.8 A). He then jumps as high as possible and makes another mark at the peak of the jump on the wall. It is important to bend the ankles, knees, and hips before explosively extending these joints from the crouch position for optimal power. Allow three trials, of which the best score counts. The score is measured by subtracting the reach height from the jump height.

A special device has also been developed to measure vertical jump height and power. The key feature in the design of the vertical jump test mat is a measuring tape feeder mounted on a rubber mat. This feeder allows the measuring tape to slide through with minimal resistance as the person jumps, but stops the tape once the apex of the jump is reached (Figure 12.8 B). The length of measuring tape pulled through the feeder indicates the height of the jump, which is clearly displayed for recording. Evaluative norms are presented in Table 12.16.

Figure 12.8 The vertical jump. **A.** Traditional jump along a wall. **B.** Using a vertical jump test mat.

Table 12.16 Norms (cm) for the vertical jump test.

Rating	Males		Females	
	Age (years)		Age (years)	
	15 – 19	20 – 29	15 – 19	20 – 29
Excellent	≥51	≥56	≥37	≥40
Above Average	37 – 50	39 – 55	29 – 36	28 – 39
Average	27 – 36	30 – 38	22 – 28	20 – 27
Below Average	18 – 26	21 – 29	15 – 21	15 – 19
Needs Improvement	≤17	≤20	≤14	≤14

Measuring Agility and Coordination

Agility, the physical ability that enables rapid and precise change of body position and direction, is important for almost every activity and sport. Testing for agility may be accomplished in many ways, but only a few simple tests will be presented here.

Coordination involves the combination of movement skill. It is important in almost all sports but also in everyday life. Coordination can be as simple as picking a dime off the floor without falling over or as complex as performing movements in a step class. Sports examples of coordination include place kicking in football, hitting a baseball or a tennis ball, foot dribbling in soccer, hand dribbling or shooting in basketball, and spiking in volleyball. Many agility and coordination tests also measure speed of movement and balance.

CAHPER Shuttle Run

Shuttle runs are used to measure the agility of individuals in running and changing direction. Both males and females age nine and up can complete this test. Marking tape, a stopwatch, and three bean bags (or three of any small object, such as blocks of wood) are the equipment needed for the test.

One bean bag is placed beside the runner on the start line, and two bean bags are placed on a line 10 metres away. The runner lies face down, hands at the sides of the chest and forehead behind the start line (Figure 12.9 A). On the starting signal, the runner (1) jumps to her feet and runs 10 metres to the line; (2) picks up one bean bag (Figure 12.9 B); (3) returns to the start line; (4) sets the bean bag down across the line; (5) picks up another bean bag; (6) returns to the line 10 metres away; (7) exchanges the bean bag she is carrying for another; and (8) runs back across the finish line.

A "ready" warning signal should be given prior to the starting signal. Administer two trials with sufficient rest between them, and record the better of the two to the nearest tenth of a second. Evaluative norms are shown in Table 12.17.

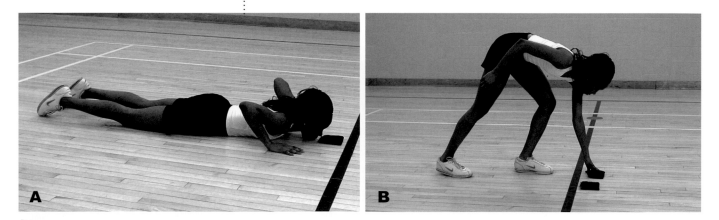

Figure 12.9 The shuttle run. **A.** Start face down at the start line. **B.** Pick up a bean bag before returning to the start line.

Recreation and Fitness Leadership

Table 12.17 Norms (sec) for the CAHPER shuttle run, boys and girls age 14–17.

Rating	Boys				Girls			
	14	15	16	17	14	15	16	17
Excellent	≤10.6	≤10.4	≤10.1	≤10.0	≤11.1	≤11.3	≤11.2	≤11.2
Above Average	10.7 – 11.2	10.5 – 11.0	10.2 – 10.7	10.1 – 10.6	11.2 – 12.0	11.4 – 12.2	11.3 – 12.0	11.3 – 11.9
Average	11.3 – 11.7	11.1 – 11.4	10.8 – 11.1	10.7 – 11.1	12.1 – 12.7	12.3 – 12.9	12.1 – 12.6	12.0 – 12.6
Below Average	11.8 – 12.3	11.5 – 12.0	11.2 – 11.8	11.2 – 11.6	12.8 – 13.5	13.0 – 13.5	12.7 – 13.4	12.7 – 13.4
Needs Improvement	≥12.4	≥12.1	≥11.9	≥11.7	≥13.6	≥13.6	≥13.5	≥13.5

Hexagonal Obstacle Test

This test is designed to assess agility, coordination, and balance. Using chalk or tape, begin by drawing or taping a hexagon on the floor (66 cm per side). To simplify the task, first draw a large circle with a radius of approximately 66 cm; then insert the lines of the hexagon. Label the lines A to F (Figure 12.10 A).

Standing in the middle of the hexagon, the client begins on signal to jump with both feet over side A and immediately back into the starting position within the hexagon. Then, without ever turning the body, he jumps over all sides to complete one round (Figure 12.10 B). The test continues until three full revolutions are completed. The time is stopped when the client's feet enter the hexagon after jumping side F for the third time. Time is recorded to the nearest tenth of a second. The best time out of two trials is kept (Table 12.18).

Table 12.18 Norms (sec) for the hexagonal obstacle test.

Rating	Males	Females
Excellent	≤10.0	≤10.5
Above Average	10.1 – 12.5	10.6 – 14.5
Average	12.6 – 15.5	14.6 – 18.5
Below Average	15.6 – 18.5	18.6 – 21.5
Needs Improvement	≥18.6	≥21.6

Putting It All Together

Physical fitness testing serves several important purposes for our fitness clients including diagnosis, goal setting, placement, motivation, and achievement. When assessing physical fitness, it is important to select

Figure 12.10 The hexagonal obstacle test. **A.** Schematic. **B.** Jump.

reliable and valid fitness tests. Reliability refers to the consistency of test scores, data, or observations; validity means that the test measures what you intend it to measure. In addition, well-developed norms for all age categories help you compare and evaluate your clients' achievements.

Components of physical fitness that are commonly assessed include cardiorespiratory endurance, body composition, muscular strength, muscular power, muscular endurance, flexibility, and agility. Although more accurate results can be obtained by using sophisticated laboratory equipment, many reliable and valid field tests (e.g., 12 minute walk–run test, vertical jump, shuttle runs, and the sit-and-reach test) have proven to be useful in assessing the major components of fitness. However, you must realize that any assessment requires thorough preparation, practice trials, and attention to detail for sound measurement and evaluation of performance. Effective measurement and evaluation of clients' physical fitness is a key component of developing their physical fitness programs.

Key Terms

absolute strength	one repetition maximum (1RM)
agility	power
cardiorespiratory endurance	relative strength
coordination	reliability
field test	running test
flexibility	skinfold measurements
hand-grip dynamometer	step test
muscular endurance	validity
norms	$\dot{V}O_2$max

Review Questions

1. Discuss six ways that fitness testing and evaluation can help a fitness client.

2. What are evaluative norms? Discuss their usefulness in interpreting test results.

3. What is the difference between reliability and validity? Why are they both important in fitness assessments?

4. Briefly describe the key components of two different tests for cardiorespiratory fitness. Explain how they can help in planning a fitness program.

5. Why is it important to have submaximal and maximal tests for cardiorespiratory fitness? When would you use each and why?

6. Describe an alternative method of assessing maximal strength without performing a one repetition maximum (1RM) test.

7. Describe one test of muscular endurance and explain how it differs from other possible tests. Give a situation in which it would be a useful diagnostic tool for you.

8. List the sites used to measure skinfolds in the YMCA skinfold test for estimating body composition.

9. List four tests that can be used to assess a client's skill-related fitness (motor abilities).

10. Describe one test of skill-related fitness and explain how it differs from other possible tests. Give a situation in which it would be a useful diagnostic tool for you.

UNIT 4

INJURY PREVENTION AND FIRST AID

13  Risk Management and Injury Prevention

14  Injury Management

15  Fitness Safety Practices

A hushed silence comes over the crowd as the player goes down hard. Within seconds the trainers are on the field assessing the injury. In these critical first minutes after the impact, decisions will be made that will have a significant effect on the outcome. Training and experience will come to bear on the treatment that is chosen and applied. Ultimately the player's recovery and return to action may depend on that initial intervention.

Later comes the second-guessing. Could the injury have been prevented? Was there a deficit in the equipment or facilities or even the training and physical preparation of the player? Was an opponent overly aggressive? Was a rule broken?

The word *accident* has been defined as anything occurring unexpectedly or without known or assignable cause. Some contend that in sport and recreation there are no accidents. Is it possible to predict every hazardous situation that might arise? Is there an appropriate response in every case? These are certainly the goals of Unit 4.

You will learn about fitness safety practices and injury prevention in fitness facilities. An informed understanding of body structure and mechanics enables a fitness instructor to evaluate common exercise techniques, avoiding or modifying those that are unsuitable for particular participants. No matter what preventive measures are taken, however, injuries do occur. Prompt and effective first aid can control the amount of damage and discomfort. It may also reduce recovery time.

The information you receive in this unit about responding to injuries is important, but it does not replace a formal training program. All recreation leaders are encouraged to complete first aid and CPR certification. When it comes to participation in physical recreation, "better safe than sorry" is an important motto that should guide all aspects of the experience.

Old Sports Injuries

Almost everyone has a story about a sports injury he or she has suffered. Sometimes the story includes mismanagement of the situation.

When I was kicked in the face by a horse, the stable owners rushed me to the hospital. During the 20-minute drive and the two-hour wait in the emergency department, my face swelled up like a balloon. If only they'd taken the time to make me an ice pack to put on my face! I would have had far less pain, and the surgery to repair my teeth and jaw wouldn't have had to wait for the swelling to subside.

The stable owners had every imaginable kind of first aid equipment for a horse injury but nothing for a rider!

In This Chapter:

CHAPTER 13
Risk Management and Injury Prevention

In this chapter, you will learn about the following:

❶ Options for managing and minimizing risk

❷ Regulations and procedures for preventing injuries and keeping participants safe

❸ Regulations and procedures to follow in the case of an accident

❹ The concepts of negligence and liability

317

Physical activity inherently presents some risk of injury, and one of the key responsibilities of the recreation and fitness leader is ensuring the safety of all those involved. Taking time to determine the risks faced by participants in your activity is the first step in minimizing and controlling those potential hazards. Although risk factors have been categorized as human, environmental, and equipment related, the most critical factor is the human element. It is humans who make poor decisions regarding situations they put their participants in (e.g., hazardous weather or dangerous surroundings). It is humans who slip up and forget critical safety practices (e.g., allowing participants to use substandard equipment or failing to provide adequate supervision). Fitness leaders have a legal obligation to provide a safe environment for participants and can be held accountable if safety regulations are not followed or are shown to be lacking. How can a fitness leader fulfill this obligation?

Although risk factors can be categorized as human, environmental, and equipment related, the human element is by far the most critical. Fitness leaders must take time to determine the risks to participants and take the necessary steps to minimize and control those potential hazards.

Risk Management

The answer to the question just posed above is risk management. **Risk management** can be defined as "reducing the chances of injury or loss by taking steps to identify, measure, and control risks." The first step in the risk management process is identifying any potential threats to your participants' safety. After determining all the potentially risky situations, the next step is deciding which ones could pose a serious risk, and the third step is determining what steps to take to deal with them.

An experienced leader will be familiar with foreseeable risks and the steps required to minimize them. Novice leaders should seek the advice of their supervisors and become familiar with standard risk management

> Safety doesn't happen by accident.
> *Anonymous*

Caution signs and warning flags are a good way to inform swimmers of any potential dangers or risks.

procedures. Attention to risk management protects everyone involved in the implementation of the program—the fitness and recreation leader, the coach, the officials, and the organization—by reducing the potential for accidents and lawsuits.

Options for Managing Risk

There are five options for managing risk. As a person in a leadership role, it is your responsibility to decide whether to retain, reduce, or avoid the risk. Other options include taking time to correct the risky situation and obtaining liability insurance to transfer the possible costs to another entity.

Retaining the Risk

Although it may seem counter-intuitive, retaining the risk is an acceptable option – the risk may be more perceived than real. That perception of risk may be what attracts people to the activity. This is certainly the case in extreme sports such as bungee jumping, mountain climbing, and skydiving. When all safety precautions are in place, and with correct training and supervision, these activities are relatively safe, yet they still elicit the thrill that some people are seeking in their recreational pursuits.

Reducing the Risk

In general, risks can be put into three categories. **Environmental risks** include such things as weather conditions and where the activity takes place. Compare the risk of canoeing on a calm lake in sunny weather with tackling white-water rapids in a steady drizzle.

Equipment risk involves game and personal equipment. Something as simple as tying your shoelaces and putting long hair in a ponytail can prevent injury. Finally, **human risk** factors include the participants' personal characteristics and behaviours. Matching competitors of unequal strength and ability in a judo class or not taking into account a participant's risk-taking tendencies are examples of poor attention to human factors.

Parents, coaches, officials, and event organizers can also be a source of risk. Their behaviours and decisions can make the difference between a safe activity and a risky one. In fact, since environmental and equipment factors are things leaders need to make decisions about, it could be stated that *all* risk factors contain a human element. Fortunately, there are many risk-reduction procedures that can be followed. This chapter outlines them in great detail.

Retaining the risk for some activities such as skydiving, rock climbing, and bungee jumping is an acceptable option, since the risks are more perceived than real.

Avoiding the Risk

Of course, in certain situations the risk is so great that the activity is avoided altogether. For instance, it is unsafe to swim in the dark, to skate on a lake or river when the ice is not thick enough, or to practice an aerial stunt at circus camp without a safety net.

Taking Time to Correct the Risk

In some cases, a risky situation can be remedied quickly. Spilled water or broken glass on a playing surface can be cleaned up during a time-out. It never hurts to stop an activity when you perceive risk, and you will likely be commended for your quick thinking and concern for your participants' safety.

Transferring the Risk

Finally, all agencies offering recreation programs, personal trainers working with individuals, teachers in the school system, and so on, have liability insurance policies. These insurance policies offer protection after the fact. If an injury occurs and the victim sues the individual or agency, the insurance company either settles the lawsuit out of court or pays the assessed liability and court costs so that the individual coach or recreation staff person is protected from personal financial loss.

It is always a good idea to stop an activity when a risky situation arises, such as moisture build-up on a playing surface.

Five Options for Managing Risk

Retain the risk:
- Accept the risk as an inherent part of the activity (often the risk is what attracts participants to the activity).
- Alert participants about the risks.

Reduce the risk:
- Wear protective equipment.
- Modify the rules.
- Change the environment (e.g., padded goalposts).

Avoid the risk:
- Certain activities may prove to be too risky and are eliminated from the program. This is at the discretion of the coordinators.

Take time to correct the risky situation:
- Suspend the activity until the risk is eliminated (e.g., the weather improves, faulty equipment is repaired or replaced).

Transfer the risk:
- Obtain insurance to ward against charges of negligence and liability.
- Have adult participants sign a waiver form whereby they accept full responsibility for any injury.
- Hire first aid staff to be present at the event.

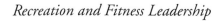

Recreation and Fitness Leadership

Proactive and Reactive Strategies

A fitness and recreation leader needs to be both proactive and reactive as a risk manager. To be **proactive**, imagine the participants taking part in an activity, and list all the risks they might encounter (Table 13.1). For each of these inherent risks, choose one of the response options just outlined. Being **reactive** means responding appropriately and immediately when a situation arises that could add to risk (Table 13.2). Before an accident happens, you should try to change the situation or warn the participants of potential risks ahead of time. When any accident occurs, identify the cause and, when possible, eliminate it.

Table 13.1 Determining risks of your activity and applying remedies.

Playground Climbing Structure	
Potential Risk	**Remedy**
Hard landing on ground	• Spread load of bark chips • Rake the sand after a rainstorm
Cuts and scrapes	• Check entire structure for rough edges, splinters, and so on at beginning of season and weekly thereafter
Fingers catch in tire-swing chain	• Cover chain with rubber tubing
Strangulation	• Ban scarves, hood strings • Post a sign • Supervise closely

Table 13.2 Appropriate and immediate reaction to unsafe situations.

Risk	Remedy
Ceiling fixture falls to the floor and shatters	• Cordon off the area with pylons or benches • Call maintenance to clean up
Gymnastics mat is torn	• Put the mat in the storage room until it is repaired, or discard it
Wire cable on the volleyball net is frayed	• Repair temporarily with duct tape • Replace cable
Water bottle has exploded on the playing surface	• Stop the activity • Wipe up water with towel

Some risks are not foreseeable, however. For example, a participant may have a medical condition that has not been diagnosed. News reports of apparently healthy athletes collapsing during a practice or game from a previously undiagnosed condition, such as a congenital heart deformity, are rare but not unheard of.

Risk Management Procedures

*S*everal standard procedures must be implemented in order to fulfill the responsibility for risk management. Think of this as a jigsaw puzzle in which all the pieces need to be in place to create a complete picture. If even one piece is missing, the potential for harm is amplified.

Medical Information and Contact Forms

All participants should be required to complete and submit a medical information form before they participate in an activity for the first time. The **Par-Q form** (Figure 13.1) is used throughout the fitness field in Canada, or your organization may develop its own form. This form should ask for contact information in case of accident or injury. The completed forms must be accessible to staff at all times and must be shown to emergency medical personnel when an injury occurs. The form must be witnessed and signed by a parent or guardian if the participant is under the age of majority (either 18 or 19 depending on what province you live in).

> **Safety is something that happens between your ears, not something you hold in your hands.**
> *Jeff Cooper*

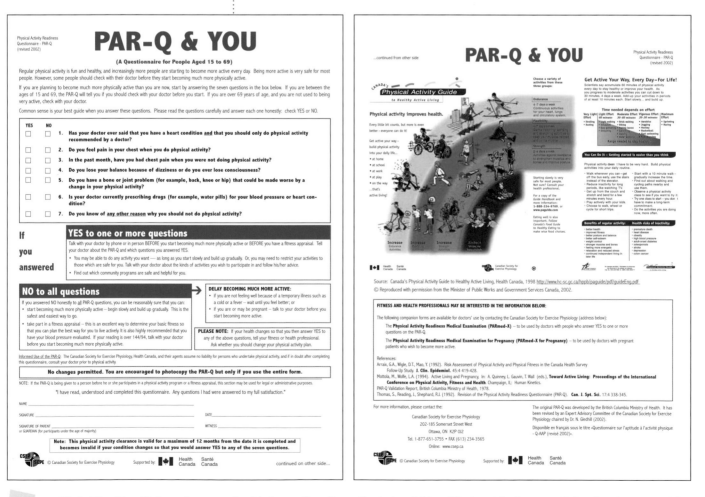

Figure 13.1 The Par-Q form is a medical information form that should be filled out before participating in an activity for the first time.

Would you know what to do if . . .

- a child in your soccer program is stung by a bee

- a child in your day camp accidentally eats a dessert with peanut butter as an ingredient

. . . and starts to develop a skin rash and has difficulty breathing?

You realize the child is going into **anaphylactic shock** – the result of a severe life-threatening allergy to bees or peanut butter.

If you had checked these children's medical information forms, you would have taken steps to prevent the incidents. Moreover you would have the first aid treatment (an EpiPen) on hand to deal with these medical emergencies.

But what would happen if you didn't know?

Risk Warnings

Medical information forms are often combined with **notification of risk** statements (Figure 13.2). If the participants are minors, parents or guardians are asked to acknowledge the risks of the activity. Legally, they do not have the authority to sign away the child's right to sue for damages

---

Appendix A
Sample Secondary Interschool Athletic Activity Participation Form

This form should be completed on behalf of each team member participating in secondary interschool athletic activities and returned to the teacher/coach prior to the first competition.

STUDENT ATHLETE NAME _____ SCHOOL _____
HOME ADDRESS _____ POSTAL CODE _____
HOME PHONE # _____ HEALTH CARE # _____
PARENT/ GUARDIAN _____ WORK PHONE # _____
STUDENT ATHLETE'S PHYSICIAN _____ PHONE # _____
EMERGENCY CONTACT NAME _____ PHONE # _____

NOTE: An annual medical examination is recommended.

MEDICAL INFORMATION

1. Date of last complete medical examination: _____

2. Date of last tetanus immunization: _____

3. Is your son/daughter/ward allergic to any drugs, foods or medication/other? Yes _____ No _____ If yes, provide details: _____

4. Does your son/daughter/ward take any prescription drugs? Yes _____ No _____
If yes, provide details: _____

5. What medication(s) should the participant have on hand during the interschool athletic activity? _____
Who should administer the medication? _____
I, the parent, give permission for the teacher/coach/teacher to administer this medication(s) to the student athlete as directed or needed.
Signature: _____
Or
Although the student athlete can under normal circumstances administer his/her own medication, I, the parent, give permission for the teacher/coach/teacher to administer the medication if an injury/illness prevents the student athlete from doing so themselves.
Signature: _____

6. Does your son/daughter/ward wear a medical alert bracelet _____, neck chain _____ or carry a medical alert card? Yes _____ No _____
If yes, please specify what is written on it: _____

7. Does your son/daughter/ward wear eyeglasses? Yes _____ No _____ contact lenses? Yes _____ No _____

Appendix A
continued

8. Please indicate if your son/daughter/ward has been subject to any of the following and provide pertinent details:
epilepsy, diabetes, orthopedic problems, deaf, hard of hearing, asthma, allergies
_____
concussion or back conditions or injuries (in the past two years)
_____
arthritis or rheumatism; chronic nosebleeds; dizziness; fainting; headaches; hernia; swollen or hyper mobile joints, trick or lock knee: _____
Any other medical information that will limit participation? _____

9. Should your son/daughter/ward sustain an injury or contract an illness requiring medical attention during the competitive season, notify the teacher/coach and complete the "Request to Resume Athletic Participation Form", if applicable.

10. **MEDICAL SERVICES AUTHORIZATION**
In case of emergency medical or hospital services being required by the above listed student athlete, and with the understanding that every reasonable effort will be made by the school/hospital to contact me, my signature on this form authorizes medical personnel and/or hospital to administer medical and/or surgical services including anesthesia and drugs. I understand that any cost will be my responsibility.

Signature of parent/guardian: _____ **Date:** _____

STUDENT ATHLETE ACCIDENT INSURANCE NOTICE
The (name of School Board) does not provide any accidental death, disability, dismemberment/medical/dental expenses insurance on behalf of the student athletes participating in the activity. For coverage of injuries, you are encouraged to consider the **Student Accident Insurance Plan** made available by the school to parents at the beginning and throughout the school year.

"School/Board student procedure/expectation may be included here."

TRANSPORTATION INSURANCE NOTICE
"Include your specific Transportation Policy in this space"

ELEMENTS OF RISK NOTICE
The risk of injury exists in every athletic activity. However, due to the nature of some activities, the risk of injury may increase. Injuries may range from minor strains and sprains to more serious injuries, including death. The safety and well-being of participants is a prime concern and attempts are made to manage as effectively as possible, the foreseeable risks inherent in physical activity.

Figure 13.2 A sample medical information and risk form.

when that child reaches the age of majority. Adults (age 18 and over) may be asked to sign a waiver form, which indicates that they accept the risk and absolves the organizers of responsibility for injuries or death.

Signed waivers and notification of risk forms are useful tools in the risk management process. However, although they act as a deterrent, they do not prevent a person from suing an individual, organization, or company should an injury or death occur as a result of apparent failure to manage the risk effectively.

Warnings to participants may be verbal or visual. It is the leader's responsibility to point out hazards. In addition, leaders need to be vigilant and should caution participants about misbehaviour or inattention that represents a safety risk. Make sure participants understand all safety procedures. Post signs or use pylons to indicate hazardous areas.

Signs or pylons can be used by leaders to warn participants of potential hazards or risks.

Emergency Action Plan

An emergency action plan (EAP) is a sheet of paper posted near the telephone that lists important contact numbers, the names of the people who will take charge in the event of an emergency, and directions to the site and to the nearest hospital (Figure 13.3). An EAP should be available in each facility or site where you lead your recreation or leisure activity. When you go to a new site, always locate the EAP; ask other staff members or participants if you do not see one posted. If an EAP is not available, take the responsibility yourself to find out what you need to know.

Emergency Drills

Every activity supervisor needs to be aware of the steps to take in case of an accident or emergency. Emergency drills, fire drills, and evacuation drills are all valuable training measures. In many cases, these training exercises are mandated by the organization or the government. Details of how to respond in an emergency are provided in the next chapter.

Telephone Access

You must always have easy access to a telephone in case of an emergency. Remember, important contact information should be posted next to the phone. When off-site, a telephone or fully charged cell phone must be readily available.

All supervisors and staff members must be informed about the emergency action plan and evacuation procedures in their facility in case of an accident or emergency.

First Aid Training

The minimum certification for a fitness leader is standard first aid and Basic Rescuer CPR (Level C). Ideally, every fitness leader has up-to-date certification. When this is not the case, an individual trained in first aid must

Recreation and Fitness Leadership

Contact Information for the Emergency Action Plan

Emergency phone number:	**9-1-1 for all emergencies**
Facility manager Joe Smith:	(905) 872-8323 – cell (905) 872-4092 – home
Program director Nancy Jones:	(905) 872-5682 – cell (905) 872-3387 – home
Phone number of home facility:	(905) 872-6657
Address of home facility	**Newmarket Municipal Sports Centre** 123 Park Lane, between Chestnut St. and Poplar St. Newmarket ON **Ambulance to use side entrance on Poplar St.**
Address of nearest hospital:	**Mercy General Hospital** 1234 Queen Elizabeth Drive Newmarket ON (905) 875-6000
Charge person (1st option): Charge person (2nd option): Charge person (3rd option):	Suzy Chalmers (coach) Joey Lemieux (assistant coach) Angela Stevens (parent, nurse)
Call person (1st option): Call person (2nd option): Call person (3rd option):	Brad MacKenzie (parent) Sheila Stevens (parent) Stefano Martinez (parent)

Only one of the above listed charge persons takes the lead if two are present.

Figure 13.3 Sample emergency action plan.

be on-site whenever an activity is going on. A list of the trained personnel and when they are on duty must be posted. A trained individual will assume the role of charge person in case of an incident (see Chapter 14).

Agencies That Train and Certify First Aid Practitioners

- Canadian Red Cross
- Canadian Ski Patrol
- Lifesaving Society
- St. John Ambulance
- YMCA

First Aid Kit

A fully stocked first aid kit should be readily accessible (see the box *Recommended First Aid Kit Contents*). As well as the usual instruments and dressings, it should contain items for the first aider's protection against blood and bodily fluids. For outdoor activities, wearing a fanny pack kit is recommended. Always check the contents of your first aid kit before leaving the home site.

Recommended First Aid Kit Contents

A complete first aid kit is essential. This kit must be carefully prepared in order to treat the most common injuries. Furthermore, it must be accessible to those responsible for the team. Here is a list of what a first aid kit should contain.

Content	Use
• Disposable gloves • Biohazard kit • Plastic face guard (for artificial respiration)	• Personal safety
Disinfectants	
• Liquid antiseptic soap • Antibiotic cream/lotion/spray	• Cleaning skin around lesions • Controlling infection
Dressings	
• Sterile gauze pads (3 x 3, 4 x 4) • Adhesive tape (37.5 mm) • Ocular dressings • Sterile gauze rolls (50, 70, 100 mm) • Adhesive bandages (Band-Aid type, butterfly closures) • Elastic bandages (100, 150 mm) • Adhesive elastic bandages • Triangular bandages and safety pins	 • Covering the eye • Dry compression • Protection of minor lesions • Compression • Multiple uses but primarily to act as an arm support in case of a fracture
Drug products and ointments	
• Zinc ointment • Xylocaine spray	• Scratches or blisters • Burns
Other useful items	
• Cleaning solution for foreign bodies • Scissors • Tongue depressor • Body temperature thermometer • Chemical cold bags (if you don't have access to real ice) • Plastic bags • Tools	• Dislodging foreign bodies • Multiple uses • Multiple uses • Checking body temperature in case of trauma • For ice cubes • Minor repair of equipment

Accident Report Forms and Follow-Up

Whenever first aid is administered, it should be noted in an **accident log book**. A typical entry includes the name of the person treated, which contact person was notified, the name of the person(s) who administered treatment, the date and time, the nature of the injury, the cause of the injury, the first aid action taken, the follow-up care administered by medical professionals, and the date of return to activity (Figure 13.4).

Whenever first aid is administered, it should be recorded in an accident log book, and an accident/incident report form should be filled out for future reference.

In addition to this in-house reporting procedure, if you are working in a school or for an agency or a sports organization, there will likely be an official **accident/incident report form** (Figure 13.5) to complete. A copy of this form will be submitted to the organization's insurance company in case of future legal action.

From time to time, read all the accident report forms and look for patterns of incidents. Whenever possible, make changes in procedures to prevent similar occurrences, and devise strategies to correct any apparent problems.

A final piece of the follow-up is ensuring that the injured person receives adequate professional medical attention, including rehabilitation if required. In all cases, the participant's return to activity must be cleared by a medical professional or parent and monitored by the fitness leader.

Date/Time	Injured person	Nature of injury Cause of injury	First aid Administered by whom?	Who was notified? Follow-up Return to activity
03/07/2013 3:10 p.m.	Charlie Black	• Bruised elbow • Misjudged flip turn and hit side of pool	• Ice pack; sling • B. Singh (coach)	• Grandmother (Mrs. Jones) • Advised to rest, elevate arm, keep ice pack on, and see a physician • Back in class 08/07/2013
04/07/2013 5:15 p.m.	Samantha Lecroix	• Bruised tailbone • Running on deck, slipped and fell	• Ice pack • R. Bernstein (lifeguard)	• Stepfather (Mr. Brodeur) • Advised to rest, use ice pack, and see a physician • Back at pool 11/07/2013

Figure 13.4 Sample accident log book.

Criteria for Return to Activity

A significant cause of reinjury is allowing a participant to return to action before healing or rehabilitation is complete. Participants are often eager to get back in the game, and a wise fitness leader will put them through

Accident Report Form

Date of report _____ /_____ /_____
dd   mm   yyyy

PATIENT INFORMATION

LAST NAME:	FIRST NAME:
STREET ADDRESS:	CITY:
POSTAL CODE:	PHONE: (　　　)
E-MAIL:	AGE:

SEX: ___M ___F	HEIGHT: _____ WEIGHT: _____	DOB: _____ / _____ / _____ dd / mm / yyyy

KNOWN MEDICAL CONDITIONS/ALLERGIES:

INCIDENT INFORMATION

DATE & TIME OF INCIDENT: _____ / _____ / _____ _____ AM dd mm yyyy PM	TIME OF FIRST INTERVENTION: _____ AM PM	TIME OF MEDICAL SUPPORT ARRIVAL: _____ AM PM

CHARGE PERSON, DESCRIBE THE INCIDENT: (what took place, where it took place, the signs and symptoms of the patient)

PATIENT, DESCRIBE THE INCIDENT: (see above)

EVENT & CONDITIONS: (in what event did the incident take place, location of incident, surface quality, light, weather, and so on)

ACTIONS TAKEN/INTERVENTION:

After treatment, the patient was:

☐ Sent home   ☐ Sent to hospital/a clinic   ☐ Returned to activity

OVER...

Figure 13.5 Sample accident report form.

Accident Report Form (page 2)

CHARGE PERSON iNFORMATION

LAST NAME:	FIRST NAME:
STREET ADDRESS:	CITY:
POSTAL CODE:	PHONE: ( )
E-MAIL:	AGE:
ROLE: (coach, assistant, parent, official, bystander, therapist)	

WITNESS INFORMATION (someone who observed the incident and the response, not the charge person)

LAST NAME:	FIRST NAME:
STREET ADDRESS:	CITY:
POSTAL CODE:	PHONE: ( )
E-MAIL:	AGE:

OTHER COMMENTS OR REMARKS

FORM COMPLETED BY:

_____   _____
PRINT NAME   SIGNATURE

a series of progressively more demanding physical tasks specific to the activity to determine if they are ready to return. This testing is necessary even when a physician determines that an injury is minor. Return to activity is discussed in more detail in Chapter 14.

Facility Safety Checks

Inspect facilities on a daily basis and before each activity begins (Figure 13.6). Have a clear mental picture of what a safe facility looks like. Take steps to ensure problems are corrected immediately. Otherwise, modify your planned activities. Annual or biannual safety checks performed by professionals trained in this procedure are recommended.

It is important to inspect facilities for safety hazards on a daily basis before each activity begins.

A SITE NAME: _____

INSPECT FOR:	MEETS SAFE GUIDELINES		COMMENT/FOLLOW-UP ACTION
	YES	NO	
GYMNASIUM SPACE • free of "stored" furniture/boxes/equipment along perimeter walls and corners			
FLOORS • clean and dry			
• provides for safe foot traction			
• clear of objects that may cause tripping/slipping			
• floor sockets covered and flush with floor			
• floor plates secure, hooks and plate in good condition and flush with floor			
ENTRANCES/EXITS • free of obstructions			
• no doorknobs, protruding handles on gym side of door			
• doors open away from gym area			
STAIRS • clear of obstacles			
• stair treads in good condition			
• railings secure			
• free of protruding nails, cracks, or splinters			
CEILING • tiles and meshings on lights secure			
WALLS • all outlets, switches, registers, etc. that pose an unreasonable hazard must be flush with wall surface or padded			
• free of protruding hooks, nails, etc.			

B INSPECT FOR:	MEETS SAFE GUIDELINES		COMMENT/FOLLOW-UP ACTION
	YES	NO	
BASKETBALL BACKSTOP			
• backboards in good condition			
• cable and attachments from backboard to wall secure			
• rims secure and straight			
• Velcro strips on walls behind backboards in good condition to hold mats			
• winch not located directly below a wall-mounted backboard			

Figure 13.6 A. Sample safety checklist for gymnasium facilities. **B.** Sport-specific basketball example.

Equipment Safety Checks

Participants' personal equipment must meet established safety standards, as must equipment supplied by the organization. The participant must wear appropriate clothing and footwear for the activity and mandated safety equipment (e.g., mouthguards, helmets, goggles, gloves). Check that safety equipment fits the wearer, that shoelaces are tied, and that all loose jewellery is removed.

Personal and non-personal equipment safety checks are necessary to ensure the safety of all participants.

Recreation and Fitness Leadership

Supervision

The required level of **supervision** will vary depending on the age, experience, and characteristics of the participants (see the box *Levels of Supervision*). Be aware of participants who are daredevils, who challenge authority, or who have special needs. Supervision requirements may be greater for those individuals than for others.

There is a danger in simply setting a maximum number of participants per supervisor; this tactic does not take into consideration the age, personalities, and needs of the participants. Unfortunately, program budgets are often drawn up based on maximum ratios. Volunteers and leaders in training may be recruited to assist with supervision, but as a general rule, they cannot be left in charge of a group.

Levels of Supervision

When the activity is recognized as carrying a lower level of risk, or when the participants are not beginners, the supervisor, if not present, must be readily available and her location must be known to the participants. This is called **in-the-area** supervision. A good example is a jogging club. Members stay in groups of three or four. If one runner is injured, another can go to the coach or supervisor for help, while the injured party is not left alone.

For most activities, the supervisor must be **on-site** – visible to the participants and readily accessible. For example, the supervisor may walk from event to event at a track and field meet or practice. A fitness club employee will move among the clients, answering questions and monitoring the safe use of machines and other equipment, but will also step into the office for various reasons.

For higher-risk activities or when the participants are novices, the supervisor must provide **constant visual** supervision. While a supervisor is watching one activity, other activities may be going on in the immediate area. A lifeguard provides this kind of supervision, as does a rock climbing instructor introducing a group of beginners to the activity.

Rules of Conduct

Rules of conduct must be communicated effectively. Whether this consists of a posted list, a "contract" to be signed by participants, or some other means, the rules must be clear, concise, and visible (see the boxes *Safety at the Go-Kart Track* and *Backyard Trampoline Safety*). Be sure to use language that will be easily understood by the reader. Often a guided discussion with the participants leads to increased compliance.

Safety at the Go-Kart Track

- Minimum height: 4' 8"
- Minimum age: 8
- Helmets must be worn; chin straps must be fastened.
- Long hair must be tied back.
- Stay in cart if you crash or stop.
- Do not bump other carts. You will have to leave the track. No refunds.

Backyard Trampoline Safety

- Always supervise children.
- Allow only one person at a time.
- No child under six should bounce alone on the trampoline; an adult must be on the trampoline bed within arm's reach.
- Do not try skills that involve inversion (somersaults) unless trained how to do them by a certified instructor.
- Shock-absorbing padding must completely cover the exposed frame, springs, and hooks.
- Try to place the trampoline away from structures and play areas.
- Consider using a safety net enclosure around the trampoline.
- Climb on and off carefully. Do not jump from the bed to the ground.

When participants don't follow the trampoline safety rules, they put themselves at risk for sustaining serious injuries.

Recreation and Fitness Leadership

Commitment to Fair Play

Many injuries occur as a result of participants' attempts to gain an unfair advantage over their opponents. A cross-check while the referee's back is turned is a typical example. All participants, including coaches, managers, and officials, must be committed to encouraging **fair play** and punishing rule infractions.

Good Sports Make Good Sport

Following are the five fair play principles:

❶ Respect the rules.

❷ Respect the officials and their decisions.

❸ Respect your opponents.

❹ Give everyone an equal chance to participate.

❺ Maintain your self-control at all times.

Selecting Appropriate Activities

It is vital to select activities that are appropriate for the participants' age, fitness level, and skill level, especially if planning for special populations such as children, pregnant women, persons with disabilities, and older adults. Do the research to find accepted guidelines, and follow them strictly. In all cases use common sense: Do not expect a participant to do something that requires more maturity, size, fitness, or skill than he has.

Be aware that many participants will strive to get your approval and may not speak up if they are not really ready to try the activity you have planned for them. Alternately, they may not want to show weakness in front of their peers. Look for signs that a person is not psychologically prepared for an activity. Hesitation, dilated pupils, sweaty palms, and upset stomach or nausea are indications that the participant is fearful about some aspect of the activity. If this could present a safety risk, delay the activity until the participant has regained control and focus.

CAUTION

Do you know what signs to look for? Hesitation, dilated pupils, sweaty palms, and upset stomach are indications that a participant is fearful about some aspect of the proposed activity.

Establishing Participants' Readiness for Activity

Before the activity gets under way, determine the participants' physical health and mental alertness. Stress and lack of sleep may have a negative impact on a person's ability to concentrate and participate. Similarly,

being under the influence of alcohol or drugs will have a detrimental and perhaps even dangerous effect on performance. Do a check on previous injuries and chronic conditions to evaluate the level of participation to expect. Make appropriate modifications to the program if necessary. For instance, it may be inadvisable to ask someone with a head cold or ear infection to attempt activities requiring good balance.

Insist on a sufficient warm-up at the beginning of an activity and a cool-down after activity. For more on warming up and cooling down, see chapter 15.

Environmental Safety

Pay attention to those weather reports! Exercise in hot and humid or cold conditions requires special precautions. Heat stroke and hypothermia are life-threatening conditions. Avoid being out-of-doors during a lightning storm. Be aware that heavy rain can cause floods and landslides, and even a light rain will make roads and grass slick. Would it be wise to play soccer or go for a bike ride in those conditions?

Exercising in the Heat

Adequate water consumption is essential to stay hydrated during bouts of physical activity, especially when exercising in hot, humid weather.

Exercising in hot, humid weather can carry significant risks. Water lost as a result of heavy sweating can lead to **dehydration**, which can reduce performance, decrease the body's ability to dissipate heat, and endanger health. Adequate water consumption is essential. Particular attention should be paid to drinking enough fluids during the first few hot days of spring or summer, when participants are not yet acclimatized to hot and humid weather.

The feeling of thirst is not a good indicator of a need for water. In fact, dehydration has already started if a participant feels thirsty. Follow these guidelines to maintain adequate hydration levels before, during, and after participation in physical activity:

▶ Before exercise, participants should drink 400 to 600 ml of fluid (one average-sized bottle of water).

▶ During exercise, participants should drink 150 to 250 ml of fluid every 15 minutes. Remind participants to drink, lead by example, and never restrict them from drinking.

▶ After exercise, participants should rehydrate by drinking as much fluid as thirst dictates, even forcing themselves to drink if necessary.

▶ Beverages should be cool (8 to 10 °C) and not too sweet; children prefer flavoured sport drinks, and these can promote drinking.

Recreation and Fitness Leadership

- ► Tell the participants to bring a personal water bottle; make sure each bottle is clean and well identified.

- ► Tell the participants to monitor their hydration levels by checking their urine. If it is dark, there is not much of it, and it has a strong smell, the participants are most likely dehydrated and should force themselves to drink.

- ► Know the signs of heat exhaustion and heat stroke. Start first aid procedures immediately if you suspect these medical conditions.

During exercise, the muscles produce heat. This heat must be dissipated, otherwise the body runs the risk of "overheating." Overheating can result in a serious, potentially life-threatening condition. High temperatures and high relative humidity make it hard for the body to dissipate heat; heavy sweating occurs, but the water lost does not help cool the body. Children run a higher risk of overheating when exercising in the heat because their sweating mechanism is not fully developed. In addition, children tend to not drink enough during exercise. See the box *Beat the Heat* for some good advice on exercising in hot weather.

*Can you taste the salt? Excessive perspiration due to exercise in the heat or prolonged vigorous activity (60 minutes or more) depletes the body not only of water but also of **electrolytes** (sodium and potassium) that are necessary for optimal cardiovascular performance. These can be replenished by drinking sport drinks, either commercial brands or home-made. Try diluting orange juice by half with water and adding a tiny pinch of salt to make a low-cost sport drink.*

Beat the Heat

If the humidex is above 30 °C, in particular if it exceeds 35 °C:

- Tell participants to bring extra water or sport drinks; make sure there will be access to water during the practice or the competition, and bring a big jug of fluids.

- Tell participants to dress in loosely fitting, lightweight, and light-coloured clothes.

- Plan for low-intensity activities.

- Plan for shorter work bouts, with frequent and longer pauses.

- Schedule workouts early in the morning or during the evening; avoid the hours between 9:00 a.m. and 6:00 p.m.

- Consider alternatives to physical exercise.

Sun Sense

Remind participants to take steps to prevent overexposure to harmful UV rays, which can damage skin and eyes over the long term. Avoid scheduling outdoor activities for the middle of the day when the sun's rays are most direct. Encourage participants to wear a hat and a long-sleeved shirt, to apply sunscreen (with an SPF of at least 30), and to wear UVA- and UVB-blocking sunglasses.

Preventing overexposure to harmful UV rays includes applying sunscreen with an SPF of at least 30 when planning outdoor activities.

Exercising in the Cold

Exercising in the cold is a fact of life for most Canadians. However, there is no reason to be housebound in the winter months. Taking the necessary precautions ensures safe participation in the huge variety of outdoor fall, winter, and spring activities that Canada is noted for. Whether you are skiing, skating, or building snowmen, a few simple steps can be taken to prevent **hypothermia**. See the box *The Cold Hard Facts*.

The Cold Hard Facts

The colder the environment, the faster a participant's body temperature will decrease. Keep the following points in mind when exercising in the cold.

- During exercise in a cold environment, the skin can become wet as a result of sweating or exposure to rain or snow. A wet skin surface cools the body faster than when it is dry.

- Cold, dry air makes it difficult to breathe for some people who have asthma, although it is generally easier to tolerate the cold when the air is dry.

- Children get cold much faster than adults, and their skin is more prone to freezing. People with less body fat usually have less tolerance for cold than those with more body fat.

- Muscles and other soft tissues that are cold are more susceptible to injuries such as pulls and tears, in particular if the efforts produced are sudden and intense.

- In very dry cold environments, water vapour lost through breathing and evaporation of sweat from exposed surfaces may lead to dehydration.

- The type of fabric worn can either wick moisture from the body surface (e.g., synthetics such as Gore-Tex or polypropylene), which results in less risk of heat loss, or trap it there (e.g., cotton or nylon), which results in greater risk of heat loss.

Safety Measures to Avoid Cold Injuries

When exercising in the cold . . .

- Make sure participants wear sufficient clothing for the weather conditions, and layer clothing as follows:

  Layer closest to the skin: Polypropylene, close fitting (wicking effect)

  Second layer: Fleece or wool, slight room between first layer and second layer for "trapped air" effect

  Third layer: Windbreaking, water repellent, breathable layer

- When it is very cold, make sure exposed skin is kept to a minimum.

- Once the body has warmed up, and if the temperature is not too cold, consider removal of the second layer of clothes during exercise to avoid excessive sweating. Have participants add a layer or use blankets to keep warm during breaks or pauses.

- Apply antiperspirant to the feet before exercising to reduce sweating of the feet (which is usually followed by cooling of the feet). Doing the same on the palms of the hands may reduce the feeling of cold for people who tend to sweat a lot in their gloves or mitts.

- Make sure participants hydrate when they exercise in the cold.

Determining Negligence and Liability

Fitness leaders, coaches, and recreation organizations have a legal obligation to provide a safe environment. If the participants are minors, leaders are expected to know more than the average parent about keeping activities safe. If they have received special instruction or training on safety procedures, they are expected to apply it.

Negligence

Negligence is a legal term referring to behaviour that fails to meet a reasonable standard of care. Conduct is deemed negligent when *all four* of the following criteria occur.

❶ *The leader is responsible for the participants.*

- This is a given in your involvement as a student leader, but if you are under 18, your adult supervisor has the "duty of care" for both you and the participants.

❷ *The leader fails to meet a reasonable standard of care.*

- The leader does something incorrectly or fails to act.
- The law expects the leader or coach to act as other reasonable leaders or coaches would act in the same circumstances. The court will refer to written and unwritten standards, case law, and expert witnesses.

❸ *The participant experiences harm.*

- The participant sustains an injury.

❹ *The failure to meet the standard has caused or substantially contributed to the harm.*

- The leader's action or inaction is directly related to the injury.

To avoid negligence, recreation leaders must be aware of the standard of care expected of them. With this knowledge, they can take steps to make sure their behaviour – and the behaviour of their employees – exceeds these expectations.

> *Safety is a cheap and effective insurance policy.*
> *Anonymous*

Liability

The term liability refers to which person or persons a judge decides should bear the blame for a particular incident or occurrence. Liability may be split among the coach or leader, the participant, the facility owner, and the equipment manufacturer. Percentage figures are often used to express the degree of liability borne by the various parties involved.

Consider the following example. At an indoor rock climbing facility,

a certified instructor is teaching a group of four beginners how to climb the wall and rappel (descend) back to the ground. The instructor fails to check the knot one of the participants has made. This participant starts to climb, reaches the top, and returns to the ground without incident. Since there was no harm, there is no negligence.

On his second climb, the participant decides to remove his helmet at the top and throw it to the ground. Then he lets go of the rope, intending to return to the ground as fast as possible. As he lands, the knot slips; he loses his balance, falls, hits his head, and sustains a head injury. His family sues the rock climbing facility.

A judge would determine how much of the blame lies with the instructor for not checking the knot and how much with the participant for disobeying the safety rules and being a daredevil. A key question to consider is whether or not the failure of the knot was instrumental in causing the fall, or if the participant would have fallen anyway because of the speed of the descent. As an employee, the instructor would be covered by the owner's liability insurance. Although the parents signed a notification of risk statement, they still have the right to sue if they believe the instructor was at fault.

Ultimately, the judge determines which person or persons should bear the blame for a particular incident or occurrence.

Putting It All Together

Accidents and injuries can occur even when the best preventive measures are in place. Self-blame is appropriate only when the leader acknowledges making a mistake. On the other hand, feelings of regret are a natural response when a person in your care suffers an injury, even if you did everything you ought to have done.

An essential strategy for managing risk is being proactive. Analyze the activity, the surroundings, and the participants, and take steps to minimize or eliminate any potential dangers. Know what to do when a safety issue arises – failing to act or reacting inappropriately can increase the risk to participants. Establish safety regulations and rules of conduct, and when accidents and injuries do occur – and they will – learn from them. Record all the details so that procedures can be reviewed and altered as necessary.

This chapter provides all the information you need in order to be a first-class risk manager. Now it is up to you to apply what you know. Be vigilant. Do not make compromises. Keep up to date. Maintain your first aid certification. Your participants count on you to protect them to the best of your ability.

Key Terms

accident log book
accident/incident report form
anaphylactic shock
dehydration
electrolytes
emergency action plan (EAP)
environmental risk
equipment risk
fair play
human risk

hypothermia
liability
negligence
notification of risk
Par-Q form
proactive
reactive
risk management
supervision
waiver form

Review Questions

1. Define risk management.

2. List five options for managing risk. Give an example for each.

3. List eight risk management procedures.

4. How can keeping accurate records help you be better prepared in the case of an emergency? How can they help you prevent accidents in the future?

5. Distinguish between the three levels of supervision.

6. Obtain the safety rules for a local sports or fitness facility. Evaluate how well they are communicated to the participants.

7. What steps should participants take to stay sufficiently hydrated during activity?

8. Give five tips for exercising in extreme heat.

9. What safety measures should be taken when exercising in the cold?

10. Distinguish between negligence and liability.

In This Chapter:

CHAPTER 14
Injury Management

In this chapter, you will learn about the following:

❶ How being prepared for emergencies can facilitate the decision-making process

❷ Developing an emergency response plan

❸ Injuries that commonly occur in the recreation and fitness environment

❹ Specific skills that can help others in emergency situations

The purpose of this chapter is to indicate the steps a fitness leader should take in the event of an injury or medical emergency. Most injuries in the recreation and fitness fields involve the soft tissues, a grouping that includes the skin, muscles, ligaments, and tendons. These injuries are usually minor and not life-threatening. However, a soft tissue injury that is not cared for properly can easily escalate into a chronic condition that may plague a person's efforts to lead an active life. Every fitness leader must be able to apply the appropriate first aid measures for soft tissue injuries as presented later in this chapter. Follow-up diagnosis and treatment by an appropriate health care professional should also be sought.

More serious injuries and emergencies, such as fractures, head and neck injuries, heart attacks, and strokes, require immediate professional medical attention. However, making the correct response as a first aider on the scene can have a significant impact on the final outcome. How these medical conditions are handled in the minutes after their occurrence or onset is critical. Fitness leaders need to know the signs and symptoms and take immediate action.

Since injuries cannot always be prevented, fitness leaders must be prepared to respond appropriately in the event of an injury or medical emergency.

The Importance of Being Prepared

Despite our efforts to take all the necessary precautions described in the previous chapter, accidents do happen and injuries occur. Being adequately prepared to handle any injuries that arise will increase your confidence and help you stay calm and focused. It is highly recommended that every recreation leader pursue certification in CPR – cardiopulmonary resuscitation. Your skill in performing CPR may even be called on to aid a spectator rather than a participant. A goal of the Heart and Stroke Foundation of Canada is to have every teenager and adult trained in administering CPR.

Knowing what to do, whether through completing a first aid training course or having gained prior experience by dealing with or observing similar situations, greatly enhances the decision-making process. A first aid responder must consider all possible courses of action and very quickly make the appropriate decision. Recreation leaders are expected

It is highly recommended that every recreation leader pursue certification in cardiopulmonary resuscitation (CPR) and complete a first aid training course to prepare themselves for emergency situations.

to handle emergencies knowledgeably, confidently, and competently. The outcomes to strive for are limiting further harm, reducing pain and suffering, and facilitating a quick return to activity without long-term symptoms. You may even save a life.

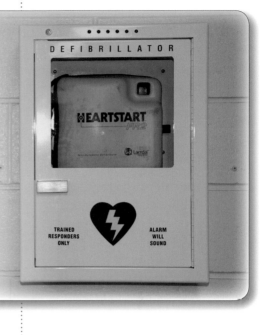

Restoring Rhythm

The placement of automatic external defibrillators (or AEDs, devices that help restore the heartbeat to a regular rhythm) in public places such as airports, schools, fitness facilities, and sports facilities allows for early intervention in the event of cardiac arrest, thus improving survival rates.

The Advanced Coronary Treatment (ACT) Foundation is a national charitable organization with the goal of establishing a CPR and AED program in every Canadian high school. The foundation raises funds for mannequins and resources, helps schools set up their programs, and arranges CPR and defibrillator training for teachers so they can instruct their students. ACT is well on its way to accomplishing its mission of empowering young Canadians to save lives.

Emergency Response

Emergency response describes the steps you take when responding to emergency situations. An emergency response plan should be designed, practiced, and modified whenever changes in your situation warrant it (see the box *Every Step You Take*). Advance planning will give you the confidence to handle the situation in a responsible and clear-headed manner.

Approach and Assessment

When an accident occurs, the first step is to control the environment to prevent further harm. The charge person should stop all participants, if applicable, and direct them to an alternate location or activity. Then he should instruct others to protect the injured participant and himself from harm (e.g., by removing any objects, glass, and so on that could hamper treatment). If the accident happens outdoors, it is important to shelter the charge person and the injured person from the elements and any traffic.

After asking someone to get the first aid kit, the charge person starts an initial assessment that will take only seconds. If any of the following life-threatening conditions is present, or if the person in charge does not feel prepared to deal with whatever symptoms are apparent, he or she

> Knowledge is of no value unless you put it into practice.
> *Anton Chekhov*

Every Step You Take

An emergency response plan needs to include the following preparatory steps:

1. Prepare and fully stock a first aid kit. This kit must be accessible at all times. For off-site activities, strap a fanny pack first aid kit around your waist.

2. A **charge person** must be designated. If you have current first aid qualifications, the charge person may be you. Otherwise, there must be a person qualified in first aid in the immediate vicinity that you can call on to handle an emergency situation.

3. Telephone contact with Emergency Medical Services (EMS) must be readily available. Either have a fully charged cell phone with you, or have access to a telephone.

4. Have emergency phone numbers on hand (facility manager, fire, police, ambulance) as well as participants' contact numbers (parents/guardians, next of kin, family doctor). Post a list of emergency telephone numbers beside the telephone. This list forms part of the emergency action plan discussed in the previous chapter.

5. Designate in advance a **call person** whose job it is to contact EMS if the charge person determines the situation warrants it. The charge person tells the call person the nature of the injury so that this information can be passed on to EMS. It is important that this step be completed accurately because the EMS dispatcher will determine if this is a high-priority situation based on the information given.

6. A written set of directions to the site should be posted near the phone. Include information such as the nearest intersection, one-way streets, and which entrance to use. The call person will read these directions to the EMS dispatcher.

7. Medical profiles for each participant, along with signed consent forms to authorize medical treatment in an emergency, should be readily available. Give this information to the emergency medical personnel.

tells the call person to contact EMS with the information that there is a patient with one or more of the following symptoms:

► The patient is not breathing.

► The patient does not have a pulse.

► The patient is bleeding profusely.

► The patient has impaired consciousness.

► The patient has injured the back, neck, or head.

► The patient has visible major trauma, with deformation to a limb.

► The patient cannot move his or her arms or legs or has lost feeling in them.

Recreation and Fitness Leadership

Treatment

After donning disposable gloves, the charge person begins the appropriate treatment: artificial respiration without cardiac compression for a nonbreathing victim; CPR if there is no pulse; direct pressure with a compression bandage for severe bleeding; rest and immobilization for fractures and for head, neck, and back injuries. Unconscious victims should be rolled over into the semi-prone (or recovery) position (Figure 14.1) unless there is an indication that a spinal injury may have occurred. In this position, fluids will drain from the mouth rather than accumulate in the throat, where they could block the breathing passages. If a spinal injury is suspected, do not move the injured person. No matter how careful you are, turning the victim can cause further damage and even paralysis.

Figure 14.1 As long as no spinal injury is suspected, unconscious victims should be rolled over into the semi-prone, or recovery, position to help keep breathing passages clear.

Other staff members or adults on hand may assist by moving spectators away from the scene, thus preparing clear access for the EMS team, or by bringing needed equipment and supplies, such as the first aid kit, blankets, and cold packs.

Secondary Assessment and Treatment

If the injured person does not exhibit any of the previously listed symptoms, the charge person can continue the assessment by determining the mechanism of injury. The injured person and those who witnessed the

---

Allergic Reactions

For some people, common foods that most of us enjoy can cause a severe allergic reaction (e.g., anaphylactic shock). A simple peanut butter sandwich can be deadly for a person with a severe peanut allergy. Insect stings are another common cause of these life-threatening reactions. Symptoms of anaphylactic shock include red, itchy skin; swelling of the tongue and throat (often leading to difficulty breathing); and a rapid or irregular heartbeat.

Contact EMS immediately if a severe allergic reaction is suspected. Anaphylactic shock is usually treated with an injection of epinephrine. People who are known to have severe reactions often carry an EpiPen, a device that allows for self-administration of the drug. Recreation leaders should know how to use an EpiPen in case the victim loses consciousness or is too young to administer the medication himself.

---

accident can provide details. The charge person applies appropriate first aid based on the information given, signs that she observes (e.g., unusual skin colour), and symptoms the victim reports (e.g., pain and impaired mobility). Throughout the assessment and treatment, the charge person must try to keep the injured person calm. Showing confidence and caring through tone of voice and body language will achieve this. In addition, treat the victim for **shock** if necessary (see the box *Symptoms of Shock*).

If the injured person is able to move herself to a safer area or a more comfortable position, encourage this. Do not attempt to move an injured person yourself unless your first aid training has given you the necessary skills and you have other people to assist you.

Even at this stage, EMS may be called in. For instance, if no one qualified in first aid is available to make the secondary assessment if symptoms worsen, or if the victim starts to show signs of head injury, EMS should be notified.

EMS should be notified if no one qualified in first aid is available to make the secondary assessment.

Symptoms of Shock

Shock is a depression of the circulatory system that may be present with any injury or illness. It may even occur in a fitness class as a result of overexertion or dehydration. When a person is in shock, not enough oxygen is supplied to the vital organs. Shock can be life-threatening and needs to be treated immediately.

Signs

- Pale skin (or bluish-gray as shock progresses)
- Cold, clammy skin
- Profuse sweating
- Shaking
- Vomiting
- Decreased consciousness (fainting)
- Breathing irregularities
- Weak, rapid pulse

Symptoms

The person may report:

- Feelings of anxiety or doom
- Confusion
- Dizziness
- Nausea
- Feeling faint
- Extreme thirst
- Pain

Treatment

- Loosen tight clothing at neck, waist, ankles, and wrists.
- Raise the victim's legs and feet above the level of the heart if possible, except in the case of neck and spinal injuries, heart attack, or stroke.
- Cover the victim to preserve body heat.
- Place a blanket under the victim, as long as movement will not aggravate injuries.
- Give nothing to eat or drink (moistening the victim's lips is all right).

It is at this stage, too, that the call person should notify the victim's emergency contacts. They may be told to go directly to the hospital emergency department where the victim is being transported, or in less severe cases, they may be advised to pick up the injured person and take him to the ER or a walk-in clinic themselves.

Follow-Up

The previous chapter gave details on completing an accident report form in order to evaluate whether or not preventive action should have taken place. Another important aspect of the follow-up is simply assuring that the injured person seeks medical attention. A phone call to the person or her family is in order. The next step in the follow-up is to monitor the victim's return to activity. Returning to action too soon is a common cause of subsequent injury.

Soft Tissue Injuries

Without question, the most common injuries in the fitness and recreation fields are soft tissue injuries. This category includes injury to skin, muscles, tendons, and ligaments. At times, underlying structures such as internal organs may be involved. Falls, impacts with obstacles or other participants, and simply moving in a way that is beyond the body's capabilities are the usual causes (see Table 14.1).

The body's response to soft tissue injury is **inflammation**, which is an increase in local blood circulation. The increased blood flow brings white blood cells to the area. These are the cells that "mop up" damaged cells and bacteria. Inflammation begins immediately and can last from two to four days. The signs of soft tissue injury are easy to remember by using the mnemonic SHARP.

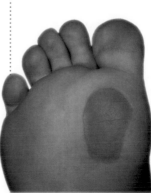

Looking SHARP

S = Swelling
H = Heat
A = Altered function
R = Redness
P = Pain

SHARP Signs of Soft Tissue Injury

Swelling – Damaged cells release their contents into surrounding tissues, which causes swelling or puffiness at the site of the injury. This results in immobilization of the injured area, the body's way to prevent movement and decrease pain. To assess the amount of swelling, compare the injured area with the uninjured area on the opposite limb. Swelling is the most critical factor in slowing down recovery time. Thus, it is essential to limit swelling (e.g., by applying pressure and ice) as soon as possible and take other steps to limit movement and ease pain.

Heat – Increased circulation to the injured area brings warm blood to the surface. This temperature change, experienced as heat, is usually quite noticeable and goes hand in hand with swelling.

Table 14.1 Summary of soft tissue injuries and causes.

Soft Tissue Type	Function	Type of Injury	Example
Muscle	Causes movement at joints by contracting and pulling on tendons that are attached to bones	**Strain** – stretching or tearing of muscle or muscle–tendon tissue	A hockey goalie does the splits to stop a puck and tears the muscle on the back of the leg.
		Bruise (contusion) – bleeding in the muscle tissue caused by a direct blow	Two outfielders collide while chasing down a fly ball, leaving one with a bruised thigh from the impact of the other player's knee.
Tendon	Joins muscle to bone (e.g., Achilles tendon attaches calf muscles to heel)	See *strain* above	A tennis player reaches for a drop shot and overstretches the calf muscles. He feels a sharp pain in or above the heel.
		Tendinitis – inflammation of a tendon, most commonly caused by overuse	A young volleyball player develops patellar tendinitis (jumper's knee) after increasing the frequency of her jumping drills.
Ligament	Noncontracting tissue joining bone to bone; stabilizes joints	**Sprain** – ligament fibres are stretched and/or partially or completely torn **Dislocation** – ligament tearing is severe enough to allow bone end surfaces to separate	A basketball player lands awkwardly after a jump shot, causing her ankle to roll over. She hears a popping sound, which is an indicator of a ligament injury.
Cartilage	Semi-bone tissue found either on the ends of bones or wedged between two adjacent bone surfaces to provide a gliding surface or act as a moderate shock absorber in the joint	**Torn cartilage** – tearing of cartilage tissue, usually as a result of a forceful twisting injury	A downhill skier catches his ski on a gate and violently twists his knee.
Skin	Seals out air, water, germs Evaporation of sweat for cooling	**Laceration** – a cut	A speed skater cuts her hand on a competitor's skate blade.
		Abrasion – a rough, broken surface	A cyclist takes a tumble and gets a nasty asphalt burn.
		Blister – a fluid-filled pocket on the skin	A triathlete gets a blister on his heel while breaking in new running shoes.

Altered function – An injured person may report that he cannot move the limb as normal. Altered function can be assessed effectively by comparing the range of movement of the injured limb with that of the uninjured limb.

Recreation and Fitness Leadership

Redness – Increased local circulation at the site of the injury also causes redness. Think about your last mosquito bite.

Pain – Inflammation coupled with pain signals from stretched and torn nerve endings is felt as pain. Ask the injured person to assess the pain on a scale of 1 to 10. Your actions to reduce pain will be greatly appreciated.

PIER Treatment for Soft Tissue Injury

Immediate treatment can limit the inflammation stage and allow the body to begin healing sooner. It will also prevent further damage and reduce pain. General treatment for soft tissue injuries follows another mnemonic, PIER.

Pressure – Whether the damage is under the skin or external, the most important step is to apply direct pressure. This action closes off the blood vessels to the damaged cells, thus reducing swelling and loss of blood. Put on disposable gloves before contacting an open wound. At the very least, have a layer of cloth, plastic wrap, or paper between your skin and the wound. Pressure can even be applied to a bruise in order to limit its extent and the time it takes to fade away. Use the heel of the hand. An elastic bandage (e.g., Tensor) is commonly used to apply pressure to sprains and strains and could be used for bruises as well. Placing a piece of thicker padding directly over the injured area adds to the impact of the elastic bandage. This padding can be fashioned from a piece of dense foam (such as what mouse pads are made of!).

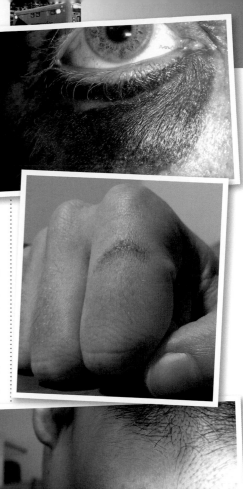

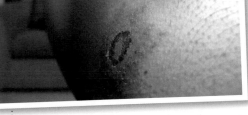

Swelling, heat, redness, and pain – the body's inflammatory response – are sure signs of soft tissue injury.

Ice – Using ice to treat an acute injury has two primary functions. As the cold temperature numbs the area, pain is reduced and the victim feels more comfortable. In addition, circulation diminishes and thus swelling is limited. Chemical ice packs, crushed ice cubes in a plastic bag, or a bag of frozen peas can provide this cooling effect. Apply ice for 15 to 20 minutes at a time every hour or so during the first 24 to 48 hours after the accident.

Ice or Heat?

Ice is the best immediate treatment for acute injuries because it reduces swelling and pain. After 48 hours, when the swelling has subsided, heat is often used to accelerate the recovery process. Heat increases blood flow to the area, removing damaged cells and supplying healing nutrients.

Heat is also an effective treatment for stiff, sore muscles and for chronic joint pain. Athletes with chronic pain often apply heat before a training session or competition in order to stimulate blood flow and relax tissues. After the activity, ice can be used to control inflammation.

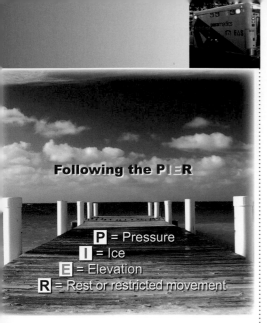

Following the PIER

P = Pressure
I = Ice
E = Elevation
R = Rest or restricted movement

Elevation – Elevating an injured limb encourages venous blood flow towards the heart and is another important treatment to limit the effects of an injury to soft tissue. Prop up an injured arm or leg so that it is above the level of the heart. If the torso is injured, have the victim lie on the uninjured area, with the injured area on top.

Rest or restricted movement – The injured person must cease activity and rest or restrict movement of the injured area. Taping and splints may be used to further reduce movement of the injured body part (see the box *Taping an Ankle Sprain*). Correct taping of a sprain will also bring the edges of the damaged tissue into contact with each other so that they will heal in the proper position. If this step is not taken, the joint will be "loose" and subject to chronic sprains.

Taping an Ankle Sprain

The first aider:

1. Assesses the situation for hazards

2. Asks: How did it happen? Where does it hurt? Can you move it?

3. Asks a bystander to assist by stabilizing the wounded ankle

4. Flexes and inverts/everts the victim's ankle depending on the location of the sprain

5. Applies horseshoe pad to injured side of ankle (Image 1)

6. Wets 0.5 meter of Tensor bandage with a water bottle or tap water

7. Performs one figure-8 wrap around the ankle, starting with the wet end of the Tensor bandage

8. Applies Tensor bandage in correct direction (up towards the knee on the injured side) (Image 2)

9. Places ice pack on injured side over top of wet Tensor (Image 3)

10. Continues to wrap the ankle with figure-8s to hold ice pack in place (Image 4)

11. Secures the Tensor bandage and checks toes for colour and coldness. Loosens bandage if circulation is being cut off.

12. Insists victim rests with foot elevated

13. Follows up by ensuring that the victim receives professional medical care and by completing an accident report

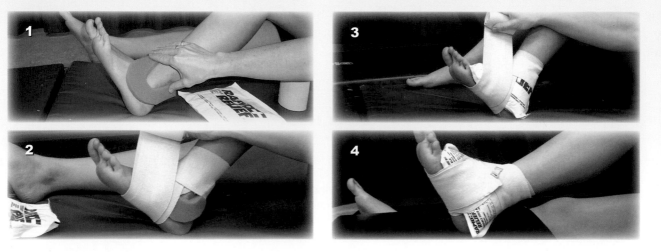

Recreation and Fitness Leadership

Return to Activity

Monitor a participant's return to activity after a minor injury. Allow her to resume activity only if there is no pain, flexibility is normal, strength can be demonstrated, and she shows the ability to perform the movements required by the activity. Be aware that keen participants may try to fake full recovery.

Assessing Readiness to Return to Action

A progressive series of activities for a participant with an injury to the lower leg includes many of the following:

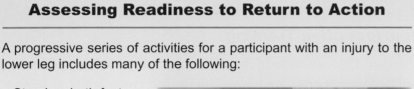

- Stand on both feet.
- Rise on toes.
- Do a knee bend.
- Walk in a straight line.
- Walk in a circle.
- Jump on the spot.
- Hop on the injured leg.
- Jog in a straight line.
- Jog in a circle.
- If the activity requires the ability to change speed and direction quickly, the participant must be able to run and cut from side to side without pain.

Rehabilitation

Rehabilitation promotes physical restoration of strength and flexibility to the injured tissue. A physiotherapist, chiropractor, athletic therapist, kinesiologist or other qualified health care professional will apply techniques and will implement and guide the participant's exercise program. Various methods of rehabilitation can be used depending on the type and the extent of the injury. A few of these methods are described in this section. Protective taping or braces are often used in conjunction with these treatments during rehabilitation.

Physiotherapists, chiropractors, massage therapists, or other health care professionals can help clients restore their strength and flexibility to injured tissues.

Cryotherapy

Cryotherapy involves using ice for the first 48 hours postinjury to reduce swelling. An easy way to apply ice is to freeze water in foam drinking cups. Expose a layer of ice by tearing off the top 2 cm of the cup. Rub the

 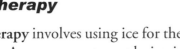

affected area until it feels numb. Move the joint actively through its range of movement until the numbness wears off. Repeat these steps three or four times.

Massage Therapy and Ultrasound

When the pain and swelling have subsided, individuals can work on rebuilding strength and flexibility. Manual **massage therapy** and similar **ultrasound** treatments can help break down scar tissue that formed as a result of the injury.

Proprioceptive Training

In almost all cases of soft tissue damage, nerve damage also occurs. Damaged nerve fibres, combined with the soft tissue injury, compromise the body's ability to sense position in space, known as **proprioception**. Beyond rehabilitation exercises for strength and flexibility, the retraining of nerve pathways must be included in the program to restore balance, coordination, and agility to preinjury levels. The main reason ankle sprains reoccur is decreased proprioception after the initial sprain.

*W*hat is proprioception? Proprioception is the ability to sense the position of a joint in space. Nerve endings within the tendons relay information to the brain, where it is interpreted. Impulses are sent out to contract the muscles to maintain stability.

A Balance Training Plan for Ankle Sprains

Standing on the floor, balance on both feet with eyes open, then with eyes closed. Stand on the injured leg with eyes open, then with eyes closed. When these tasks have been mastered, use a balance board or balance beam in the same sequence. To restore dynamic balance, stand on the balance board while holding dumbbells. Perform symmetrical arm movements first, then try asymmetrical movements.

Fractures

A **fracture** is an injury to the body's hard tissue, bone. A bone fracture (i.e., a broken bone) may be simple or compound. If the bone protrudes through the skin, the fracture is compound and presents a much more serious situation than a simple fracture. Tissue damage is extensive, and the possibility of infection is strong. Regardless of whether the fracture is compound or simple, the first aider's main response is to immobilize the limb in the position it is in. *Do not attempt to straighten the limb!* Learn the proper immobilization techniques by taking an emergency first aid course. An open (compound) fracture should be covered to reduce the chance of infection. In a scenario involving a simple fracture, ice may be applied. In some cases it may be possible to elevate the injured limb after it has been immobilized.

Head Injuries and Concussions

Aconcussion is an injury to the brain that results when the spongy brain strikes the hard inside surface of the skull. This can happen as a result of a direct blow to the head or from striking another body part in such a way that the shock is transmitted through the body to the head.

In simple terms, a concussion is a bruised brain. In a severe concussion (grade 3), swelling puts pressure on the brain tissue, potentially causing lasting brain damage. In a mild grade 1 concussion, the swelling is limited and recedes quickly. All levels of concussion require professional medical attention. And remember, a person can suffer a concussion without losing consciousness.

A concussion shows itself as a temporary alteration in mental state along with physical symptoms. Changes to mental state may include dizziness, loss of consciousness, lethargy, memory loss, confusion or disorientation, lack of focus, ringing in the ears, seeing stars or flashing lights, speech impairment, balance impairment, problems with sight, and a vacant stare. Physical symptoms include pain, headache, nausea (which may not happen until hours later), and a major decrease in performance. Other signs may include slow responses to simple questions, inappropriate emotional responses or behaviours, and difficulty following directions. Some symptoms may not appear immediately. Any person who has suffered a head injury should be carefully observed for several hours, including during sleep.

If you suspect a concussion, contact Emergency Medical Services immediately. Keep the victim calm and resting until the ambulance arrives. If the person is unconscious, monitor his breathing. The most appropriate position for an unconscious person is the semi-prone position, which allows fluids (saliva, vomit) to flow out of the mouth. However, if there is any indication of possible neck or back injury, *do not move the victim.*

The road to recovery from a concussion can be long and frustrating. Make sure the person follows doctor's orders to the letter.

In simple terms, a concussion is a bruised brain, which can happen as a result of a direct blow to the head or from striking another body part in such a way that the shock is transmitted through the body to the head.

Did You Know?

Helmets are a good idea for activities such as bicycling, in-line skating, and scooter riding. Skateboarders need special helmets that provide more coverage for the back of the head (especially for beginners who tend to fall backwards more often).

Research has shown that a properly fitted bicycle helmet offers up to 88 percent protection from brain injury.

Always replace helmets that have sustained a significant impact. Helmets are effective for one fall – one time use only! Also, avoid buying "used" helmets to ensure maximum protection.

Cardiovascular Events

The risk of developing a cardiovascular condition is linked with controllable factors such as cigarette smoking, elevated blood pressure, elevated blood cholesterol, diabetes, obesity, lack of exercise, and excessive stress. Some of the noncontrollable factors include age, gender, and genetics.

The heart acts as a pump, continuously circulating blood to the lungs and to all parts of the body. The heart itself gets its blood supply through two coronary arteries. If these arteries or their branches – which cover the entire surface of the heart, or pericardium – become narrowed or blocked, a part of the heart will not receive the oxygen it needs. This will cause a cardiovascular emergency. Risk factors that can be controlled include cigarette smoking, elevated blood pressure, elevated blood cholesterol, diabetes, obesity, lack of exercise, and excessive stress. A person's age, gender, and family history (genetics) also play a significant role. The risk of developing a cardiovascular condition can be reduced considerably by adopting a healthy lifestyle.

Heart Attack

A **heart attack** is most often caused by the blockage of a coronary artery that is already narrowed. The blood clot blocks the flow of oxygen-carrying blood to the heart muscle itself. A section of the heart muscle dies. If a large portion of the heart is affected, death results. If only a small portion is affected, recovery is possible.

Cardiac Arrest

When the heart stops pumping blood, **cardiac arrest** occurs. A heart attack is only one of several possible causes of cardiac arrest. The others are electrical shock, poisoning, drug overdose, drowning, suffocation, chest trauma, and stroke. In older active populations, the incidence of cardiac arrest is greater than in the average population.

Angina

A temporary shortage of oxygen to the heart muscle results in **angina** – translated roughly as pain in the chest. The signs and symptoms of angina are similar to a heart attack, except they are often brought on by physical effort or stress and should be relieved by rest and medication. There is no heart damage in angina as there is in a heart attack. Angina sufferers usually wear a medic alert bracelet and carry nitroglycerine tablets with them to take in case of an attack.

Stroke

When a portion of brain tissue dies because of a shortage of oxygen, this condition is referred to as a **stroke**. A stroke can be caused by a blockage in the circulation, similar to a heart attack. In fact, many people

Suffering a stroke or other cardiovascular event can be life-changing.

now refer to stroke as "brain attack" because the mechanism is the same. Another cause of a stroke is a ruptured blood vessel in the brain (called a *hemorrhagic stroke*). If the stroke happens in an area controlling heart action, cardiac arrest results.

Symptoms and Response

The symptoms of a heart attack are shortness of breath, pale colour, sweating, vomiting, and unconsciousness. The person may complain of crushing chest pain; pain spreading to the neck, jaw, shoulders, and/or arms; fear or a feeling of doom; and indigestion or nausea.

In all cases, contact Emergency Medical Services immediately, and give a clear description of the symptoms. Reduce the workload of the victim's heart by keeping him immobile. Try to prevent his condition from getting worse. Usually a semi-sitting position is most comfortable. Loosen tight clothing at the neck, chest, and waist, and reassure the person (if he is still conscious). Ask if he has angina and has any medication available. If the person goes into cardiac arrest, start **cardiopulmonary resuscitation (CPR)**.

*A*re you familiar with the symptoms of a heart attack? Aside from crushing chest pain, a person suffering a heart attack may exhibit shortness of breath, pale colour, sweating, vomiting, and unconsciousness.

You are never too young to start pursuing certification in CPR. It can be a life-saving experience.

The symptoms of a stroke usually occur suddenly and include weakness or numbness of the face, arm, or leg, especially on one side of the body; vision problems; difficulty speaking or understanding; loss of balance or coordination; confusion; and severe headache. If one or more of these symptoms are present, contact EMS immediately. The damage caused by a stroke can be stopped and even reversed if proper treatment is administered within a few hours after the onset of symptoms.

Putting It All Together

This chapter provides examples of how to handle the most common first aid situations in the field of recreation and leisure. It is important to be prepared, by establishing and practicing an emergency response plan and by getting trained in first aid and CPR. Dealing with a soft tissue injury is relatively straightforward, yet proper treatment is vital to ensure a quick return to activity.

More serious conditions such as compound fractures, concussions, heart attacks, and strokes require professional intervention. Contact Emergency Medical Services immediately. However, you still play an important role in the treatment process by monitoring the victim's condition and minimizing further damage until professional medical assistance arrives.

Key Terms

abrasion	fracture
angina	heart attack
blister	inflammation
call person	laceration
cardiac arrest	massage therapy
cardiopulmonary resuscitation (CPR)	PIER
	proprioception
charge person	rehabilitation
concussion	SHARP
contusion	shock
cryotherapy	sprain
dislocation	strain
Emergency Medical Services (EMS)	stroke
	tendinitis
emergency response plan	ultrasound

Review Questions

1. List seven features of a well-designed emergency response plan.

2. What symptoms indicate the need for immediate contact with Emergency Medical Services?

3. Describe the treatment for shock.

4. List and define six common soft tissue injuries.

5. Explain the mnemonic SHARP.

6. Explain the mnemonic PIER.

7. Develop a test for an upper limb injury to determine if a participant is ready to return to a volleyball game.

Recreation and Fitness Leadership

8. Distinguish between a simple and a compound fracture.

9. What is a concussion? What are the symptoms?

10. Distinguish between heart attack, cardiac arrest, angina, and stroke.

CAREER PROFILE

NAME: Silken Laumann
OCCUPATION: Inspirational Speaker

▶ *What do you do?*

I am a mom, a former Olympic rower, a professional inspirational speaker, and the founder of my charity, Silken's ActiveKids Movement.

▶ *What is unique about your job?*

My job is different every day! I could be speaking to a group of parents, inspiring them to play with their kids; or I could be speaking to youth and encouraging them to never give up and to always follow their dreams. My job is very emotionally rewarding.

One reason I love my job is that it gives me the opportunity to continue to grow and learn and then share that with other people. I think by sharing my life in an open way, I help people see that they too have the privilege of having dreams and realizing their own greatness.

▶ *Why did you choose a career in professional speaking? What was your motivation for pursuing this field?*

Following my accident and Olympic experiences, I wanted to share my story and inspire people. Anything is possible when you set your mind to it. How wonderful it is to share this message and hopefully impact people in a positive way.

▶ *How competitive is the field?*

I don't think of my job as competitive because everybody is unique and can only share their own truth and experiences. We all have something of value to share!

▶ *What do you enjoy most about your profession?*

I enjoy connecting with people and inspiring them to achieve.

▶ *What career advice would you give to students interested in entering this field?*

Always set goals for yourself, and don't give up on your dreams.

In This Chapter:

CHAPTER 15
Fitness Safety Practices

In this chapter, you will learn about the following:

❶ Guidelines for the safe use of fitness facilities and equipment

❷ The structure of the body's musculoskeletal system and how it dictates safe movement patterns

❸ Evaluating the safety and effectiveness of exercises

❹ Prescribing exercise programs for different client populations

> ## "The door to safety swings on the hinges of common sense."
> Anonymous

Since the fitness environment has many potential hazards, fitness leaders must be aware of the precautions and guidelines for the facilities, equipment, and exercises they use and recommend.

Fitness leaders need to be aware of many cautions and guidelines for the facilities, equipment, and exercises they use and recommend. This information goes well beyond the essential knowledge of risk management and response to injuries that has been described in detail in the previous chapters. The fitness environment has potential hazards that are specific to it alone; the vast variety of equipment, large and small, that is used in the fitness field comes with numerous precautions for use; the exercises themselves can be hazardous if not instructed and performed properly. Knowledge of human anatomy and correct body mechanics is essential in order to select and design safe and effective exercise programs. Adapting programs for clients with chronic medical conditions adds an additional challenge. Some basic information is provided here, but you are advised to seek information from your teacher or a qualified medical or fitness professional regarding necessary program adaptations.

Reliable and complete information can be accessed from professional organizations such as Canadian Fitness Professionals Inc. (Can-Fit-Pro). The manufacturers and distributors of fitness equipment are more than willing to provide information in the interest of increasing customer satisfaction. Safety documents such as the Canadian Fitness Safety Standards and individual provincial safety standards for physical education set out requirements that must be met. Numerous books and Internet sites are also available. Selected sites are presented in the box *Web Resources.*

Web Resources

- American Council on Exercise
- Canadian Fitness Professionals Inc.
- Canadian Forces Personnel and Family Support Services
- Canadian Society for Exercise Physiology
- National Fitness Leadership Alliance
- Sport Information Resource Centre

Fitness Facility and Equipment Safety Guidelines

I t is easy to find guidelines for fitness facilities and equipment. Fitness clubs have their own document, the Canadian Fitness Safety Standards, which delineates standards and guidelines for all aspects of commercial fitness programming. All people involved in the fitness industry, from personal trainers to club owners to managers, have a duty to be informed and apply these safety standards. Some of the standards that fitness facilities must meet are presented in Table 15.1.

The Ontario Physical Education Safety Guidelines include specific guidelines for every activity in the elementary and secondary physical

Exercise classes must allow each participant unrestricted and safe movement.

The Fitness Environment

The safety standards and guidelines that fitness facilities must meet are set out in a standardized Canadian Fitness Safety Standards document. All facility personnel have a duty to be informed and to apply these standards, as outlined below in Table 15.1.

Table 15.1 Canadian safety standards for fitness facilities.

Standard #1
• All fitness-related environments and equipment shall be clean, well maintained, and free from hazards.

Standard #2
• Access to a clean drinking water supply is required at or near all physical activity areas.

Standard #3
• The number of participants in an exercise class is based on the square footage that allows each participant unrestricted and safe movement in various types of exercises. Participant numbers may also be defined by building code restrictions and/or fire code regulations.

Standard #4
• All fitness testing equipment shall be checked, cleaned, and calibrated as required.

Standard #5
• Floors in wet areas shall have a nonslip surface with adequate drainage to prevent pooling of water.

Standard #6
• Whirlpools, spas, and tubs shall comply with the Recommended Standards for the Operation of Public Spas (Ministry of Health & Long-Term Care Act, June 2001).

Standard #7
• Electrical panels shall be covered. Receptacles located in wet areas of a building and associated with the pool, such as a locker and change room, require ground fault circuit interrupters of the Class A type.

Standard #8
• A fire alarm system shall be installed in a building as determined by building code requirements. (Ontario Building Code 3.2.4.1) Portable fire extinguishers shall be installed in all buildings. (OBC 3.2.5.17 or existing provincial/ territorial code or regulations as applicable)

education school program. The guidelines are divided into sections for curricular programming, intramural events, and interschool activities. The complete document is available to school boards across the country through the Ontario Physical and Health Education Association. The guidelines that cover fitness activities such as aerobics, aerobic steps, chinning bar, peg board, circuit training, slides, and tubing is presented in Table 15.2.

Following is a list of safety guidelines for the weight room compiled from several sources:

▶ Work on your own program. Do not compete with others.

▶ A T-shirt, shorts or track pants, and running shoes must be worn.

▶ Ask the staff if you are unsure of how to do something.

▶ Maintain correct posture. Use controlled movements avoiding the use of momentum.

   ▶ Wherever possible, use the full range of movement of the joints.

   ▶ Select an appropriate resistance. Do not overload the bar or machine.

   ▶ Adjust weight stacks carefully. Avoid placing fingers between weights.

   ▶ Always use safety bar collars on the barbell.

   ▶ Have a spotter when lifting free weights above the body.

▶ Breathe during efforts: Exhale during the work phase and inhale during the return phase.

▶ Remain properly hydrated.

▶ Stop if you feel faint or feel any sort of pain or stiffness whatsoever.

▶ Return all weights to their proper locations. Do not leave weight on machines, and do not leave loose weights or dumbbells on the floor.

▶ Use antiseptic spray and towels to clean equipment after use.

▶ Remember to warm up, cool down, and stretch.

In summary, follow the risk management procedures for every facility and piece of equipment, large or small, that is used in the fitness program. Be **proactive**: Imagine what could go wrong. Take the necessary steps to eliminate or reduce the risk. At the very least, warn the participants about any potential risks.

Keeping the weight room and other fitness facilities in order and adhering to basic safety guidelines will enhance the experience for all fitness leaders and participants.

Be proactive: Imagine what could go wrong and take steps to eliminate or reduce risks.

Recreation and Fitness Leadership

Table 15.2 Physical education safety guidelines (March 1999).

Equipment

- Stationary bicycles, benches, chinning bars, peg boards, and other equipment used in fitness activities must be in good repair.

- Electrical equipment must be in good working order.

- Steps and/or slides must be in good repair and equipped with nonslip treads.

- Tubing/elastic strips must be the proper tension and length for the level of participant and must be in good repair.

Clothing/Footwear

- Suitable clothing and footwear must be worn.

- No jewellery.

Facilities

- Floor area must be free of all obstacles (e.g., piano, tables and chairs).

- Allow adequate space between fitness activities/equipment in order to provide free flow of motion.

Supervision

- On-site supervision for initial instruction, followed by in-the-area supervision.

Special Rules

- Fitness activities must be modified based on the age and ability level of students, the facilities, and equipment available.

- Students must be instructed in the proper use of the equipment before using it.

- Where the fitness activities constitute the main part of the lesson, a proper warm-up and cool-down must be provided.

- Use proper progression of activities:
  1. Warm-up
  2. Muscle strength
  3. Endurance
  4. Peak work activities
  5. Cool-down activities

- Permit students to work at personal levels of intensity (e.g., students who can make responsible decisions related to low impact to high impact and low intensity to high intensity).

- Stress correct body alignment for injury prevention.

Exercise Prescription

The human body is capable of any movement that it has been trained to execute. We have all seen people perform athletic stunts that seem impossible, from the contortionist to the slalom ski racer to the weightlifter. Each elite performance is the result of an extensive, well-designed training program to make these moves seem effortless.

Loud Noise: Another Environmental Hazard

We are exposed to loud noises all the time, many beyond our control (e.g., machinery, music concerts, school band practices). But are you aware of the damage to your hearing caused by overamplified music in a fitness class or listening to an iPod at full volume while jogging or running on a treadmill?

If your fitness instructor has jacked up the volume of the audio equipment, move as far away as possible from the source, wear earplugs, and ask the instructor to turn down the volume.

Setting headphone volumes to a safe level is key. Damage occurs when the ear is exposed to 85 dBA or more of sound for an extended period of time. Most portable music players produce this volume at setting 4 or 5, or half the maximum volume on the dial. If you are using music to drown out background noise, you have probably set the volume in the danger zone. Repeat exposure at these levels will cause permanent hearing loss over time.

Wearing headphones during aerobic exercise increases the danger since the blood flow is diverted from the ears to the limbs, leaving the inner ear more vulnerable to damage. In addition, if you are jogging in your community, you may miss the sound of hazards such as automobiles, aggressive dogs, or muggers.

Hearing protection is a sound investment.
Anonymous

The steps in developing the programs to produce these results are the same as the steps in selecting exercises for fitness participants. The process begins with an understanding of the musculoskeletal structures involved in movement. Next is knowledge of the movements that the body can perform without harm. Working on this base of knowledge that respects the limitations of body structure and the need for correct body mechanics, consider the client's goals and individual body characteristics in order to select exercises that are safe, effective, and specific.

Understanding the Limitations of Human Anatomy

A rudimentary understanding of the body's musculoskeletal system is necessary before any step in exercise selection. In brief, the framework for movement is the **skeleton** (Figures 15.1 and 15.2). Muscles are attached to the skeleton at several points. When muscles contract, movement occurs at joints.

A good starting point is to look at the body in the neutral **anatomical position** and learn terms to describe the various planes of movement and the relative location of body parts (Figure 15.3). When in the anatomical position, the body is standing erect, facing forward, with the arms hanging at the sides, palms facing forward. The legs are straight, and the heels and feet are together and parallel to each other. This position is universally accepted as the starting reference point for describing the human body.

The anatomical position is used as the starting reference point for describing the human body.

Recreation and Fitness Leadership

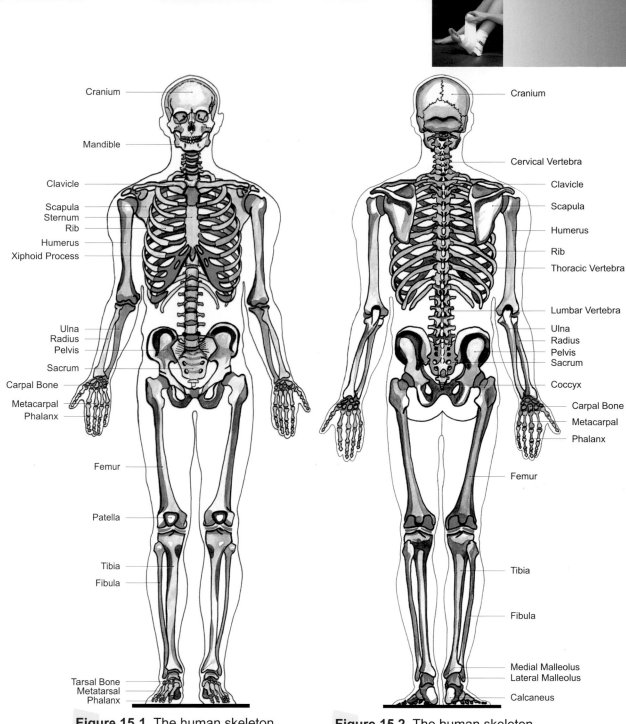

Figure 15.1 The human skeleton, anterior view.

Figure 15.2 The human skeleton, posterior view.

Did You Know?

Have you ever wondered why the thumbs are turned out in anatomical position?

Anatomical position originated with the early students of medicine in the 1500s. They relied on grave robbers to procure bodies for dissection since it was illegal to desecrate the human body at that time. When they laid a body on the slab, they felt it was more logical to have the lower arm bones (ulna and radius) lie side by side rather than crossed.

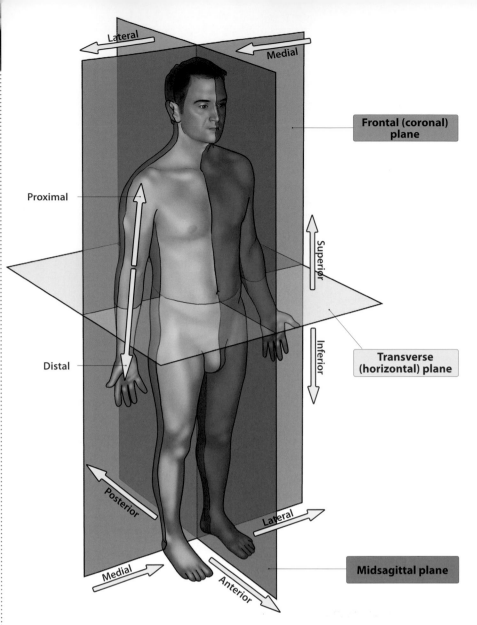

Figure 15.3 Anatomical position, directional terms, and planes of the body.

Labels in figure:
Lateral
Medial
Frontal (coronal) plane
Proximal
Superior
Distal
Inferior
Transverse (horizontal) plane
Posterior
Lateral
Medial
Anterior
Midsagittal plane

Joints of the Human Body

A joint is basically the point of connection between two or more bones. The stability and integrity of joints are maintained by strands of connective tissue called ligaments, which hold the bones together. Joints allow movement as well as provide mechanical support for the body.

Classification of Joints

There are three classifications of joints, based on the amount of movement each allows. Immovable joints, such as the fused sutures between the bones of the cranium, allow no movement. Slightly movable joints are found in the vertebral column, the sacroiliac joint, and the tibiofibular joint, where a fibrocartilage disc separates the bones. Freely movable joints have inelastic ligaments and strong muscles to maintain the integrity of the joint while allowing for a wide range of movement. The three major types of movable joints, or synovial joints (Figure 15.4), referred to in fitness are described in Table 15.3.

Recreation and Fitness Leadership

Table 15.3 Types of synovial joints.

	Type	Movement	Examples
	Hinge	Movement in one plane only: closing and opening	Elbow, knee, fingers
	Plane (gliding)	Movement in two planes of movement: forward and backward, side to side	Wrist, ankle
	Ball and socket	Movement in all planes: greatest range of movement	Shoulder, hip

Hinge Joint This type of joint has one articulating surface that is convex and another that is concave. Examples include the elbow joint and the joints of the fingers.

Plane (Gliding) Joint This joint permits gliding movements as in the bones of the wrist. The bone surfaces involved are nearly flat, so the only movement allowed is a gliding action. Another example of such a joint is the facet joints of the vertebrae.

Ball and Socket Joint A rounded bone is fitted into a cup-like receptacle. This is the kind of joint found at the shoulder and the hip where rotation in all three planes of movement is possible.

Describing Joint Movement

There is a common vocabulary to describe the movements that are possible at each joint (Figure 15.5). These terms are presented in Table 15.4.

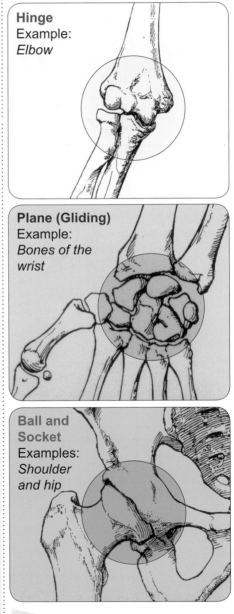

Hinge
Example:
Elbow

Plane (Gliding)
Example:
Bones of the wrist

Ball and
Socket
Examples:
Shoulder and hip

Figure 15.4 Examples of typical synovial joints in the body.

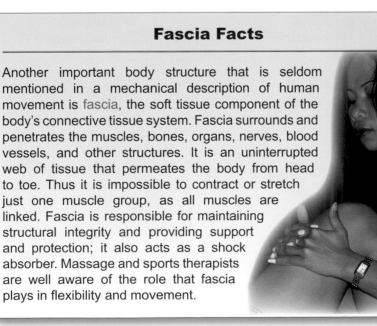

Fascia Facts

Another important body structure that is seldom mentioned in a mechanical description of human movement is fascia, the soft tissue component of the body's connective tissue system. Fascia surrounds and penetrates the muscles, bones, organs, nerves, blood vessels, and other structures. It is an uninterrupted web of tissue that permeates the body from head to toe. Thus it is impossible to contract or stretch just one muscle group, as all muscles are linked. Fascia is responsible for maintaining structural integrity and providing support and protection; it also acts as a shock absorber. Massage and sports therapists are well aware of the role that fascia plays in flexibility and movement.

Flexion

Extension

Dorsiflexion

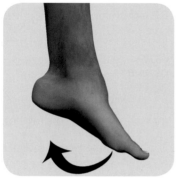

Plantar Flexion

Abduction

Adduction

Rotation

Pronation

Supination

Inversion

Eversion

Circumduction

Figure 15.5 Major body movements around joints.

Recreation and Fitness Leadership

Table 15.4 Common vocabulary of exercise movements.

Action	Description	Occurs At	Notes
Group 1: movements in the sagittal plane (forward and backward)			
Flexion	Bending toward the fetal position: curling the body, making fists	Spine Elbows Knees Hips Ankles Wrists Fingers	Hyperextended positions can be dangerous (e.g., landing with hyperextended knees)
Extension	Straightening and returning toward the neutral anatomical position		
Hyperextension	Moving beyond the neutral position: leaning backward, pressing the knees backward, straightening the elbows beyond 180 degrees		
Dorsiflexion	Moving the toes toward the shin	Ankles	
Plantar flexion	Pointing the foot		
Group 2: movements in the frontal plane (side to side)			
Abduction	Moving a bone away from the midline of the body	Shoulders Hips	In front of or behind the body
Adduction	Moving a bone toward the midline or across the midline		
Elevation	Raising the shoulders	Shoulders	
Depression	Returning the shoulders to neutral position		
Lateral flexion	Side bend	Spine	
Group 3: movement within a body segment			
Rotation	The bone turns on its own internal long axis	Spine Leg Arm	Medial rotation: front of limb moves toward the midline Lateral rotation: movement away from the midline
Pronation	Radius moves to cross over the ulna	Lower arms	
Supination	Radius returns to neutral anatomical position		
Inversion	Inside edge of the foot lifts off the floor	Ankle	
Eversion	Outside edge of the foot lifts off the floor		
Group 4: circling movements			
Circumduction	The free end of the limb moves in a circle	Hips Shoulders Fingers at knuckle	
Group 5: movements in the horizontal plane			
Protraction	Rounding the shoulders	Shoulder blades	
Retraction	Pulling the shoulder blades back to neutral position		

Muscles of the Human Body

Muscles allow the skeleton to move. Most muscles are attached from one bone to another, with a joint in between. The attachment closer to the centre of the body is the muscle's **origin**. The attachment farther away from the centre of the body is the muscle's **insertion**. The origin of the muscle is usually attached to more stationary parts, whereas the insertion is attached to more mobile structures of the skeleton. Remember, muscles can act only on the joints they cross.

There are more than 600 muscles in the human body. Figures 15.6 and 15.7 identify the major superficial muscles, and Table 15.5 presents the common names of some major muscles and their everyday movements.

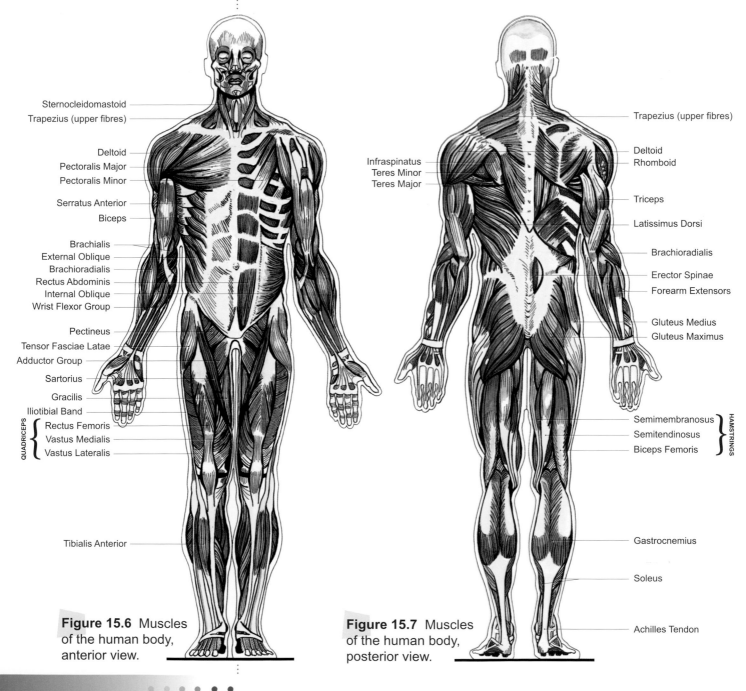

Figure 15.6 Muscles of the human body, anterior view.

Figure 15.7 Muscles of the human body, posterior view.

Recreation and Fitness Leadership

Table 15.5 Your muscles: Love 'em and learn 'em.

Muscle	Common Name	Everyday Movements
Deltoids	Delts	Raising your upper arm in all directions
Trapezius	Traps	Shrugging your shoulders, lifting arm out to side
Latissimus dorsi	Lats	Pulling and dragging
Rhomboids		Pulling shoulder blades together for good posture
Erector spinae		Straightening your spine (standing up after tying shoelaces), maintaining good posture
Pectorals	Pecs	Pushing, hugging
Biceps		Bending your elbow, lifting, carrying
Triceps		Straightening your elbow, assisting with pushing
Forearm muscles		Hand and wrist actions (waving goodbye, using a screwdriver, typing)
Rectus abdominis	Abs	Keeping you stable while you move other muscles, sitting up from lying down
Internal and external obliques	Obliques	Twisting to look behind you, doing a side bend Adds power to throwing and kicking
Gluteus maximus	Glutes	Jumping, climbing stairs, standing up from sitting, straightening leg behind you
Gluteus medius		Stepping sideways, ice skating, in-line skating
Leg adductors	Inner thighs	Crossing legs
Quadriceps	Quads	Straightening your knee, bending the hip (walking, running, stair climbing, skiing, skating, hopping, skipping, jumping, kicking)
Hamstrings	Hams	Bending your knee, extending the hip (help when standing up from sitting)
Gastrocnemius and soleus	Calves	Standing on toes, jumping
Tibialis anterior	Shin muscle	Tapping your toes, squishing a bug (ankle flexion)

Balanced Muscular Development

A well-designed exercise program develops the muscles equally on both sides of a joint or corrects an existing imbalance, which can lead to an injury. For example, it is easy to overdevelop the quadriceps while ignoring the hamstrings. When this happens, the knee joint may hyperextend when landing for a jump.

Generally, muscles work in pairs (Table 15.6). One muscle contracts to cause movement in one direction; its matching muscle contracts to cause movement in the other direction. The muscle producing the desired action is called the **agonist**, or **prime mover**; its opposing muscle is called the **antagonist**. Antagonists play a very important role in controlling the speed of action. Other muscles surrounding the joint and assisting the prime mover are called synergists. Muscle groups closer to the torso and in the torso provide a stable base of support for the movement. These are called stabilizers and postural muscles.

An example of programming for balanced development is including both knee lifts and hamstring curls in an aerobics class. Similarly, curl-ups need to be paired with back extension exercises.

Table 15.6 Common muscle pairs.

Joint	Muscle Pairs
Elbow	Biceps and triceps
Knee	Quadriceps and hamstrings
Ankle	Tibialis anterior and soleus/gastrocnemius
Torso	Rectus abdominis and erector spinae Internal obliques and external obliques

Types of Muscle Contraction

Muscles can either shorten or lengthen as they contract. When acting as the prime mover, they shorten and are said to be performing a concentric contraction. When acting as antagonists to slow the action, they are lengthening. This is called eccentric contraction.

A third type of muscle action is known as an isometric contraction (Figure 15.8). The muscle exerts force (contracts) to counteract an equal opposing force. There is no change in muscle length and no movement (e.g., pushing against an immovable object, contracting opposing pairs of muscles to hold a position for stability).

Most exercises contain both concentric and eccentric phases. A curl-up with a held position is an example that also includes an isometric phase (Figure 15.9).

Do you know the difference? The differences between concentric, eccentric, and isometric contractions are small but significant. Can you think of specific exercises or actions that involve these different contraction phases?

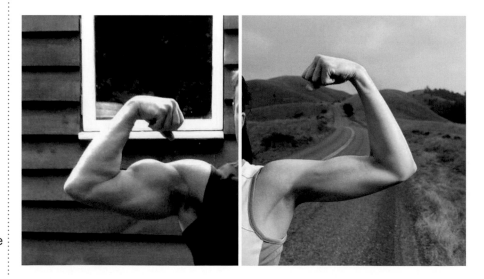

Figure 15.8 Holding a flexed pose is an example of an isometric contraction, since there is no change in muscle length and no movement.

Recreation and Fitness Leadership

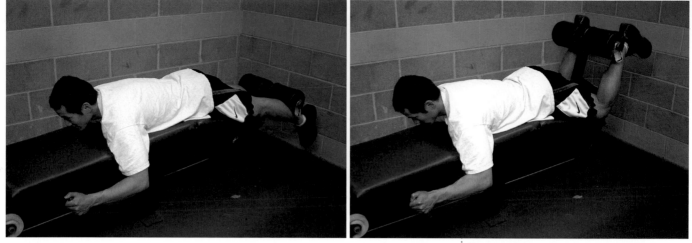

In summary, when designing an exercise program or a group fitness class, select a variety of exercises that utilize all the safe possible movements at all joints. Table 15.7 shows various possibilities.

Figure 15.9 A leg curl may contain concentric, eccentric, and isometric phases. The concentric phase occurs during the curling action and the eccentric phase during the lowering action of the exercise. An isometric phase occurs if the weight is held in one position without any movement.

Table 15.7 Summary of joint movements.

Joint	Movements
Shoulder joint (humerus, acromion)	Flexion/extension Abduction/adduction Medial/lateral rotation Circumduction Transverse (horizontal) flexion/extension
Shoulder girdle (scapula, clavicle)	Elevation/depression Protraction/retraction Upward/downward rotation
Elbow joint	Flexion/extension
Radioulnar joint	Pronation/supination
Wrist joint	Flexion/extension Radial flexion/ulnar flexion
Vertebral column	Flexion/extension Lateral flexion Rotation
Lumbosacral joint	Flexion/extension (pelvic tilt forward and backward)
Hip joint	Flexion/extension Abduction/adduction Medial/lateral rotation Circumduction
Knee joint	Flexion/extension Note: circumduction possible while lower leg is suspended in the air with a bent knee
Ankle joint	Plantar flexion/dorsiflexion Eversion/inversion

Understanding the Role of Correct Body Alignment

Executing exercises correctly and knowing why the chosen technique is correct are integral parts of the safety and enjoyment of a fitness activity. The logic behind correct exercise technique is valuable to leaders and participants alike. Respect for the inherent limitations of body structure and understanding of correct body mechanics guide the selection of safe and effective exercises.

According to the definition given by *Webster's New World College Dictionary*, alignment is the "proper positioning or state of adjustment of parts in relation to each other." Although this definition is particularly descriptive of mechanical devices, it is certainly appropriate when considering the human body in motion. Failure to pay attention to correct alignment can result in pain and injury.

There are four important alignment issues:

❶ Neutral lumbar spine

❷ Disc compression

❸ Hip, knee, and ankle alignment

❹ Sickle foot

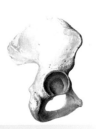

*P*roper pelvic position
An ideal pelvic position (or tilt) is achieved by maintaining a balance of strength and flexibility in the muscles acting on the pelvis.

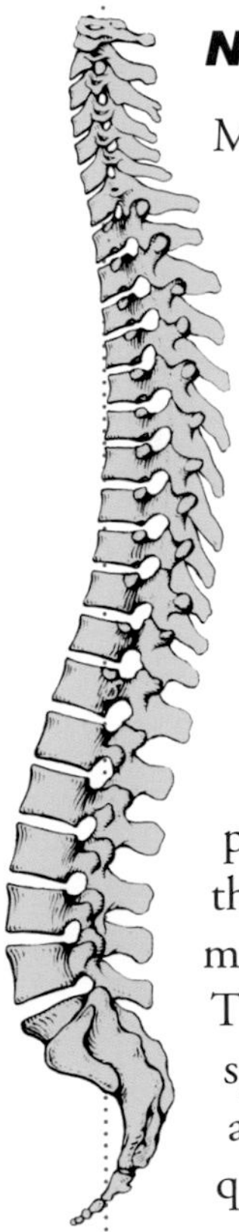

Neutral Lumbar Spine

Many powerful muscles of the body are attached to the pelvis (Figure 15.10). The condition of these muscles directly or indirectly influences the tilt or angle of the pelvis, which in turn affects the degree of compression of the lumbar discs. A **neutral lumbar curve** is the position that causes the least stress for an individual. Normally there is a slight curve in the lower back. Do not attempt to flatten the lower back. Isometric contraction of the lower abdominals prior to exertion is a useful technique for maintaining the normal curve. The correct pelvic position for exercise is achieved by maintaining a good balance of strength and flexibility in the muscles acting on the pelvis.

Lordosis (swayback) is a common postural problem for many participants. In this condition, the pelvis tilts forward as a result of weak abdominal muscles and tight iliopsoas and quadriceps muscles. The primary activities to correct excessive lumbar spine extension should target abdominal and hamstring strengthening along with quadriceps and lower back stretching.

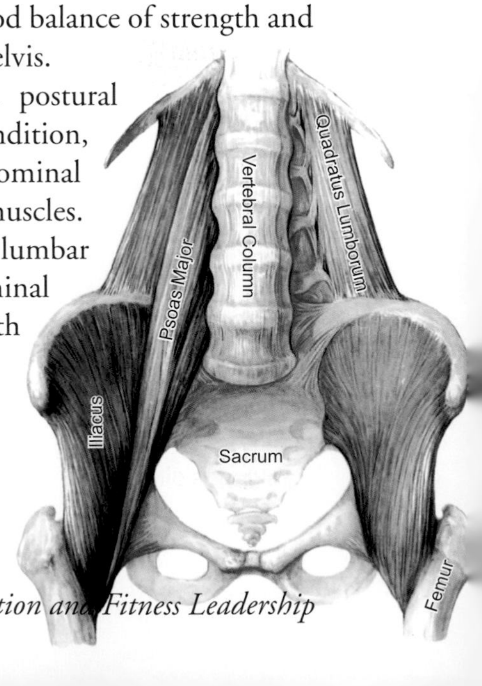

Figure 15.10 Many powerful muscles are attached to the pelvis, including the quadriceps, hamstrings, iliopsoas, and rectus abdominis.

Recreation and Fitness Leadership

Disc Compression

The spine consists of a stack of **vertebrae** (Figure 15.11) that forms three curves. The front portion of the spine contains vertebral bodies separated by shock-absorbing discs. This part of the spine serves supporting, weight-bearing, and shock-absorbing functions. On the back of each vertebra is a spinous process (the part you feel under the skin) (Figure 15.12). Vertebrae articulate (slide along each other) on surfaces called **facets**, allowing limited movement of the spine. The different regions of the vertebral column allow varying degrees of movement. The sacral and thoracic areas of the spine have the least amount of movement, and the cervical and lumbar regions are the most mobile.

Of course, the spinal cord runs down the spine in a protected channel formed by the vertebrae. Spinal nerves exit from each side, carrying impulses to and from muscles, skin, and organs. If the spine is excessively flexed or hyperextended, the spinal cord can be damaged or severed, which can result in paralysis. Spinal nerves can also be compressed, resulting in pain and mobility problems.

A **vertebral disc** is a self-contained fluid system that absorbs shock through compression. Excessive uneven pressure on the discs may weaken the disc wall and result in a bulge, tear, or rupture of the wall (ruptured disc). This puts pressure on the nerves exiting the spinal cord in that area.

The facets determine the range and kinds of movement the spine is capable of. For instance, in the lower back (lumbar region), they allow only flexion and extension and limit lateral flexion (side bending) and rotation.

Two very long ligaments run along the front and back of the spine to provide support. The posterior ligament narrows as it nears the bottom of the spine, resulting in an inherent weakness in the lower back.

The exercises that are problematic for the spine are those that require excessive flexing, extending, and twisting in spinal regions not designed to allow this. Yet all these exercises play a part in the fitness regimes we follow and the sports we do. For instance, full head circles and many of the advanced positions in yoga (asanas) might be inadvisable for a person with neck or back problems. Developing the musculature to control the speed of the movements is vital, as is core training to develop the stabilizer muscles (see the boxes *Riding for the Disabled* and *Core Training*).

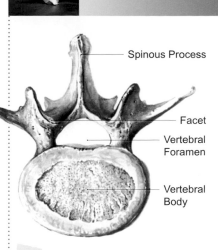

Figure 15.11 Vertebra, top view.

Did you know?
The anterior portions of the vertebrae serve a weight-bearing function, while the posterior portions facilitate gliding and guiding.

Figure 15.12 Vertebra, side view.

Riding for the Disabled

Therapeutic riding offers many lifelong benefits to its participants, including improved balance through the activation of the core muscles and increased confidence and self-esteem. Under the supervision of specially trained physiotherapists, skilled equestrian staff, and dedicated volunteers, riders gain greater physical, cognitive, psychological, and social skills.

Core Training

A fitness trend that is here to stay is the recognition that core strength and stability play a role in every move we make. A strong core not only prevents back pain but also provides a stable foundation for all limb movements. All the muscles that enable us to throw, strike, kick, catch, jump, land, and so on function more effectively by working from a firm base, the point of attachment to the spine and pelvis. Even golfers are now being encouraged to activate their core muscles prior to swinging a club, and core work in hockey has increased greatly at all levels to reduce muscle tears in the abdomen and groin. This awareness of body alignment and balanced muscular contraction is called **mindfulness** and has its roots in Eastern exercise modalities such as yoga and a system of training devised in the mid-1900s called Pilates. Today most fitness programs have accepted and promote the concept of core conditioning.

What is the core? The area of the body from the diaphragm to the base of the pelvis, including the lumbar and sacral spine and the abdominal and back muscles (Figure 15.13). A strong core and the awareness of effectively activating the muscles prevent injuries related to disc compression and incorrect pelvic tilt.

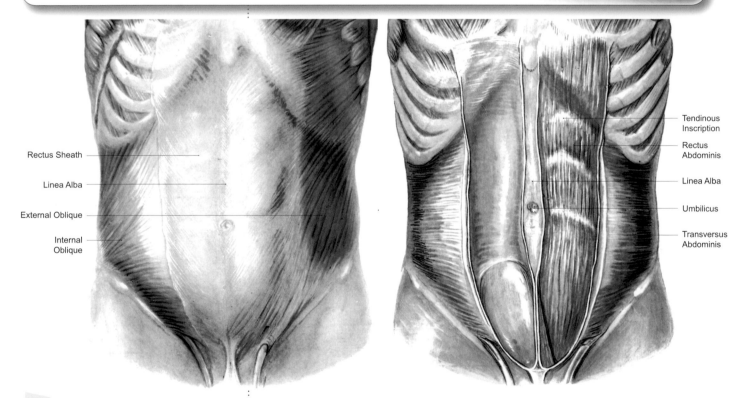

Figure 15.13 The muscles of the abdomen.

Hip, Knee, and Ankle Alignment

The knee is a hinge joint and thus is designed to move in one plane. An intricate combination of ligaments, tendons, and muscles provides support for the knee joint (Figure 15.14). **Cartilage** forms a shock-absorbing cushion on the articular surfaces (i.e., where the bones of the knee meet). The collateral ligaments on the sides of the knee resist sideways forces, and the cruciate ligaments within the knee limit forward and backward slippage of the femur on the tibia. Strong thigh and leg muscles aid in maintaining the integrity of the knee joint. Proper leg

Core exercises using a weighted ball can help not only to prevent back pain but also to provide a stable foundation for all movements.

alignment while bearing weight is accomplished by keeping the knee, ankle, and foot in the same plane.

An area of controversy in knee bending (squatting) activities is the degree of knee flexion that is safe. Some authorities recommend a bend of no more than 90 degrees from full extension. This is a worthwhile caution for unfit or older participants. On the other hand, children play in deep squat positions as a matter of course; with training, deep squats offer no injury potential as long as alignment and balance are maintained.

Figure 15.14 The knee joint. **A.** Anterior view. **B.** Posterior view.

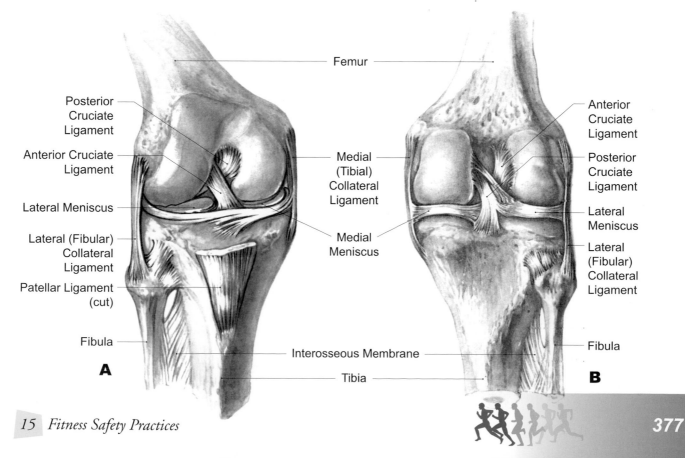

Sickle Foot

Alignment of the foot and ankle in a relaxed position has implications for weight-bearing activities. If the foot naturally turns in (like a sickle), there is a much higher chance of landing on the edge of the foot and rolling over the ankle. The result is a sprain. Exercises to balance the strength and flexibility of both sides of the ankle can prevent most of these injuries. Supportive footwear, such as high-cut running shoes, ankle braces, and orthotics may also help.

If a damaged ligament heals in a lengthened state (resulting in a "loose" ankle), it is more likely that future sprains will occur. This highlights the importance of inverting or everting the ankle in the opposite direction to the mode of injury when applying first aid to a sprained ankle. The goal is to push the torn ends of the ligament toward each other so that they will heal in the normal position. Rehabilitation exercises will complete the process of repair to the ligament (Figure 15.15).

Figure 15.15 Ankle strengthening exercises using tubing are a good way to rehabilitate a sprained ankle.

Dangerous Exercises?

It is not appropriate to ban certain exercises because they are inherently "dangerous." Most exercises are safe for the average participant. But for untrained or unfit or injured clients, some exercises should be avoided. Others should be explained carefully, demonstrated correctly, and performed under supervision at first. Controlling the speed of the exercise will also reduce the possibility of injury.

Some of the exercises and activities that are considered inappropriate for certain populations are listed below:

► Leg raises while lying straight, straight-leg sit-ups, jack-knives

► Duck walks, full squat jumps

► Hurdler's stretch

► "W" sit (sitting with bent knees and pelvis on floor between heels)

► Yoga plow, shoulder stand

► Bridge, backbend, cobra rocker

► Side bends

► Full head circles

► Sagging push-ups, burpees

Bridge

Hurdler's stretch

Recreation and Fitness Leadership

The Importance of Warming Up and Cooling Down

Warm-Up

Insist on a sufficient warm-up at the beginning of an activity. Typically, a warm-up consists of mild to moderate cardiorespiratory exercise to raise the heart and respiratory rate, ensuring that muscles are supplied with oxygen and that muscle temperature increases to facilitate movement. Jogging, playing a tag game, low-impact aerobics, and reviewing basic skills with game equipment are all good examples of ways to begin the warm-up. This is followed by dynamic range-of-motion exercises, to the extent that is required for the activity. For instance, focus on arm swings and circles for throwing activities or on leg raises for kicking activities. Keep these actions dynamic to maintain the elevated heart rate. Game-play simulations that mimic the main activity form the last part of the warm-up in order to prepare the mind as well as the body for the activity to follow. Reviewing previously learned skills achieves this purpose.

Cool-Down

Cooling down after activity is another area to focus on. An effective cool-down allows the heart rate and breathing to return gradually to pre-activity levels, facilitates the removal of lactic acid from the muscles (which helps eliminate postexercise muscle soreness), and leaves the participant feeling relaxed and perhaps even euphoric. Stopping suddenly after strenuous activity can result in fainting as the blood pools in the lower limbs and is not returned to the heart by muscular action. The end of the practice is also the best time to develop flexibility as the muscles are very warm. Mental preparation activities can be done effectively at this point in the workout.

A proper cool-down following strenuous activity should leave the participant feeling relaxed. It is a good time to develop flexibility as the muscles are still warm.

Evaluating the Effectiveness of Exercises

Apart from selecting exercises that respect the inherent limitations of body structure, it is important to analyze how the activities are performed to ensure that they produce the desired effects. For instance, curl-ups are supposed to develop the abdominal muscles. But performing a curl-up with feet secured or with straight legs works the hip flexor muscles far more than the abdominals (Figure 15.16). This exercise can also aggravate existing back problems if the back is allowed to arch.

Figure 15.16 Performing some exercises incorrectly can make them not only ineffective but also dangerous.

Considering Growth and Development

Exercises must be carefully selected for children and youth, whose developing bodies can be harmed by certain activities, especially when repeated too often. For instance, Little League softball restricts the number of pitches a young person can throw in the course of a game or practice. The time of the growth spurt is especially challenging because tissues often do not develop at the same rate (see the box *Osgood-Schlatter Disease*). Young, active participants may lose flexibility if the speed of long-bone growth exceeds the speed of muscle-length growth. Explain this process to your client and assist him in modifying his goals for flexibility improvement accordingly.

Osgood-Schlatter Disease

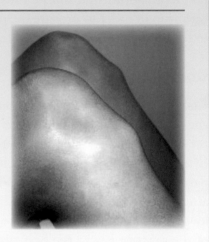

Osgood-Schlatter disease is an inflammation or fracture through the growth plate of the tibia. It is probably the most frequent cause of knee pain in children. The condition occurs most commonly in active children just starting their growth spurt, anywhere between the ages of 9 and 15 years. Both boys and girls are equally vulnerable to its debilitating effects: activity-related pain and point tenderness (pain to the touch) on the tibial tuberosity, a spot a few inches below the kneecap, or patella, where the patellar tendon inserts into the tibia. Sports requiring lots of running, jumping, kneeling, and squatting are particularly painful because whenever the quadriceps is contracted, the tendon pulls on the growth plate area. With constant pulling the tendon becomes inflamed, and bone fragments can be pulled off the growth plate. This creates a calcium deposit that will remain for life, long after the pain has gone away. The client should use pain as a guide to modify his or her activity level.

Applying ice a few times a day for 15 minutes will reduce the inflammation. Ice should also be applied immediately after activity for the same amount of time. A physiotherapist or athletic trainer can provide exercises to strengthen the leg without aggravating the condition. Occasionally, special braces or straps are worn to protect the area from contact and to decrease the stress where the tendon inserts near the growth plate.

Adapting for Physical and Mobility Limitations

All populations benefit from some form of exercise programming. Fitness leaders find employment with people of all ages, abilities, and physical conditions. Numerous courses are available to provide the information needed to design safe, effective programming for elderly people, women who are pregnant or who have recently given birth, people who are recovering from heart attacks or injuries, and people with chronic health conditions. Since asthma and arthritis are so prevalent and span a wide age range, some information on programming for these conditions is given here.

> When you gamble with safety, you bet your life.
> *Anonymous*

Recreation and Fitness Leadership

Asthma

People with asthma are encouraged to maintain a normal and healthy lifestyle, which includes exercise and other physical activities. To achieve this, they must take their prescribed medications as directed by their physicians, avoid situations that are known to trigger an attack, and monitor their symptoms and lung function.

Fortunately, there are many fitness activities that are beneficial and well tolerated by people with asthma, such as outdoor and indoor biking, aerobics, walking, and running on a treadmill. Activities that involve short intermittent periods of exertion such as volleyball, gymnastics, baseball, and wrestling are generally well tolerated.

Activities involving longer periods of exertion, such as soccer, distance running, and basketball, may be less well tolerated but can be performed if the athlete manages triggers and maintains proper medication. Cold-weather sports such as cross-country skiing and ice skating are often avoided because inhaling cold air can trigger an attack. However, many people with asthma are able to participate fully in these activities. Unless chlorine is a trigger, swimming lengths is generally well tolerated because it is performed in a warm, moist-air environment.

When working with a person with asthma, you must know which medications are prescribed and where they are kept. Select appropriate activities, and encourage a thorough warm-up that raises the breathing rate gradually. Tell your client to breathe through the nose rather than the mouth so that the air is warmed and filtered. It is recommended that people with asthma cool down very gradually at the end of their workouts. Above all, know what to do if a client's asthma symptoms worsen during exercise.

Although most activities can be adapted for people with asthma, cold-weather sports such as cross-country skiing and ice skating pose an additional concern because inhaling cold air can trigger an attack.

Arthritis

People with arthritis benefit from structured programs that include both aerobic and resistance exercise. They can experience significant improvements in symptoms, improved physical performance, and reduced pain. Aquatic aerobic training programs offered in therapeutic pools have many advantages related to the warmth and buoyancy of the water. Pools that are designed for persons with arthritis are often kept at much warmer temperatures (e.g., 26 to 28 degrees Celsius) than recreational pools and may have specialized access ramps to make entrance to the pool easier. As recommended for anyone, a person with arthritis should heed the warning signs of pain and stop doing activities that cause discomfort until the pain subsides.

Individuals with arthritis often have a limited range of motion, especially in lower-extremity joints. Decreased range of motion associated with knee and hip osteoarthritis is associated with pain, loss of function, physical limitations, and an increased risk of injury and falls. In addition, cartilage requires regular compression and decompression to stimulate remodelling and repair. The optimal daily exercise plan to maintain cartilage health should include range-of-motion exercises. Care must be taken during stretching because affected joints that are lax are easily overstretched and more vulnerable to injury. Personal trainers should seek additional training before developing programs for people with arthritis.

Putting It All Together

"Safety is as simple as ABC – **A**lways **B**e **C**areful."
Anonymous

Keeping fit can be hazardous to your health! That is hardly the message we want to send to our current and potential clients. One of our most important roles as mentors, then, is to inform and educate. In this chapter you learned where to find information about the safe use of fitness facilities and equipment. A knowledge of mechanically safe joint actions and correct body alignment will help you gain an understanding of correct exercise techniques to prevent acute and overuse injuries.

Analyzing an exercise for its effectiveness helps you make the most efficient use of available time for developing specific areas of the body. And don't forget, people with physical and mobility limitations can exercise safely if appropriate modifications are made. Use this knowledge to guide your own journey to fitness; spread the word to those who share your goals.

Key Terms

agonist (prime mover)
anatomical position
antagonist
cartilage
concentric contraction
core training
eccentric contraction
facets
fascia
insertion
isometric contraction
ligaments

lordosis
mindfulness
neutral lumbar curve
origin
proactive
skeleton
synergists
synovial joints
therapeutic riding
vertebrae
vertebral disc

Review Questions

1. List the key standards for a fitness facility.

2. List the key rules for a weight-training facility.

3. Explain how exercise can cause hearing loss for participants and fitness instructors.

4. What steps are involved in developing programs and selecting exercises for fitness participants?

5. Describe the anatomical position.

6. List three types of synovial joints, providing examples of each.

7. Define the following: extension, dorsiflexion, adduction, depression, pronation, circumduction, and protraction.

8. Explain three types of muscular contraction, providing examples of each.

9. What are the four main concerns regarding body alignment during exercise?

10. What are the benefits and concerns of exercise programs for people with arthritis?

In This Appendix:

APPENDIX
Career Opportunities

In this appendix, you will learn about the following:

❶ The education needed to become a professional in recreation and fitness leadership

❷ The career opportunities in recreation and fitness leadership

❸ How to get started on a career in recreation and fitness

385

> "Work and play are words used to describe the same thing under different circumstances."
> Mark Twain

Our society's focus is ever-changing, and for many of us, the new focus is on healthy, active living. Participation in recreation and leisure activities has become more and more popular. This increased emphasis on physical activity in today's society as a means to better health as well as improved business productivity has resulted in a corresponding expansion of career possibilities in the field of recreation and leisure services.

This appendix surveys the diverse learning and career opportunities available in the field of recreation and fitness leadership.

Education You Need

> You learn something every day if you pay attention.
> *Ray LeBlond*

To pursue a productive career in recreation and fitness leadership or related areas, it is necessary to complete either a college diploma or undergraduate degree in this field. Whether university and college programs are called recreation and fitness leadership or go by other titles, most programs deal primarily with promoting and planning recreation programs for all ages and abilities. Recreation for those with special needs, once called therapeutic recreation, is now titled adaptive recreation.

Some programs focus on sports, fitness, sport administration, or recreation and leisure; however, most programs are diverse and comprehensive enough to allow for study in many of these areas.

Career Opportunities

"So what are you going to do with that?" is the question many students face when they first tell their parents about their choice of major. The real question is, can you earn a living with that background? The answer for recreation and fitness leadership is "Yes!"

Recreation has become a multibillion-dollar industry in North America alone. That growth, coupled with an explosion of amateur and club sports, on top of concerns about health, fitness, and weight management, contributes to robust career opportunities for recreation and fitness leadership students.

NAME: David Patchell-Evans
OCCUPATION: Founder and CEO, GoodLife Fitness Clubs
EDUCATION: BA, Honours (Physical Education), University of Western Ontario

▶ *What do you do?*

I am the founder and CEO of the largest group of fitness clubs in the world owned by a single individual. GoodLife Fitness has more than 300 clubs stretching across Canada from Newfoundland to British Columbia and servicing nearly 900,000 members. My job is to lead our strategic planning team with a clear vision that demonstrates caring for our members and staff with a simple goal of making all Canadians fit and healthy.

▶ *What is unique about your job?*

Fitness club ownership has almost unlimited growth opportunity globally. The world's population for the most part is informed about the need to exercise and the health benefits of doing so, yet only an estimated 9 to 13 percent of people belong to a fitness facility. That means there is a huge population of unfit people who would benefit from a fitness membership. The other side, I would caution though, is that this is also a highly competitive and risky field. To survive and grow a thriving business, you must have a smart plan, know your ROI [return on investment] margins, and deftly adapt your business to any shifts in the market.

▶ *Why did you choose a career in fitness club ownership?*

While attending university, I had a serious motorcycle accident at age 19 that put me in rehabilitation for six months at a sports injury clinic on campus. I had come to university to do a business degree, but this time spent working out alongside athletes created a new-found interest for me in exercise physiology and biomechanics. This experience not only crystallized my interests in a physical education degree but also focused my motivation as to what I wanted to do with my life. I wanted to change lives by helping people lead their best lives through fitness.

▶ *What are the future job prospects in the field? Where is it heading?*

The profession is growing by leaps and bounds! Prospects for a career in fitness have never been brighter, and this trend will continue to outperform many other careers for decades to come. From 2000 to 2004, the fitness industry in Canada experienced a 27 percent growth. GoodLife Fitness offers a range of exciting, dynamic, and challenging careers. As a company, we believe in promotions from within and rewarding top performers with rapid advancement and management/leadership opportunities as we increase our number of clubs across Canada to 200 by 2009.

A career as a manager at a club could include a defined career path as a fitness manager, personal training regional manager, general manager, cluster manager, or divisional manager. Our management trainee program provides employees with training in fitness, leadership, business, sales, and service in order to successfully run their own multi-million-dollar world-class businesses.

▶ *What other career options are available?*

There will be jobs in related areas of teaching, group exercise instructors, sports attorneys, government (including research and writing), lifestyle coaching, sports trainers, consulting, corporate wellness, and sports medicine to name a few. Large companies will have an infrastructure of positions including marketing, public relations, operations, and human resources.

Health and Fitness

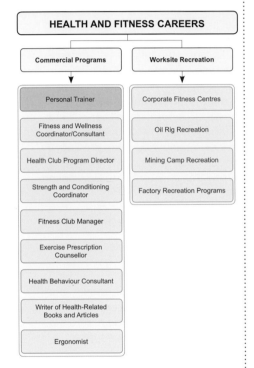

HEALTH AND FITNESS CAREERS

Commercial Programs

- Personal Trainer
- Fitness and Wellness Coordinator/Consultant
- Health Club Program Director
- Strength and Conditioning Coordinator
- Fitness Club Manager
- Exercise Prescription Counsellor
- Health Behaviour Consultant
- Writer of Health-Related Books and Articles
- Ergonomist

Worksite Recreation

- Corporate Fitness Centres
- Oil Rig Recreation
- Mining Camp Recreation
- Factory Recreation Programs

The **health and fitness industry** is a phenomenon of the late 20th century – and the explosion of career opportunities for recreation and fitness program graduates has matched its evolution. For example, GoodLife Fitness was founded by David Patchell-Evans in 1979 after a nearly debilitating motorcycle accident changed the course of his life. Today, GoodLife Fitness has over 300 fitness clubs and over 875,000 members, making it Canada's largest fitness chain and the largest privately owned fitness company in the world. Each requires a full staff, ranging from personal trainers to physiotherapists and nutritionists – from entry-level positions to experienced professionals with highly specific training.

Concerns about obesity, the increased interest in exercise and a healthy diet, and the aging of the "baby boom" generation are all contributing to a need for the knowledge, skills, and capabilities of recreation and fitness leadership students. The health and fitness industry integrates exercise, personal responsibility, and prevention in ways that meet the needs of the North American people. Decades of research and reports by Health Canada and the Fitness Industry Council of Canada point to the need for physical activity to promote health. The health services and leisure and hospitality industries have proven to be among the highest-demand positions in North America. When it comes to prospects for recreation and fitness leadership students, the opportunities seem endless.

The marketing of exercise and sports-related protective and corrective equipment such as braces, orthotics, nutritional supplements, and acute sports injury management equipment also continues to expand. Numerous stores specializing in this niche market, and employing recreation and fitness graduates, have opened up across Canada, and growth in this area is expected to continue.

Worksite Programs

Health care costs are skyrocketing, and companies are reaching out via employee health and fitness programs in an effort to manage the expense. The side benefits of improved health are improved worker productivity and reduced absenteeism.

Worksite programs first appeared in the early 1980s and exploded in the 1990s. The quality of these programs was sometimes a hiring differentiator for some companies. Commercial programs, which include private fitness clubs and gyms, the YMCA, and Curves for Women, are now part of our daily routines towards healthy, active living. Hospitals, general medical clinics, and specialized clinics such as physiotherapy facilities represent one of the largest – though often hidden – segments in the health and fitness world. These programs are more specific than commercial or public programs. Health risk identification, cardiac rehabilitation, nutrition and weight management consulting, and water exercise therapy are all found in clinical health and fitness programs.

NAME: Gregg Malpus
OCCUPATION: Sales and Product Training Manager, Tourism Vancouver, Tourism Whistler
EDUCATION: Recreation Facilities Management, Travel and Tourism, Seneca College, King Campus

▶ What do you do?

I am responsible for the training of new agents promoting Tourism Whistler or Tourism Vancouver. We are a central reservations company for Whistler and Vancouver, selling air flights, accommodations, activities, ski tickets and lessons, transportation, and so on. I train the agents who will promote and sell our product to the public. Training programs include sales improvement, vendor training (how to use the booking software), new product introduction, upcoming promotions, cross-selling, upselling, and quality control.

▶ What is unique about your job?

I have a position where I can try out the product — skiing, snowboarding, new hotels, and recreation programs. I love to try new things, and this career gives me the opportunity to do just that. I am an avid snowboarder myself and now promote resorts that offer this activity. Because I provide staff training, I know all the upcoming promotions and attractions in Whistler and Vancouver and can often try them out myself!

▶ What was your motivation for pursuing this field?

I love to try new things and be outdoors whenever possible. This career choice allows me to play and work at the same time. The nature of tourism is constant change. Something new and better comes along, and you are eager to see and try it. Once I understand the product, I then sell it to our customers. I love adventure, and this field of recreation and tourism provides many challenges and new innovative activities.

▶ How competitive is the field?

Tourism is always competitive, with new facilities and programs being created and offered all the time. What is new and flashy will often be the choice of customers. Tourism operators must constantly be upgrading and improving existing programs and facilities in order to compete in this industry.

▶ What career advice would you give to students interested in this area?

Get experience now on a part-time level. Volunteer or gain certification in tourism-based activities such as skiing and snowboarding. Try activities to make sure this is a career area you are interested in. For example, have you ever been white-water rafting, gone heli-skiing, or taken extended hiking treks? You need to have that sense of adventure but also a marketing interest in order to promote these experiences to your potential customers.

Commercial Programs

Many different types of health and fitness activities can be classified as **commercial programs**. They all have one thing in common – their objective is to generate a profit for their owners or shareholders. Some are large franchised or corporate-owned chains such as Extreme Fitness and Gold's Gym. Others are independent, locally owned and managed operations, such as Popeye's Gym in Kitchener, Ontario, or gender-specific facilities, such as Jenny Craig, Curves for Women, and Sisters Pace. YMCAs sell health club memberships to offset the cost of other programs offered by the nonprofit organization. Should YMCA health and fitness programs be included in the commercial sector? You decide.

Membership sales are the major focus of these facilities, supported by retail sales of clothing and equipment, restaurant and entertainment facilities, special events such as tennis tournaments, fees for consulting and training, and fees for weight-loss programs and accompanying specialized meals. Health and fitness is big business in sales-based facilities across North America today.

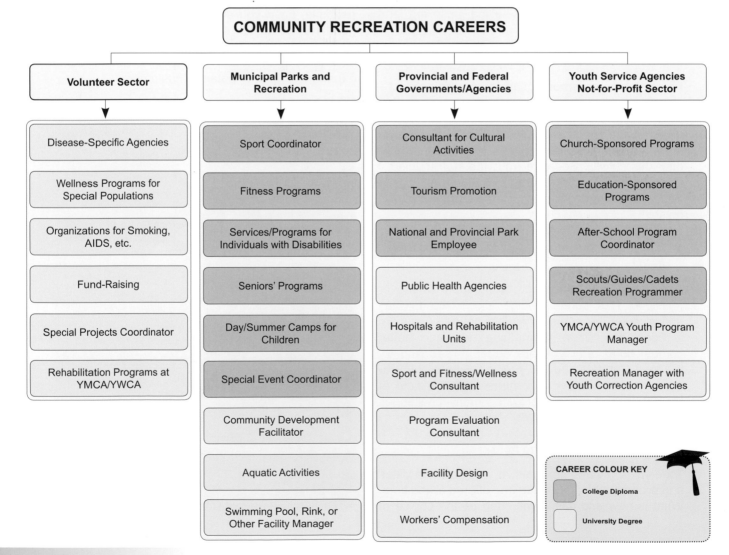

COMMUNITY RECREATION CAREERS

Volunteer Sector	Municipal Parks and Recreation	Provincial and Federal Governments/Agencies	Youth Service Agencies Not-for-Profit Sector
Disease-Specific Agencies	Sport Coordinator	Consultant for Cultural Activities	Church-Sponsored Programs
Wellness Programs for Special Populations	Fitness Programs	Tourism Promotion	Education-Sponsored Programs
Organizations for Smoking, AIDS, etc.	Services/Programs for Individuals with Disabilities	National and Provincial Park Employee	After-School Program Coordinator
Fund-Raising	Seniors' Programs	Public Health Agencies	Scouts/Guides/Cadets Recreation Programmer
Special Projects Coordinator	Day/Summer Camps for Children	Hospitals and Rehabilitation Units	YMCA/YWCA Youth Program Manager
Rehabilitation Programs at YMCA/YWCA	Special Event Coordinator	Sport and Fitness/Wellness Consultant	Recreation Manager with Youth Correction Agencies
	Community Development Facilitator	Program Evaluation Consultant	
	Aquatic Activities	Facility Design	
	Swimming Pool, Rink, or Other Facility Manager	Workers' Compensation	

CAREER COLOUR KEY

College Diploma

University Degree

Recreation and Fitness Leadership

A Career in Personal Training

Personal Training

Personal training is becoming a popular career choice for individuals who enjoy physical activity and want to share this enthusiasm with others. It can be a rewarding career, especially if you are interested in helping people meet their goals for healthy, active living. The demand for personal training is on the rise as a result of the aging "baby boom" generation, as well as concerns about the rise in obesity among children, youth, and adults.

Individuals interested in personal training will need a solid background in physical and health education through university or college courses or personal training workshops. Most trainers are certified with a reputable organization to identify themselves as quality personal trainers. To succeed in the industry, prospective trainers should learn about cardiorespiratory, strength, and flexibility training techniques. Good communication skills are required as well. You can practise your communication skills through public speaking. Develop your interpersonal skills by working on projects with peers or participating on a sports team. To be an entrepreneur in the industry, business courses will provide you with the skills to become successful in your personal training business.

Personal training is a career that addresses the health needs of the general population. It's a joy being able to meet people and learn about their unique needs and interests, then being able to provide them with an exercise program and the professional support to reach their goals. You will be in the business of improving people's quality of life by helping them become stronger and more confident through physical activity. Transforming a sedentary client into an active person is one of the greatest rewards of the personal training profession.

Program Planning

Program planning begins with a needs assessment of the clientele – what are their physical activity interests and what are the best practices in the industry? Knowing what the trends are will help you make successful choices. What space you have and how to use that space is another fundamental question. Is it a multipurpose space, or is it a dedicated space? What are the storage areas? Depending on the activity, you will also need to decide whether the flooring will be tile, rubber, carpet, or a wood sprung floor. Other items to consider include mirrors, lighting, electrical requirements, and ventilation.

After you have drawn some conclusions about these issues, the next big question is your budget. How much money will you have available to renovate the space (capital expenditures)? What is your operating budget? The operating budget includes funds for salaries, equipment and supplies, repairs, and caretaking.

Community Recreation

Community recreation programs have been around for many years, and most of us have used public facilities during our lifetimes. Multidimensional complexes built in recent years as nonprofit municipal facilities are a relatively new phenomenon. Many cities own and operate large recreational water parks, cross-country running and ski trails, downhill ski parks, tennis courts, sports fields, and even some golf courses. Every dimension of community programming employs people with a wide range of skill sets.

Common jobs in all of these programs include group exercise instructors, often focusing on aerobics programs; fitness instructors focusing on specific strength development; health and fitness counsellors who work one on one with clients to help them develop personalized programs and achieve their goals, often involving changes in lifestyle; and personal trainers, who typically cater to clients in upper income sectors.

Many people with this type of experience go on to become directors of facilities, which requires training in health and fitness disciplines as well as management training (e.g., accounting, sales management, and organizational development). These individuals require a multidisciplinary educational background and a strong foundation in recreation. Often they are called on to conduct market research, identify emerging trends in our society, and help develop plans for new facilities or equipment.

Sport Management

Sport management involves the business side of sport. Graduates of recreation and fitness programs can look for opportunities in professional sport franchises, ski resorts, corporate fitness centres, arena management,

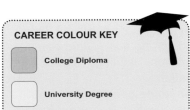

CAREER COLOUR KEY

College Diploma

University Degree

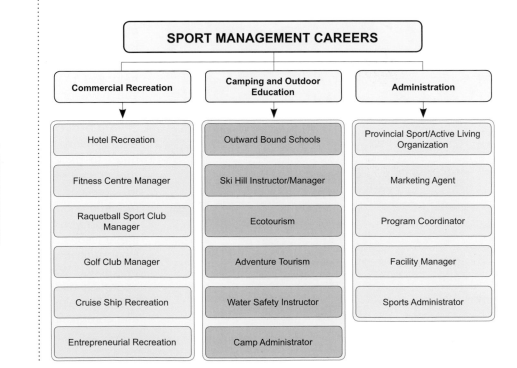

SPORT MANAGEMENT CAREERS		
Commercial Recreation	**Camping and Outdoor Education**	**Administration**
Hotel Recreation	Outward Bound Schools	Provincial Sport/Active Living Organization
Fitness Centre Manager	Ski Hill Instructor/Manager	Marketing Agent
Raquetball Sport Club Manager	Ecotourism	Program Coordinator
Golf Club Manager	Adventure Tourism	Facility Manager
Cruise Ship Recreation	Water Safety Instructor	Sports Administrator
Entrepreneurial Recreation	Camp Administrator	

college sports programs, sporting goods merchandising, sports media industries, and a wide variety of other sport-related fields.

Teaching and Coaching

Many fitness and leadership students pursue their passion for sport, exercise, and recreation by finding rewarding careers as teachers or sports coaches. There is an extremely wide diversity of roles and settings involving **teaching and coaching** – from preschool play time to intercollegiate sports, and from local sandlot games to professional sports. Coaches and teachers find roles in nonprofit organizations and corporations, often leading to management responsibilities.

The roles of teachers and coaches are so closely intertwined that they often cannot be easily differentiated. Both professions are concerned with developing and maintaining fitness and motor skill performance in various settings. One possible difference is that teachers often deal with base audiences – those with no natural selection process involved. Consequently, a wide range of capabilities and interest levels is evident in any given group. Coaches, on the other hand, often deal with a highly selective audience, one in which skill levels are more developed and where the individuals have a high degree of interest and aspiration. Which would you rather be?

Although the actions and methods of teaching and coaching are very similar, some aspects of teaching and coaching are quite different – different workdays, different audiences, and different accreditation requirements. Each professional group has its own subcultural attributes, with some members actively involved in both roles.

Many people find themselves coaching at the community level. Tee-ball, mites soccer, and tennis leagues exist for very young participants, and all require large numbers of people to coordinate, manage, and coach activities. Similarly, sport-specific clubs exist in almost every activity, all requiring coaches for various levels. National sport governing bodies have long recognized that the diversity of coaching capabilities within their sports is a serious problem, so most have developed coaching training and certification programs to help ensure adequate coaching standards – with the side benefit of making the sport more enjoyable for participants

COACHING CAREERS

Community Club Coach

Group Fitness Instructor

Personal Trainer

Coaching Certification Program Instructor

High School Coach

Sports Official

CAREER COLOUR KEY

College Diploma

University Degree

Although the roles of teachers and coaches are closely intertwined, coaches deal with a more highly selective audience, one in which skill levels are more developed and where the individuals have a high degree of interest and aspiration.

and leading to the growth of the sport. Time after time, sport after sport across the country, we can see that participation thrives when coaching excels. Coaches are the catalyst for growth in virtually every sport.

Getting Started

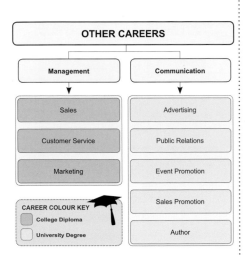

OTHER CAREERS

- Management
  - Sales
  - Customer Service
  - Marketing
- Communication
  - Advertising
  - Public Relations
  - Event Promotion
  - Sales Promotion
  - Author

CAREER COLOUR KEY
- College Diploma
- University Degree

Many students are puzzled about where or how to start their career investigation. One good idea is to identify and establish a relationship with someone already working in the field. Ask to "job shadow" that person for a day. Most professionals will be honoured by a student's request. There is no better way to determine if you will like a career than to observe the work firsthand and possibly participate in it. Many organizations offer both paid and unpaid internships so that students can learn about the job function and make informed career decisions for themselves.

When asked what skill sets or capabilities they want in employees, most CEOs respond that they want people who can communicate effectively, both verbally and in writing. That has been true for many years, and the rush into the Internet age has only intensified the need for strong communication capabilities. Recreation and fitness leadership students typically have strong interpersonal and verbal communication skills, developed through the nature of the research and curriculum that they undertake.

Putting It All Together

> *Try to learn something about everything and everything about something.*
> Thomas Henry Huxley

This appendix illustrates how education and career opportunities in recreation and fitness leadership have become much more diverse over the last several decades. This reflects both our expanding perspective of recreation as well as its impact on and reaction to trends in Canadian society.

Today's recreation and fitness professionals, more than ever, need to obtain a broad education. Both college and university recreation programs offer a broad scope of courses in marketing, managing, accounting, and programming to enable graduates to work in this challenging industry.

Key Terms

commercial programs
community recreation
health and fitness industry

sport management
teaching and coaching
worksite programs

Recreation and Fitness Leadership

NAME: Will Kopplin
OCCUPATION: Assistant Program Manager, Athletic Centre (during the summer: Program Manager, Junior Blues)
EDUCATION: BSc (Physics), University of Toronto

▶ What do you do?

I work at the University of Toronto's Athletic Centre. As well as being the home base for the Faculty of Physical Education and Health, the Athletic Centre provides opportunities for children, youth, University of Toronto students, and other members of the community to participate in physical activity at all levels, from recreation to high performance. Servicing such a large community requires a contribution from a large number of staff. There are staff to set up the equipment, program instructors, program supervisors, first aid staff, game officials, timekeepers, ticket takers, security staff, and more. As part of the program management team, I coordinate the staff from all these different areas and make sure the program or event that is taking place runs smoothly.

▶ What is unique about your job?

I would say there are very few jobs out there that offer such diversity. On any given week, I could be acting as the event manager at a varsity basketball game, presenting a trophy for intramural volleyball, sitting in the press box at a hockey game, or sitting on a disciplinary review board.

▶ What was your motivation for pursuing this field?

I have always been heavily involved in sport and in fact was a varsity athlete here at the University of Toronto. My experience as an athlete was unforgettable. Working in my field, I have the opportunity to give something back to athletics and to hopefully help others achieve the same positive experience that I had. I also find that the atmosphere surrounding athletics is one that I enjoy.

▶ How competitive is the field?

There are many opportunities to get involved in athletics management. However, depending on your career goals, it can be extremely competitive (Maple Leaf Sports and Entertainment will be needing only a handful of presidents and vice presidents in the next 10 to 20 years, for example). A career in athletics is one that you should choose because you enjoy it.

▶ What do you enjoy most about your profession?

Making a contribution to something I really enjoy and the diversity of my job portfolio are two of the main things. But mainly I enjoy the excitement that sport can provide. As an athlete, I loved the feeling of accomplishing a goal I had set for myself, whether it was learning a new skill or finishing well in competition. Although I cannot compete anymore at the level that I used to, I still find a lot of enjoyment in being a part of the athletic environment and helping an individual or team feel that same sense of accomplishment.

▶ What career advice would you give to students interested in entering this field?

Try to get involved as much as possible. Take advantage of leadership opportunities when they present themselves, and try to gain some experience in as many different areas as you can. Joining a sport committee or council, volunteering to organize (or help organize) a sporting event, and helping to coach a team are just a few of the possibilities. That way when it comes time to choose a career path, you will know what aspects of sport you enjoy most and have a good perspective on the industry.

References

Akesson, E. J., Loeb, J. A., & Wilson-Pauwels, L. (1990). *Core textbook of anatomy* (2nd ed.). Philadelphia, PA: J.B. Lippincott Company.

Anderson, M., & Hall, S. J. (1997). *Fundamentals of sports injury management*. Baltimore, MD: Williams & Wilkins.

Antonio, J., & Stout, J. R. (2002). *Supplements for endurance athletes*. Champaign, IL: Human Kinetics.

Baechle, T. R., & Earle, R. W. (2000). *Essentials of strength training and conditioning*. Champaign, IL: Human Kinetics.

Bell, A. H., & Smith, D. M. (2002). *Developing leadership abilities*. Columbus, OH: Prentice Hall.

Bompa, T. O. (1999). *Periodization: Theory and methodology of training* (4th ed.). Champaign, IL: Human Kinetics.

Canadian Society for Exercise Physiology. (1998). *The Canadian physical activity, fitness and lifestyle: CSEP's guide to healthy active living* (2nd ed.). Ottawa, ON: Canadian Society for Exercise Physiology.

Coaching Association of Canada. (2007). *National coaching certification program. Introductory module: Reference material. Version 1.1*. Ottawa, ON: Coaching Association of Canada.

Carola, R., Harley, J. P., & Noback, C. R. (1992). *Human anatomy*. New York, NY: McGraw-Hill.

DeGraaf, D. G., Jordan, D. J., & DeGraaf, K. H. (1999). *Programming for parks, recreation and leisure services: A servant leadership approach*. State College, PA: Venture Publishing, Inc.

Fedyck, H., Nadolny, D., & Cremasco, J. (1985). *Eat well, live well*. Toronto, ON: Ontario Dietetic Association.

Fielder, F. E. (1967). *A theory of leadership effectiveness*. New York, NY: Mc-Graw-Hill.

Freeman, W. H. (1997). *Physical education and sport in a changing society* (5th ed.). Boston, MA: Allyn & Bacon.

Hersey, P., Blanchard, K. H., & Johnson, D. E. (2001). *Management of organizational behavior: Leading human resources* (8th ed.). Upper Saddle River, NJ: Prentice-Hall.

Grant, D., McNamara, J., & Gianoli, P. (1989). *Exercise Danger: 30 exercises to avoid plus 100 safer and more effective alternatives*. Floreat Park, WA: Wellness Australia PTY.

Guthrie, H. (1989). *Introductory nutrition* (7th ed.). St. Louis, MO: Mosby-Year Book.

Hammer, W. I. (1999). *Functional soft tissue examination and treatment*. Baltimore, MD: Aspen Publications.

Harland, B. F. (2000). Caffeine and nutrition. *Nutrition, 16* (7-8), 522-526.

Hartmann, J., & Tunnemann, H. (2001). *Fitness and strength training for all sports*. Toronto, ON: Sport Books Publisher.

Health and Welfare Canada. (2007). *Eating well with Canada's food guide*. Ottawa, ON: Health Canada.

Health Canada. (2000). *The vitality approach: A guide for leaders*. Ottawa, ON: Health Canada.

Health Canada. (2007). *Physical activity guide to healthy active living*. Ottawa, ON: Health Canada.

Health Canada. (2007). *Physical activity guide to healthy active living for older adults*. Ottawa, ON: Health Canada.

Insel, P. M., & Roth, W. T. (1994). *Core concepts in health* (7th ed.). Mountain View, CA: Mayfield Publishing Company.

Johnson, B. L., & Nelson, J. K. (1986). *Practical measurements for evaluation in physical education* (4th ed.). New York, NY: Macmillan Publishing Company.

Katzenback, J. R., & Smith, D. K. (1999). *The wisdom of teams: Creating the high performance organization*. New York, NY: Harper Business.

Klavora, P. (2007). *Foundations of exercise science: Studying human movement and health*. Toronto, ON: Sport Books Publisher.

Leith, L. M. (1998). *Exercising your way to better mental health*. Morgantown, WV: Fitness Information Technology, Inc.

Leith, L. M. (1990). *American coaching effectiveness program sport administration*. Champaign, IL: Human Kinetics.

McArdle, W. D., Katch, F. I., & Katch, V. L. (1999). *Sports and exercise nutrition*. Baltimore, MD: Lippincott Williams & Wilkins.

Morrow, Jr., J. R., Jackson, A. W., Disch, J. G., & Mood, D. P. (1995). *Measurement and evaluation in human performance*. Champaign, IL: Human Kinetics.

Mullen, B., & Copper, C. (1994). The relationship between group cohesiveness and performance: An integration. *Psychological Bulletin* (March), 210-227.

Ontario Physical and Health Education Association. (1999). *Ontario safety guidelines for physical education*. Toronto, ON: Ontario Physical and Health Education Association.

Ontario Physical and Health Education Association. (2000). *Ontario health and physical education curriculum support: Grade K-10*. Toronto, ON: Ontario Physical and Health Education Association.

Payne, W. A., & Hahn, D. B. (1992). *Understanding your health* (3rd ed.). St. Louis, MO: Mosby-Year Book.

Robbins, S. P. (2003). *Essentials of organizational behaviour* (7th ed.). Upper Saddle River, NJ: Prentice-Hall.

Robbins, S. P., & Langton, N. (2004). *Fundamentals of organizational behavior* (2nd ed.), Upper Saddle River, NJ: Pearson Prentice-Hall Inc.

Russell, R. (2001). *Leadership in recreation*. New York, NY: McGraw-Hill.

Schindler, P. L., & Thomas, C. C. (1993). The structure of interpersonal trust in the workplace. *Psychological Reports* (October), 563-573.

Scholich, M. (1999). *Circuit training for all sports*. Toronto, ON: Sport Books Publisher.

Shils, M.E., Shike, M., & Olson, J. A. (1999). *Modern nutrition in health and disease* (9th ed.). Baltimore, MD: Lippincott Williams & Wilkins.

St. John Ambulance. (2000). *First Aid: First on the scene: Activity Book*. Ottawa, ON: St. John Ambulance.

Temertzoglou, T. (2007). *Healthy active living: Keep fit, stay healthy, have fun*. Toronto, ON: Thompson Educational Publishing Inc.

Tuckman, B. W. (1965). Developmental sequences in small groups. *Psychological Bulletin* (June), 384-399.

Vander, A. J., Sherman, J. H., & Luciano, D. S. (1994). *Human physiology* (6th ed.). New York, NY: McGraw-Hill.

Wilson, S. (1988). *Politics and leisure*. London, GB: Unwin Hyman.

Woodside, D. B., & Garfinkel, P. E. (1989). An overview of the eating disorders: Anorexia nervosa and bulimia nervosa. *N.I.N. Review*, 8, 1-4.

Glossary

accommodation: A conflict management style in which one individual appeases another party by placing that person's interests above his or her own.

action plan: A detailed sequential list of items to be accomplished, including the names of the persons responsible and the deadlines for completion.

active listening: Asking questions to better understand how someone else is feeling and why.

adjourning: The last stage in group development, when team members wrap up their activities and disband.

adjudication: A process in which a neutral third party listens to all sides of a dispute and then makes a judgment based on the available information.

agenda: A list of items to be dealt with at a meeting; also called the "order of business."

agility: The ability to execute movements at high speed with rapid changes in direction, level, or plane.

agonist (prime mover): The muscle or group of muscles that produces a desired movement.

anatomical position: A universally accepted position that is the starting reference point for describing the human body.

antagonist: A muscle or group of muscles opposing an action (i.e., working in the opposite direction).

assertive: Ensuring personal needs are met, but not at the expense of others' needs.

autocratic leadership style: The leader is in control and makes all decisions.

avoidance: A passive way of reducing conflict by means of withdrawing from the situation or other person involved.

balance: The ability to achieve and maintain body stability.

barrier: In terms of wellness, anything that prevents us from participating regularly in recreational activities.

basal metabolic rate (BMR): The minimum amount of energy the body requires to carry out all vital functions.

behaviour theory of leadership: A viewpoint suggesting that great leaders exhibit certain key behaviours across a wide range of situations.

benevolent dictator: A leader who asks for input but then makes decisions without taking the solicited advice into consideration.

body composition: The various tissues that make up the body, in particular fat/adipose tissue and muscle tissue as well as organs, bones, and fluids.

brainstorming: A group strategy that elicits a wide variety of ideas without discussion or evaluation of merit.

carbohydrates: Nutrients that make up the primary source of energy in our diets.

cardiopulmonary resuscitation: An emergency medical procedure that maintains the flow of oxygenated blood to the heart and brain in the event of cardiac arrest.

cardiorespiratory (cardiovascular) endurance: The body's ability to sustain aerobic activities such as running and skating.

challenge tournament: A tournament structure in which participants organize their own matchups.

cholesterol: An essential lipid that circulates in the blood; excessive cholesterol in the bloodstream has been linked with cardiovascular disease.

cohesiveness: The degree to which individual members are attracted to a group and want to remain in that group.

communication: The transference of meaning and understanding among group members.

comprehensive theory of leadership: This theory acknowledges the importance of considering the context within which leadership occurs.

compromise: A way of reducing conflict by having both parties "give up" something of value.

concentric contraction: A dynamic action in which the muscle shortens as it goes through its range of motion.

conflict management: The ability to effectively resolve conflict situations that arise among members of a group or team.

coordination: The ability to perform movements in the correct order and with the proper timing.

core training: An emphasis on strengthening the core area of the body, from the diaphragm to the base of the pelvis.

democratic leadership style: The leader involves all group members in planning and attempts to reach consensus.

depersonalized conflict: Conflict that stems from a difficult situation or problem.

disordered eating: Irregular and unhealthy eating patterns.

diversity: Cultural or ethnic variety in a group or population.

downward communication: Communication that flows from a higher to a lower level within an organization or group (e.g., from a coach to her athletes).

draw sheet: A schematic diagram that shows which teams play each other in a tournament.

eating disorders: Clinical disorders characterized by extreme unhealthy eating patterns and a distorted body image.

eccentric contraction: A dynamic action in which the muscle lengthens during the movement.

ecological approach: An approach to behaviour change that places the creation of supportive environments on par with the development of personal skills.

elimination tournament: A tournament structure in which teams are eliminated after a set number of losses.

emergency action plan (EAP): A sheet of paper posted near the telephone that lists important contact numbers, the names of the people who will take charge in the event of an emergency, and directions to the facility.

Emergency Medical Services (EMS): A team of medical professionals that provide acute patient care and transportation in the case of medical emergencies.

emergency response plan: A set of steps to take when responding to emergency situations.

energy balance equation: An equation used to explain weight loss, gain, or maintenance based on caloric input and caloric output.

essential fat: Fat that is essential for normal physiological functioning.

fascia: The soft tissue component of the body's connective tissue system.

fats: Nutrients that perform many important functions in the body, including protection of organs, hormone synthesis, and vitamin absorption.

fibre: Indigestible plant substances that have many health benefits, such as lowering blood cholesterol and aiding digestion.

field test: A test that measures physiological function in a simulated setting.

FITT principle: A simple method to recall the four important design elements of any training program: frequency, intensity, training time, and type of activity.

flexibility: The ability of a joint to move through its full range of motion.

focus groups: Groups that meet and discuss their thoughts and views on various subjects.

forming: A stage of group development in which team members assess one another's strengths and weaknesses, engage in social comparisons, and determine likelihood of team success.

functional foods: Foods that go beyond simply meeting basic nutrient needs by helping reduce the risk of chronic disease.

groupthink: A process in group decision making in which individual members are so concerned about seeking agreement with others that the desire for consensus overrides the best possible solution.

health belief model: A behaviour change model stipulating that a person's health-related behaviours depend on the person's perception of four critical areas.

health: The capacity to lead a satisfying life, fulfill ambitions, and accommodate to change.

"I" messages: Statements that communicate feelings and emotions, identify causes, and propose solutions without blaming others directly.

IDEAL decision-making model: A model of decision making that involves identifying a problem, discussing alternative solutions, evaluating choices, acting on one alternative, and learning from the results.

inflammation: An increase in local blood circulation in response to a soft tissue injury.

interest checklists: A list of possible activities; the respondent checks off those he or she either currently participates in or is interested in participating in.

intergroup conflict: Conflict that arises when whole groups are in conflict with each other.

interpersonal conflict: Conflict between two or more individuals who have opposing views.

intragroup conflict: Conflict that occurs when a group is split on an issue.

intrapersonal conflict: Internal conflict that arises when a person has to make a tough decision on his or her own.

isometric action: A static action in which the muscle generates force against a resistance but no visible change in muscle length occurs.

laissez-faire leadership style: The leader supports a group that is working maturely by offering guidance when asked.

lateral communication: Communication that occurs among members at the same organizational level (e.g., athletes on a team).

leadership: The ability to influence a group towards the attainment of predetermined goals.

lean body mass (LBM): The "nonfat" or "fat-free" component of the human body, primarily skeletal muscle, bone, and water.

leisure: Free time that can be spent as a person sees fit.

liability: Court determination of assignment of blame.

lifestyle: The habits, attitudes, tastes, moral standards, economic level, and so on that together constitute the mode of living of an individual or group.

ligaments: Strands of connective tissue that hold bones together at joints.

mean: Adding all the scores and dividing by the number of responses, which calculates the average score.

measures of central tendency: The central characteristics of a set of data.

median: The score that represents the middle point – usually the best representation of the sample's response.

mediation: A process in which a neutral party helps resolve a conflict without aggression or coercion.

mentor: Someone who guides and supports another person in his or her development and endeavours.

minerals: Inorganic (non-carbon-containing) materials that are needed in small amounts to perform numerous functions in the body.

minutes: The official record of a meeting, including those in attendance, all matters discussed, and all motions voted on.

mode: The most frequently occurring score in a set of data.

motor ability: A skill-related component of physical fitness, such as balance, power, speed, reaction time, coordination, or agility.

muscular endurance: The ability of muscle to maintain tension or to execute repeated movements against a submaximal resistance.

muscular strength: The ability of a muscle or muscle group to exert force against a resistance.

needs assessment: A tool that reveals the opinions and wishes of potential participants through the provision of personal feedback.

negligence: Behaviour that fails to meet an established standard of care.

norming: A stage of group development in which close relationships begin to form among team members.

norms: Acceptable standards of behaviour that are considered to be appropriate and shared by the members of a particular group; referenced standards that are linked to a clearly defined subgroup.

nutraceuticals: Purified preparations of health-promoting bioactive compounds found in some foods.

nutrition: The science of food and how the body uses it in health and disease.

obesity: An excess of body fat beyond some particular standard, usually based on age and sex.

one repetition maximum (1RM): The maximum amount of weight an individual can lift just one time.

overload principle: For improvement to occur, training demands must be higher than normal performance requirements in order to stress the capacity of the targeted muscle or system.

percentile: A point or position on a continuous scale of 100 theoretical divisions such that a certain fraction of the population of raw scores lies at or below that point.

performing: During this stage of group development, the group comes together well to perform individual functions for the good of the work team.

personality theory of leadership: A theory suggesting that a person's leadership style develops naturally based on his or her strengths and preferred behaviours.

personalized conflict: Conflict that occurs when people are in opposition to one another.

physical fitness: The ability of the body to adjust to the demands and stresses of physical effort. Often used as a measure of physical health.

PIER: A mnemonic for the general treatment of soft tissue injuries – pressure, ice, elevation, and rest or restricted movement.

power: The ability to overcome external resistance at a high rate of muscular contraction. It is a combination of strength and speed.

proactive: A proactive leader anticipates risks and plans in advance how to minimize or eliminate them.

progression principle: To ensure that a muscle group or system continues to improve, the overload stimulus must be periodically increased.

promotion: A message that informs, persuades, or reminds people about an organization's programs and services.

promotional timeline: A schedule of the various stages of the promotion process.

proprioception: The ability to sense the position of a joint in space.

proteins: Nutrients that provide important structural components for building and repairing muscles, bones, blood, enzymes, some hormones, and cell membranes.

public meetings: An open forum for the public to voice opinions, allowing ideas and information to be gathered.

publicity: The spreading of information about the details of specific events and programs.

quorum: The number of people who need to be in attendance at a meeting in order for the decisions to be official.

random sample: A sample taken from a population where everyone has an equal chance of selection.

reaction time: The time it takes to react to a stimulus.

reactive: A reactive leader responds appropriately and immediately when a situation arises that could add to risk.

recreation: Participation in an activity that a person enjoys.

rehabilitation: The physical restoration of strength and flexibility to injured tissue.

relapse prevention model: A behaviour change model that involves anticipating problems of adherence and developing appropriate solutions.

reliability: The consistency or repeatability of test scores, data, or observations.

reversibility principle: Training interruptions have a negative effect on personal fitness, resulting in stagnation or a decline in performance.

risk management: Reducing the chances of injury or loss by taking steps to identify, measure, and control risks.

role: A set of expected behaviour patterns that can be attributed to someone occupying a given position.

round-robin tournament: A tournament structure that enables each team to play every other team.

SHARP: A mnemonic for the signs of soft tissue injury – swelling, heat, altered function, redness, and pain.

situational theory of leadership: A theory of leadership that suggests a leader must learn to give up some control to individual team members as they become more mature and responsible.

skinfold measurement: A method of estimating body composition that involves measuring skinfolds at particular sites on the body with special calipers.

SMART goals: Goals that are specific, measurable, attainable, relevant, and completed within a certain time frame.

social cognitive theory: A theory of behaviour change that incorporates self-efficacy, incentive, and value placed on outcomes.

social support: Instrumental, informational, emotional, and appraising sources of support that bring about health behaviour change.

somatotyping: A system of classifying people based on body types.

specificity principle: Exercises cause specific physiological responses or changes, so to improve a particular fitness or skill component, you must select a training modality that is as close in action as it can be to the end result.

speed: The highest rate at which a movement or series of movements can be executed, or the ability to cover a given distance in the shortest possible time during an all-out effort of short duration.

statistics: A branch of mathematics that involves gathering information and collating it to determine averages.

storage fat: Fat that serves as an energy reserve and that cushions and protects internal organs.

storming: A phase of group development characterized by conflict and often open rebellion.

survey: A data-gathering technique used to assess the needs of the community or evaluate program quality or customer satisfaction.

synergists: Muscles that assist the prime mover during an action.

synovial joints: The most common joint in the human body; synovial joints have the greatest amount of movement of the three joint types.

target audience: The audience or group that a program or event is intended to serve.

time management: A person's ability to effectively allocate his or her time and resources in order to achieve personal objectives.

toil: Hard and continuous work; exhausting labour or effort.

total fitness: The functional readiness and level of effectiveness required for everything a person does; includes physical, emotional, social, spiritual, and intellectual dimensions.

tournament: A formal competition structure.

trait theory of leadership: A viewpoint suggesting that great leaders exhibit certain key personality traits across a wide range of situations.

trans fat: An unhealthy fat formed through the process of hydrogenation.

transtheoretical model: A five-stage model of behaviour change that includes precontemplation, contemplation, preparation, action, and maintenance.

upward communication: Communication that flows from a lower to a higher level within an organization or group (e.g., from students to their teacher).

validity: The extent to which a test measures what it proposes to measure.

vitality: The state of having energy, feeling great, sleeping well, having a good appetite, and feeling confident about one's appearance and capabilities.

vitamins: Organic (carbon-containing) substances that are required in small amounts for normal growth, reproduction, and maintenance of health.

waiver form: A form that may be signed by an adult, absolving the organizers of an event or program of responsibility in case of accident or injury.

wellness: The combination of health and happiness; the achievement of balance in one's mental, physical, emotional, social, environmental, and spiritual life.

win–win: A conflict-resolution style that involves attempting to solve a problem by clarifying individual needs and seeking a solution where both parties "win" or get what they need without compromise.

work group: A group of individuals interacting to share information and make decisions that will ultimately help the individual members perform in their respective areas of responsibility.

work team: A small number of individuals who are working towards a common goal. This group is marked by positive synergy.

work: The result of exertion, labour, or activity; a deed or performance.

Key Terms Index

Photo Credits

Every effort has been made to acknowledge correctly and contact the source and/or copyright holder of each picture, and Kinesiology Books Publisher apologizes for any unintentional errors or omissions, which will be corrected in future editions of this book.

	Pages
Canadian Press	6 (Wayne Gretzky), 11 (Terry Fox)
Corbis/Magma Photo Inc.	34, 38, 45, 62, 90, 190 (brain), 208, 219, 221, 244 (girl), 248 (housework, walkers), 262, 263 (muscular strength), 319 (safety equipment)
Firstlight	182, 202
Gymstick	236
Maifith Design Inc.	239 (body), 245 (figure 10.2), 265, 277 (vessels), 278, 364 (anatomical position), 366, 367 (joint schematics), 368
Niko Slana	43, 48, 109 (basketball), 117 (wall climbing and dance), 142, 166, 217, 270 (gymnast), 319 (rock climbing), 321 (playground), 333
PhotoDisc	front cover (basketball, cyclist, baseball), i, 30, 31, 41, 44, 55 (golfer), 70, 73 (cyclist), 79, 83, 87 (spiritual, physical), 117 (golfer and darts), 118, 144 (darts), 148, 165, 172 (walkers), 226, 235, 247 (background image), 248 (tennis, cycling, skiing), 256, 258, 263 (motor abilities, flexibility), 264, 270 (flexibility), 273 (motor ability), 274 (karate, sprinter, golfer), 277 (training), 280 (sit-ups), 288, 290, 293, 315, 316, 334 (stretching), 381 (skiing), back cover
Sport Books Publisher	4, 16, 20, 24, 28, 29, 37, 39, 40, 51, 55 (group), 56, 60 (gym class), 61, 65, 78 (woman walking dog), 82 (cyclist), 84, 87 (intellectual), 88, 104, 105, 106, 109 (sit-ups), 120, 122, 239 (arm), 243 (family, man sitting), 248 (ice cream), 263 (muscular endurance, body composition, students, wheelchair), 266, 269, 273 (body composition), 276, 280 (stepping), 282 (medicine ball), 291, 292 (abdominal crunch), 295, 304, 305, 306, 309, 318, 331, 343 (defibrillator), 351 (physiotherapist), 355, 373, 377 (core exercises), 379 (sit-ups), 393
Sportverlag	365, 370
Stan J. Czerniec	228 (mirror image), 231 (measurement), 240 (waist measurement), 271, 272, 282 (exercise band), 296, 299, 300 (chin-ups), 302, 308, 310, 311, 378 (ankle exercise)
University of Toronto	front cover (notebook, water polo), 1, 5, 22, 25, 27, 69, 263 (cardiorespiratory endurance), 268 (cardiorespiratory endurance), 274 (water polo, volleyball)
VEB Georg Thieme	374 (pelvis, pelvic muscles), 375 (vertebrae), 376 (abdominal muscles), 377 (knee joint)
York University	54, 140

THREE COMPANIONS TO RECREATION AND FITNESS LEADERSHIP

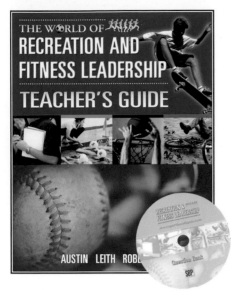

► TEACHER'S GUIDE

Facilitates instruction of core material and student evaluation

Includes a question bank on CD

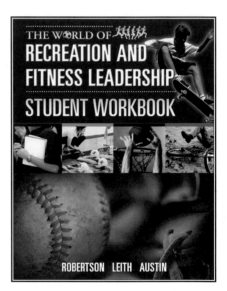

STUDENT WORKBOOK ◄

Helps instructors and students evaluate progress and learning comprehension

► GRAPHIC PACKAGE

Fully animated slides offer a great teaching and learning tool for presenting chapter material

Patricia M. Leith, BPHE (University of Toronto, 1970), BEd

Pat graduated from the University of Toronto in 1970 with a BPHE and obtained her BEd the following year. Four years of teaching with the Toronto School Board was followed by 31 years at Lindsay CVI, where she taught health and physical education and dance. She was a department head for 25 years. She contributed to writing grade 11 health curriculum materials and the Ontario Physical Education Safety Guidelines for OPHEA. Pat convened many events, including five OFSAA Gymnastics Championships. Now retired, she continues to coach her girls' gymnastics and aerobics team and to facilitate theory courses for the National Coaching Certification Program. She is a Master Learning Facilitator for Gymnastics Canada and volunteers with Gymnastics Ontario. In her spare time she goes trail riding, takes dance classes, and tends her gardens.

Debra Lea Austin, BA (Hons) PE (University of Western Ontario, 1981), BEd (Althouse College, 1982)

Recently retired, Debi was the department head of Healthy Active Living and Family Studies at Huntsville High School, where she taught for most of her teaching career. She spent much of her free time during the school year coaching sports, including senior girls' volleyball, girls' golf, badminton, girls' hockey, cross-country running, and basketball. In 1999, she coached her basketball team to an OFSAA gold medal. Debi is also a strong proponent of outdoor education in high school, and she took students on regular canoe trips every semester. Her hobbies include golf, competitive ice hockey, horseback riding, and canoeing (particularly white-water canoeing). Debi was one of the writers for the PLF 4C Ministry Profile document.

Jillian Robertson, BRLS (Brock University, 1986), MEd

Jill graduated from Brock University with a bachelor in recreation and leisure studies. Currently Jill is employed with the Barrie Minor Hockey Association as their business manager and also teaches part time at Georgian College in the recreation services, fitness, and wellness diploma programs and the golf course management degree program. Jill is also active within the community and sits on a number of volunteer committees.